P. Winfield

Coastal Hydraulics

Consulting Editor: Professor E. M. Wilson, University of Salford

Also from Macmillan

Hydraulic Behaviour of Estuaries

D. M. McDowell and B. A. O'Connor

Engineering Hydrology, second edition

E. M. Wilson

Coastal Hydraulics

A. M. Muir Wood, F.R.S., F.Eng
Sir William Halcrow & Partners

C. A. Fleming, Ph.D., M.I.C.E.
Sir William Halcrow & Partners

Second Edition

M

First edition 1969
Second edition 1981

Published by
THE MACMILLAN PRESS LTD
London and Basingstoke
Companies and representatives throughout the world

Typeset in 10/11 Times by
Multiplex techniques ltd., Orpington, Kent
and printed in Hong Kong

ISBN 0 333 26129 1

Contents

Preface to the Second Edition

The date of publication of the first edition of this book (by the first author) approximately coincided with the beginning of a period of 'mighty ferment' in the development of understanding of the physics of the sea, its motions, its forces and its capacity for erosion, sediment transport and deposition.

Whereas twelve years ago many of the phenomena of morphological change could only be developed in a qualitative sense from simple basic physical formulae, subsequent research, model testing and fullscale monitoring present many new quantitative design methods with reasonable assurance of reproducing nature, having regard to the inherent uncertainties of the sea and its energy transfers.

We need to recognise many reasons for adopting a probabilistic approach to the behaviour of the sea. Questions of uncertainty in energy transfer largely concern variations in solar radiation, directly as air/sea temperatures and indirectly as winds over the face of the sea. Additionally, wave patterns, turbulence and sea levels need to be expressed in statistical terms of magnitude and frequencies. The behaviour of a water particle at an instant of time represents the consequences of innumerable events at innumerable points in space. Hence, extreme effects are bound to be expressed in terms of exceedance.

When, however, we are concerned with the measurement of change over a long period of months or years, we may reasonably consider an estimate related to mean conditions and, if we wish, representing uncertainty in terms of a standard deviation. Even so the uncertainty may still extend to an unpredictable event causing an irreversible change.

Perhaps the single most important feature responsible for technical advance has been the increased activity offshore, particularly in relation to gas and oil. Structures of a size and cost never previously built at sea demand much data on winds, currents and waves for economic design. The availability of such data makes it possible to tackle many more maritime problems with assurance. Ever greater investigation and analysis, essential to reliable prediction, can be justified by the increasing capacity and reduced costs of computers, with associated advances in programming, and the process snowballs as monitoring of the outturn permits comparison with hindcasting.

Whereas, in consequence, the first edition was conceived much as an introduction to the marine environment, at a time of only slight sea tang in a first-degree course in civil engineering, the second edition is more ambitious in

attempting to combine a reasonable coverage of the basic physics with an
adequate handbook for tackling simpler problems and a book of reference for
the more complex ones. The ubiquity of the programmable pocket calculator,
even for the most isolated engineer, implies that the complexity of a
recommended method of analysis may be considered primarily in relation to
the economic benefit that this allows. In the first edition, the isolated engineer
was assumed to rely on observation, slide rule and power of logic only.

This has been a difficult book to write, particularly in relation to selection of
material in order to combine immediately useful advice with introductions to
developments still at a stage of major growth. The authors wish to acknowledge
the help, advice and criticism from many of their colleagues in and around Sir
William Halcrow & Partners including particularly W.L. Wood, L. Summers,
C.J. Antonakis, J.E. Clifford, P.S. Godfrey, R.J. Maddrell and M. O'Leary.
The authors will welcome criticism towards, perhaps, an improved third
edition. Finally, we would like to thank Mrs Iris Golding for her valuable work
in typing the drafts and Mrs Margaret Powers for preparation of the figures.

Notation

Symbol	Brief Definition	Dimensions
A	Amplitude of tidal constituent	—
A	Highest wave crest	L
B	Height of tidal bore	L
b	Distance between wave orthogonals	L
b	Breakwater gap width	L
b_0	Distance between wave orthogonals in deep water	L
C_c	Contraction coefficient	—
C_v	Velocity coefficient	—
C	Wave celerity	LT^{-1}
C_D	Drag coefficient	—
C_L	Lift coefficient	—
Ch	Chezy coefficient	—
C	Friction coefficient	—
C_g	Wave group velocity	LT^{-1}
C	Lowest wave trough	L
$C_{D_{90}}$	Chezy coefficient with D_{90} roughness length	—
C_M	Mass coefficient	—
C_n	Ratio of wave group velocity to celerity	—
C_0	Wave celerity in deep water	LT^{-1}
C_s	Wave celerity in shallow water	LT^{-1}
c	Concentration of sediment	—
c	Bottom energy coefficient	—
$\hat{c}$	Maximum volumetric concentration	—
c_0	Reference concentration	—
$\bar{c}_b$	Average concentration in bed load	—
cn	Jacobian elliptic function	—
D_{35}	Grain diameter (35% finer than)	L
D_{50}	Grain diameter (50% finer than)	L
D_{90}	Grain diameter (90% finer than)	L
D_{gr}	Dimensionless grain size	—
d	Diameter	L
d	North declination	—
$\hat{d}_0$	Maximum water particle orbit at bed	L

Symbol	Brief Definition	Dimensions
E	Earth's mass	M
E_k	Kinetic energy of wave per unit width	MLT^{-2}
E_p	Potential energy of wave per unit width	MLT^{-2}
E_t	Total energy of wave per unit width	MLT^{-2}
E	Phase of tide rising force	—
E	Total energy of wave per unit area	MT^{-2}
E_f	Dissipation of energy per unit area of bed	MT^{-2}
e	Radius of the Earth	L
e	Void ratio	—
F_r	Froude number	—
F	Fetch	L
F_e	Effective fetch	L
F	Force	MLT^{-2}
F_{wc}	Dimensionless coefficient	—
f	Frequency	T^{-1}
f	Friction parameter	—
f_c	Current friction factor	—
f_e	Wave energy factor	—
f_p	Peak energy frequency	T^{-1}
f_w	Wave friction factor	—
g	Acceleration due to Earth's gravitational force at surface level	LT^{-2}
g	Phase lag constant	—
H	Wave height	L
$\bar{H}$	Mean wave height	L
H_{max}	Maximum wave height	L
H_{rms}	Equivalent root-mean-square wave height	L
H_s	Significant wave height (average height of highest one-third waves)	L
$H_{1/10}$	Average height of highest 10% waves	L
$H_{1/100}$	Average height of highest 1% waves	L
H_I	Incident wave height	L
H_R	Reflected wave height	L
H_T	Transmitted wave height	L
H_b	Wave height at breaking	L
H_{des}	Design wave height	L
H_0	Deep water wave height	L
h	Sea depth	L
h	Beach height	L
h_0	Height of median sea level, between wave crest and trough, above mean sea level	L
$\bar{h}$	Mean depth	L
h_b	Breaker depth	L
h_s	Depth at toe of structure	L
I_{wc}	Dimensionless coefficient	—
I_1	Immersed sediment transport rate	MLT^{-3}

Symbol	Brief Definition	Dimensions
K_D	Coefficient for breakwater armouring	—
k	Tidal phase lag	—
k	$2\pi/L$	L^{-1}
k_N	Roughness length	L
K_r	Wave height refraction coefficient	—
K_s	Wave height shoaling coefficient	—
K_f	Wave height friction coefficient	—
K	Dimensionless coefficient for bulk sediment transport	—
K', K''	Coefficients for bulk sediment transport	$M^{-1}L^2T^2$
L	Wave length	L
L_0	Wave length in deep water	L
L_{sol}	'Length' of solitary wave	L
l	North latitude	—
l	Mixing length	L
l	Length of basin	L
M	Solitary wave factor ($2\pi/L_{sol}$)	L^{-1}
M	Moon's mass	M
M_2	Tidal constituent (principal lunar)	—
N_s	Stability number for breakwater armouring	—
N	Dimensionless constant in longshore	—
N_z	Number of zero crossings	—
N_K	Keulegan–Carpenter number	—
n	Tidal speed number	T^{-1}
n	Empirical exponent	—
P	Wave power per unit width	MLT^{-3}
P_n	Normal tidal tractive force	LT^{-2}
P_t	Tangential tidal tractive force	LT^{-2}
P_s	Static component of wave pressure	L
P_v	Dynamic component of water pressure	L
P	Dimensionless parameter in longshore current model	—
P	Cumulative probability	—
P	Empirical constant	—
P_j	Empirical coefficient	—
p	Water pressure	$ML^{-1}T^{-2}$
p_0	Atmospheric pressure	$ML^{-1}T^{-2}$
p	Power per unit area	MT^{-3}
p	Normal dispersive stress	$ML^{-1}T^{-2}$
p	Porosity of sediment	—
Q	Volumetric sediment transport rate	L^3T^{-1}
Q	Overtopping rate	L^3T^{-1}
Q_g	Longshore transport rate (with groynes)	L^3T^{-1}
Q_0	Longshore transport rate (without groynes)	L^3T^{-1}
Q_p	Transport rate passing a breakwater	L^3T^{-1}
Q_x	Longshore transport rate upstream of a groyne	L^3T^{-1}
q_b	Volumetric rate of bed transport per unit width	L^2T^{-1}

Symbol	Brief Definition	Dimensions
q_s	Volumetric rate of suspended transport per unit width	L^2T^{-1}
R	Wave run-up	L
R	Hydraulic radius	L
R	Overfill ratio	—
Re	Reynolds number	—
r	Distance between Earth and Moon	L
r	Coefficient of wave run-up	—
S	Strouhal number	—
S	Wind slope of sea surface	—
S	Length of cylinder	L
S	Distance from wall	L
S_{ij}	Momentum flux tensor	—
S^{nn}	Spectral density of surface elevation	—
S^{mm}	Spectral density of mud line bending moment	—
S_2	Tidal constituent (principal solar)	—
s	Distance along wave orthogonal	—
s	Bed slope	—
s_f	Friction slope	—
T	Wave period	T
T	Fundamental mode of oscillation	T
T_p	Corresponding to peak energy of spectrum	T
T_{sol}	'Period' of solitary wave	T
t	Time	T
U	Wind velocity	LT^{-1}
U	Group velocity of waves	LT^{-1}
U_0	Group velocity of waves in deep water	LT^{-1}
U_g	Gradient wind	LT^{-1}
$\bar{U}$	Mass transport velocity under waves	LT^{-1}
Ur	Ursell number	—
u	Tidal current	LT^{-1}
u	Orbital velocity of waves (horizontal)	LT^{-1}
$\hat{u}$	Maximum orbital velocity	LT^{-1}
$\hat{u}_0$	Maximum orbital velocity at the bed	LT^{-1}
u	Velocity in x-coordinate direction	LT^{-1}
$\bar{u}$	Depth mean velocity	LT^{-1}
u'	Velocity fluctuation	LT^{-1}
V	Dimensionless longshore current velocity	LT^{-1}
V	Velocity normal to member	LT^{-1}
V_s	Speed of vessel	LT^{-1}
v	Velocity in y-coordinate direction or general current velocity	LT^{-1}
v'	Velocity fluctuation	LT^{-1}
v_0	Maximum longshore current velocity with no mixing	LT^{-1}
v_*	Shear velocity	LT^{-1}

Symbol	Brief Definition	Dimensions
v_{*c}	Shear velocity due to current alone	LT^{-1}
v_{*wc}	Shear velocity due to wave and current	LT^{-1}
$\hat{v}$	Maximum velocity at the free surface	LT^{-1}
$\bar{v}$	Depth mean velocity	LT^{-1}
v_n	Velocity normal to wave direction	LT^{-1}
v_p	Velocity parallel to wave direction	LT^{-1}
v_b	Mean velocity of sediment in bed load	LT^{-1}
W	Weight of breakwater armour	M
W	Width of fetch	L
w	Velocity in z-coordinate direction	LT^{-1}
w_s	Particle fall velocity	LT^{-1}
w	Orbital velocity of waves (vertical)	LT^{-1}
$\hat{w}$	Maximum orbital velocity	LT^{-1}
X	Body force in x-direction	MLT^{-2}
X	Horizontal water particle displacement	L
X	Non-dimensional x-coordinate	—
X	Non-dimensional horizontal length for solitary wave	—
x	Distance to centre of the Moon	L
Y	Body force in y-direction	MLT^{-2}
Y	Non-dimensional y-coordinate	—
Y	Non-dimensional vertical length for solitary wave	—
Z	Longitude of point on Earth's surface relative to Moon	—
Z'	Dimensionless bed load thickness	—
z	Vertical distance with origin at water surface	L
z'	Vertical distance with origin at the bed	L
z_0	Bed load thickness or reference level	L
α	Friction angle (angle of repose)	—
α	Angle between wave crest and contour	—
α	Angle of inclination of face of seawall	—
α	Phase lag angle	—
α_b	Angle of wave incidence at breaker line	—
β	Angle of inclination of bed to horizontal	—
β	Ray separation factor	—
β	Angle of shoreline at breakwater	—
γ	Non-dimensional height of solitary wave crest	—
γ	Wave breaking index	—
γ_s	Density ratio	—
Δ	Damage parameter for rubble mound	—
Δ	Volume of non-dimensional solitary wave/unit width	L^2
Δ_r	Bed form height	L
Δ_s	Relative density ratio	—
δ	Phi mean difference	—

Symbol	Brief Definition	Dimensions
ϵ	Dimensionless block factor	—
ϵ	Spectral width parameter	—
ϵ	Coefficient of eddy viscosity	L^2T^{-1}
ϵ_s	Sediment diffusion coefficient	L^2T^{-1}
ϵ_0	Reference eddy viscosity (at z_0)	L^2T^{-1}
ϵ'	Normalised diffusion coefficient	—
ζ	Vertical water particle excursion	L
η	Water surface elevation	L
η	Efficiency	—
θ	Latitude	—
θ	Angle of wave crest relative to x-axis	—
θ	Shield's relative stress parameter	—
θ_0	Angle between shadow line and breakwater	—
θ_b	Angle between wave orthogonal and beach normal at breaking	—
κ	Von Kármán's constant	—
λ_r	Bed form wavelength	L
μ	Non-dimensional surface elevation for solitary wave	—
μ	Molecular viscosity	L^2T^{-1}
μ_e	Pseudo-horizontal eddy viscosity	L^2T^{-1}
μ	Ripple factor	—
μ	Phi mean	—
ν	Coefficient of dynamic viscosity	$ML^{-1}T^{-1}$
ξ	Horizontal water particle excursion	L
ξ	Horizontal water particle excursion at the bed	L
ξ	Exponent in sediment concentration distribution	—
ρ	Water density	ML^{-3}
ρ_a	Air density	ML^{-3}
ρ_r	Rock density	ML^{-3}
ρ_s	Sediment grain density	ML^{-3}
σ	$2\pi/T$ where T is wave period	T^{-1}
σ	Standard deviation	—
σ	Phi sorting or phi standard deviation	—
σ_r	Phi sorting ratio	
τ	Shear stress	$ML^{-1}T^{-2}$
τ_d	Dispersed shear stress	$ML^{-1}T^{-2}$
τ_t	Critical threshold stress	$ML^{-1}T^{-2}$
τ_0	Shear stress at the bed	$ML^{-1}T^{-2}$
τ_s	Shear stress at the surface	$ML^{-1}T^{-2}$
τ_{wc}	Shear stress due to waves and currents	$ML^{-1}T^{-2}$
τ_c	Shear stress due to currents alone	$ML^{-1}T^{-2}$
ϕ	Angle of friction	—
ϕ	Velocity potential	L^2T^{-1}
ϕ_0	Phase lead of maximum shear stress	—
ψ	Stream function	L^2T^{-1}

Symbol	Brief Definition	Dimensions
ψ	Wind stress and atmospheric pressure term	$ML^{-1}T^{-2}$
Ω	Earth's angular spin velocity	T^{-1}
Ω	Force potential	—
ω	Vorticity	T^{-1}

1

Basic Hydraulics

It is probable that recent graduates in civil engineering will be familiar with the basic hydraulic theory assumed in the subsequent chapters. Those further removed from a period of academic instruction may find it helpful to make use of one or more sections of this chapter which endeavours to set out in simple terms the most fundamental aspects of the theory of hydraulics in relation to the dynamics of the sea.

1.1 Equations of Motion of Ideal Fluids

To simplify the mathematical description of fluid flow where the influences of viscosity and compressibility are small, an ideal incompressible fluid with no viscosity is first considered. The equations of continuity and motion which govern fluid flow are based respectively on the principle of the conservation of mass and on Newton's laws.

The general equation of continuity in an incompressible fluid may be expressed in cartesian coordinates x, y, z and velocity components u, v, w (figure 1.1) as

$$\frac{\partial u}{\partial x} + \frac{\partial v}{\partial y} + \frac{\partial w}{\partial z} = 0 \text{ or } \nabla \cdot u = 0 \tag{1.1}$$

We may define a stream function, ψ, such that

$$u = \frac{\partial \psi}{\partial z} - \frac{\partial \psi}{\partial y}, \ v = \frac{\partial \psi}{\partial x} - \frac{\partial \psi}{\partial z}, \ w = -\frac{\partial \psi}{\partial x} + \frac{\partial \psi}{\partial y} \text{ (or } u = \nabla \psi) \tag{1.2}$$

which will be found to satisfy equation 1.1.

Vorticity for a two-dimensional element of fluid (figure 1.1) may be defined as

$$\omega = \frac{\partial u}{\partial z} - \frac{\partial w}{\partial x} \tag{1.3}$$

that is, from equation 1.2* $\qquad \omega = \nabla^2 \cdot \psi$

*Derivatives in terms of y omitted for two dimensions.

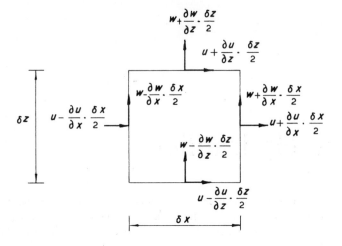

Figure 1.1 *Reference diagram for fluid motion*

Thus, rotational flow contains vortices whereas irrotational flow requires that the integral of velocity along and around the boundary of any element within the body of the fluid shall be zero.

Irrotational flow requires that everywhere $\partial u/\partial z = \partial w/\partial x$ so then vorticity, $\omega = \nabla^2 \psi = 0$. For irrotational flow *only* we can then define a velocity potential ϕ such that

$$u = \frac{\partial \phi}{\partial x} , \quad v = \frac{\partial \phi}{\partial y} , \quad w = \frac{\partial \phi}{\partial z} \text{ or } \boldsymbol{u} = \nabla \phi \tag{1.4}$$

The continuity equation 1.1 provides, by substitution from equation 1.4, Laplace's equation

$$\frac{\partial^2 \phi}{\partial x^2} + \frac{\partial^2 \phi}{\partial y^2} + \frac{\partial^2 \phi}{\partial z^2} = 0 \text{ or } \nabla^2 \phi = 0 \tag{1.5}$$

Comparison of the slopes of stream functions (which become streamlines for potential flow) and the slopes of potential functions, by means of equations 1.2 and 1.4, establishes that they represent families of orthogonals. Hence, if the mesh is square at one point in a problem concerning potential flow, the mesh will be square (when reduced infinitesimally) everywhere and this provides the basis for approximate sketching of potential flow nets.

The Euler equations of motion describe what is happening at a point in a fluid and may be expressed as

$$\frac{\partial \boldsymbol{u}}{\partial t} + \boldsymbol{u} \cdot \nabla \boldsymbol{u} = \boldsymbol{F} - \frac{1}{\rho} \nabla p \tag{1.6}$$

which may be written as

$$\frac{\partial u}{\partial t} + \tfrac{1}{2}\nabla u^2 + (\nabla \times u) \times u = F - \frac{1}{\rho}\nabla p \tag{1.7}$$

[Compare with the Lagrangian form of the equations of motion of a particle of the fluid where x, y, z are *not* independent variables but depend upon the initial coordinates, x_0, y_0, z_0, of the (same) particle, as well as the time t.]

For an irrotational, incompressible flow, $\nabla \times u = 0$ and $(1/\rho)\nabla p = \nabla(p/\rho)$. If we express the external force F as the gradient of a force potential, $F = -\nabla\Omega$ (say), equation 1.7 may be written as

$$\nabla \left(\frac{\partial \phi}{\partial t} + \tfrac{1}{2}|u|^2 + \Omega + \frac{p}{\rho}\right) = 0 \tag{1.8}$$

The expression in parentheses in equation 1.8 is not a function of the space coordinates and only an arbitrary function of time. Integrating

$$\frac{\partial \phi}{\partial t} + \tfrac{1}{2}|u|^2 + \Omega + \frac{p}{\rho} = F(t) \tag{1.9}$$

where $F(t)$ is a constant of integration. This is the general form of Bernoulli's theorem. If external forces are only due to gravity, $\Omega = gz$. The equation may be solved for many situations by applying appropriate boundary conditions.

(1) *Rigid boundary.* There is no transport normal to the boundary so $d\phi/d\gamma = 0$ where γ is the direction normal to the boundary.

(2) *Free boundary.* (a) The kinematic condition at the free surface is that the fluid particle at the surface remains at the surface. If the surface is described as $z = \eta(x, t)$, in two dimensions

$$w = u\frac{\partial \eta}{\partial x} + \frac{\partial \eta}{\partial t} \tag{1.10}$$

(b) A second condition is that the pressure remains constant along the free surface, which we may take to be zero without loss of generality.

The relevant equations for waves may be developed as

$$\nabla^2 \phi = 0 \text{ throughout the volume}$$

$$\frac{d\phi}{d\gamma} = 0 \text{ at rigid boundary}$$

$$\left.\begin{aligned}
\frac{\partial \phi}{\partial t} + \tfrac{1}{2}|u|^2 + g\eta &= 0 \\
\frac{\partial \eta}{\partial t} + u\frac{\partial \eta}{\partial x} &= w
\end{aligned}\right\} \text{ at the free surface } (p = 0)$$

and alternative forms of the resulting equations are discussed in chapter 3.

1.2 Viscous Flow

The viscosity of real fluids opposes any force causing relative motion within a fluid through shearing forces.

The coefficient of viscosity μ is defined by the shear stress resulting from a velocity gradient in a transverse direction. Thus $\tau_{xz} = \mu(\partial u/\partial z)$. Hence, by reference to figures 1.2 and 1.3, the momentum equations for two-dimensional flow, for predominantly horizontal flow, can readily be derived as

$$\frac{\partial u}{\partial t} + u\frac{\partial u}{\partial x} + v\frac{\partial u}{\partial y} = \frac{X}{\rho} - \frac{1}{\rho}\frac{\partial p}{\partial x} + \frac{\mu}{\rho}\left(\frac{\partial^2 u}{\partial x^2} + \frac{\partial^2 u}{\partial y^2}\right) \tag{1.11}$$

$$\frac{\partial v}{\partial t} + u\frac{\partial v}{\partial x} + v\frac{\partial v}{\partial y} = \frac{Y}{\rho} - \frac{1}{\rho}\frac{\partial p}{\partial y} + \frac{\mu}{\rho}\left(\frac{\partial^2 v}{\partial x^2} + \frac{\partial^2 v}{\partial y^2}\right) \tag{1.12}$$

where X and Y are body forces in x and y-directions.

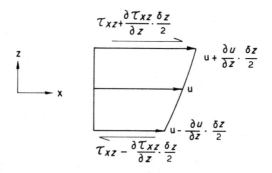

Figure 1.2 *Reference diagram for laminar flow*

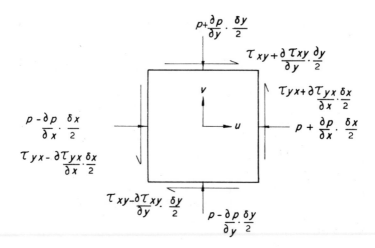

Figure 1.3 *Forces on fluid element*

If the pressure is hydrostatic (that is, vertical velocities are small) $p = \rho g \eta$ where η is surface elevation and

$$\frac{1}{\rho}\frac{\partial p}{\partial x} = g\frac{\partial \eta}{\partial x} \text{ and } \frac{1}{\rho}\frac{\partial p}{\partial y} = g\frac{\partial \eta}{\partial y}$$

in equations 1.11 and 1.12.

If we reduce the equations of motion to a non-dimensional form with L a characteristic length, U a characteristic velocity and T a characteristic time, non-dimensional variables x_*, y_*, u_*, v_*, η_* and t_* are

$$x_* = \frac{x}{L}, \ y_* = \frac{y}{L}, \ u_* = \frac{u}{U}, \ v_* = \frac{v}{U}, \ \eta_* = \frac{\eta}{L} \text{ and } t_* = \frac{t}{T}$$

Equation 1.11 may now be rewritten

$$\frac{U}{T}\frac{\partial u_*}{\partial t_*} + \frac{U^2}{L}\left(u_*\frac{\partial u_*}{\partial x_*} + v_*\frac{\partial u_*}{\partial y_*}\right) = \frac{X}{\rho} - g\frac{\partial \eta_*}{\partial x_*} + \frac{\mu}{\rho}\frac{U}{L^2}\left(\frac{\partial^2 u_*}{\partial x_*^2} + \frac{\partial^2 u_*}{\partial y_*^2}\right)$$

or

$$\frac{\partial u_*}{\partial t_*} + u_*\frac{\partial u_*}{\partial x_*} + v_*\frac{\partial u_*}{\partial y_*} = \frac{LX}{U^2\rho} - \frac{gL}{U^2}\frac{\partial \eta_*}{\partial x_*} + \frac{\mu}{\rho LU}\left(\frac{\partial^2 u_*}{\partial x_*^2} + \frac{\partial^2 u_*}{\partial y_*^2}\right) \ (1.13)$$

(if $T = L/U$). Now Froude number $Fr = U/(gL)^{1/2}$ and Reynolds number $Re = \rho LU/\mu$, thus

$$\frac{\partial u_*}{\partial t_*} + u_*\frac{\partial u_*}{\partial x_*} + v_*\frac{\partial u_*}{\partial y_*} = \frac{LX}{U^2\rho} - \frac{1}{Fr^2}\frac{\partial \eta_*}{\partial x_*} + \frac{1}{Re}\left(\frac{\partial^2 u_*}{\partial x_*^2} + \frac{\partial^2 u_*}{\partial y_*^2}\right) \ (1.14)$$

and

$$\frac{\partial v_*}{\partial t_*} + v_*\frac{\partial v_*}{\partial y_*} + u_*\frac{\partial v_*}{\partial x_*} = \frac{LY}{U^2\rho} - \frac{1}{Fr^2}\frac{\partial \eta_*}{\partial y_*} + \frac{1}{Re}\left(\frac{\partial^2 v_*}{\partial x_*^2} + \frac{\partial^2 v_*}{\partial y_*^2}\right) \ (1.15)$$

If $T \neq L/U$, equation 1.11 may be written

$$\frac{L}{TU}\frac{\partial u_*}{\partial t_*} + u_*\frac{\partial u_*}{\partial x_*} + v_*\frac{\partial u_*}{\partial y_*}$$

$$= \frac{LX}{U^2\rho} - \frac{Lg}{U^2}\frac{\partial \eta_*}{\partial x_*} + \frac{\mu}{\rho LU}\left(\frac{\partial^2 v_*}{\partial x_*^2} + \frac{\partial^2 v_*}{\partial y_*^2}\right) \quad (1.16)$$

where Strouhal number $S = L/TU$ and the left-hand side of equation 1.16 may be written as

$$S\frac{\partial u_*}{\partial t_*} + u_*\frac{\partial u_*}{\partial x_*} + v_*\frac{\partial u_*}{\partial y_*}$$

When the flow is turbulent the variable instantaneous flow may be considered as the sum of an ensemble average $(\bar{u}, \bar{v})$ and instantaneous fluctuations (u', v'), ignoring effects of varying pressure, temperature and external forces, that is, $u = \bar{u} + u'$, $v = \bar{v} + v'$.

Subsituting for u and v into the left-hand side of equation 1.11, adding the quantity $u'(\partial u'/\partial x + \partial v'/\partial y)$, which for reasons of continuity must be zero, and averaging over the ensemble yields

$$
\frac{\partial \bar{u}}{\partial t} + \bar{u}\frac{\partial \bar{u}}{\partial x} + \bar{v}\frac{\partial \bar{u}}{\partial y}
$$
$$
= \frac{X}{\rho} - \frac{1}{\rho}\frac{\partial p}{\partial x} + \frac{\mu}{\rho}\left(\frac{\partial^2 \bar{u}}{\partial x^2} + \frac{\partial^2 \bar{u}}{\partial y^2}\right) - \left(\frac{\partial \overline{u'u'}}{\partial x} + \frac{\partial \overline{u'v'}}{\partial y}\right)
$$
(1.17)

where $\overline{u'u'}$ and $\overline{u'v'}$ are ensemble averages. Using the Boussinesq analogy (see section 1.3.4) these terms may be written as

$$
\overline{u'u'} = -\epsilon\frac{\partial \bar{u}}{\partial x} \,, \quad \overline{u'v'} = -\epsilon\frac{\partial \bar{u}}{\partial y}
$$
(1.18)

so that equation 1.17 reduces to

$$
\frac{\partial \bar{u}}{\partial t} + \bar{u}\frac{\partial \bar{u}}{\partial x} + \bar{v}\frac{\partial \bar{u}}{\partial y} = \frac{X}{\rho} - \frac{1}{\rho}\frac{\partial p}{\partial x} + (\nu + \epsilon)\left(\frac{\partial^2 \bar{u}}{\partial x^2} + \frac{\partial^2 \bar{u}}{\partial y^2}\right)
$$
(1.19)

where ν is the kinematic viscosity $(= \mu/\rho)$ and ϵ is the coefficient of eddy viscosity. A similar equation results from operating on equation 1.12.

For channel flow in one direction over a bed of gentle slope s with a relatively low free surface gradient, the equation of continuity and of momentum (figure 1.4) are respectively

$$
\frac{\partial \eta}{\partial t} + \bar{u}\frac{\partial \eta}{\partial x} + \bar{h}\frac{\partial \bar{u}}{\partial x} = 0
$$
(1.20)

and

$$
g\frac{\partial \eta}{\partial x} + \frac{\partial \bar{u}}{\partial t} + \bar{u}\frac{\partial \bar{u}}{\partial x} + g\left(s_f - s\right) = 0
$$
(1.21)

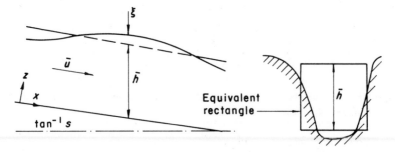

Figure 1.4 *Reference diagram for channel flow*

where $\bar{u}$, $\bar{h}$ indicate cross-sectional mean values and s_f (friction slope) is determined in relation to a flow equation, such as

$$s_f = \frac{\bar{u}\,|\bar{u}|}{Ch^2 R} \quad \text{or} \quad s_f = \frac{n^2\,\bar{u}\,|\bar{u}|}{R^{4/3}} \tag{1.22}$$

where Ch is the Chezy coefficient, n is the Manning coefficient and, for wide channels R (hydraulic radius) $= \bar{h}$.

Section 2.7 briefly describes the different numerical methods of solving the marine applications of these equations. For flow in one dimension with the ability to specify the boundary conditions at time $t = t_0$, the method of characteristics may be applied to equations 1.20 and 1.21, by combining them to yield an hyperbolic equation of the form $\partial^2\bar{u}/\partial x^2 - A\,\partial^2\bar{u}/\partial t^2 = B$. If $E_1 =$ lefthand side of equation 1.20 and $E_2 =$ lefthand side of equation 1.21 and the characteristic velocity $C = (gh)^{1/2}$ then

$$E_1 \pm \frac{C}{g}\,E_2 \tag{1.23}$$

$$= \frac{\partial\eta}{\partial t} + (\bar{u} \pm C)\,\frac{\partial\eta}{\partial x} \pm \frac{C}{g}\left[\frac{\partial\bar{u}}{\partial t} + (\bar{u} \pm C)\,\frac{\partial\bar{u}}{\partial x}\right] + C(s_f - s) = 0$$

An operator D $[= \partial/\partial t + (\partial x/\partial t)\,(\partial/\partial x) = \partial/\partial t + (\bar{u} \pm C)\,\partial/\partial x$, where $\partial x/\partial t = u \pm C]$ corresponds to a positive or negative characteristic.

Along such a characteristic equation 1.23 may be written

$$D\eta \pm \frac{C}{g}\,D\bar{u} = \pm C(s - s_f) \tag{1.24}$$

which readily lends itself to stepwise solution by considering points of intersection of characteristics in (x, t) space, starting from points on the boundary $t = t_0$ for which values of η and $\bar{u}$ are known (figure 1.5).

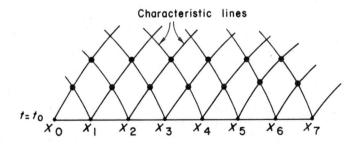

Characteristic lines

$t = t_0$

$x_0 \quad x_1 \quad x_2 \quad x_3 \quad x_4 \quad x_5 \quad x_6 \quad x_7$

Figure 1.5 *Reference diagram for characteristics for one-dimensional flow*

1.3 Sediment Transport

Natural sediments can be broadly described as cohesive or non-cohesive. The
behaviour of the former can be influenced by electromagnetic forces in
addition to physical drag and lift hydrodynamic forces. Marine sediments on
an open coastline are non-cohesive, and their movement depends on the
motions of the sea and on the physical properties of the individual particles,
described further below.

1.3.1 Particle Size

The most common method of measuring sediment size distribution is by
sieving and plotting the results as weight of material retained against sieve size
to produce a cumulative size frequency curve. The technique tends to measure
the minor dimensions of the particles and is unsatisfactory for very fine sands.
Other methods of sediment size measurements include equivalent or sediment-
action diameter, triaxial dimensions or nominal diameter. As the terminal fall
velocity of particles is one of the most important parameters used to describe
sediment motion, the first of these methods may be the most appropriate since
the problem of shape factor is largely eliminated. However, this method can be
misleading because the fall velocity of a patchy cloud of grains may not be the
same as for grains uniformly dispersed throughout a fluid or for single grains.

Natural sediments tend to be irregular in shape, and definition by a single
dimension can be somewhat incomplete. Shape can influence the hydraulic
characteristics of particles, principally the drag and lift forces, depending on
the Reynolds number. One of the more useful descriptions of particle shape has
been suggested by McNown and Malaika.[1] Using three mutually perpendicular axes, a shape factor is defined as the ratio of the shortest dimension
to the square root of the product of the other two dimensions. However, it
should be noted that this does not differentiate between a cube and a sphere.
Generally, if the equivalent sedimentation diameter is known the problem of
shape can be avoided.

Several different values can be taken from cumulative size frequency curves
and used as the representative particle size for sediment transport calculations.
This is because in heterogenous sediments at low stages of flow there is a greater
proportion of the finer fractions than the coarser fractions in movement and the
proportions can change with flow conditions. Thus any one representative
particle size applied to the whole range of flows is probably inadequate,
because the effective sediment size will vary with the transport rate. In the
absence of any more satisfactory evidence to indicate the appropriate particular
representative diameter it is customary to use a value of D_{50} (50 per cent finer
than).

In pure water, the coefficient of viscosity μ is 1.31×10^{-3} kg/m s at $10°C$
with a temperature variation of about -0.03×10^{-3} (kg/m s) per $°C$.
(Kinematic viscosity $\nu = 1.792 \times 10^{-6} \exp(-0.042T^{0.87}) \, 0 < T < 30°C$.)

In sea water of density 1025 kg/m^3, the coefficient of viscosity μ is about
8 per cent greater than that of fresh water at the same temperature (that is ν
is about 6 per cent greater).

1.3.2 Fall Velocity

The terminal fall velocity of particles is important when relating sediment properties to theories of grain motion. The fall velocity is principally a function of size, shape, density and fluid viscosity, but may also be influenced by sediment concentration. The terminal fall velocity is estimated by equating the drag forces on a particle falling through a fluid to the gravitational force so that

$$w_s = \left[\frac{4}{3} \frac{gD (\rho_s - \rho)}{C_D \rho} \right]^{1/2} \tag{1.25}$$

where C_D is a dimensionless drag coefficient, D is a representative diameter, g is acceleration due to gravity, ρ_s and ρ are the density of solid and fluid respectively and w_s is the terminal fall velocity. The problem reduces to one of finding a drag coefficient for a particular sediment and flow condition. For high values of Reynolds number ($Re \geqslant 500$) the drag coefficient is approximately 0.5 because inertial forces predominate over viscous forces. For small values of Re (unity or less) the fall velocity is governed by Stokes' Law where

$$w_s = \frac{g}{18} \left(\frac{\rho_s - \rho}{\mu} \right) D^2 \tag{1.26}$$

in which μ is the coefficient of viscosity.

Figure 1.6 illustrates the ranges of equations 1.25 and 1.26 together with the transition region, for particles of quartz density, $\rho_s/\rho = 2.65$. This value corresponds approximately to the specific density of most natural rock particles, larger than fine silts or clays, commonly found in the open sea.

At 20°C the fall velocity for particles of median size 60×10^{-6} $< D_{50} < 6000 \times 10^{-6}$ m is given by

$$\log \left(\frac{1}{w_s} \right) = 0.447 (\log D_{50})^2 + 1.961 \log D_{50} + 2.736 \tag{1.27}$$

Elata and Ippen [2] found that a uniform suspension of neutrally buoyant spheres behaved as a Newtonian fluid but appeared to exhibit an effectively higher viscosity dependent on, and increasing with volumetric concentration. However, there are few theoretical and experimental data in general relating to the settling velocity of dispersed particles at high concentration. The viscosity of diluted suspensions may normally be considered approximately to correspond to that of the clear fluid.[3,4]

Some other expressions [5] generally relate to stable suspensions and may not correspond to conditions in oscillatory flow. Temperature affects viscosity and hence the behaviour of suspended sediments. (see section 1.3.1).

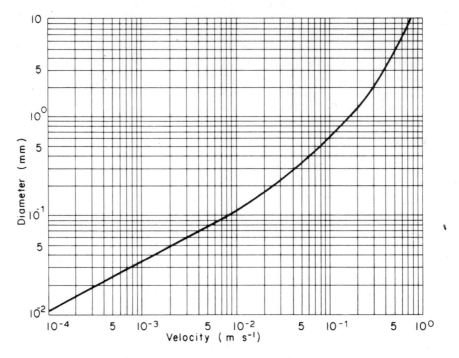

Figure 1.6 *Terminal fall velocities for quartz particles*

1.3.3 Critical or Threshold Stress

The critical or threshold stress is the shear stress acting on the bed at the stage of
flow at which sediment movement can be considered to have started. This is not
a well-defined condition. As soon as a substantial number of particles are in
motion the situation may be complicated by impact forces between the moving
and the stationary grains, although these effects are thought to be small. Clearly,
different particles may be subject to a variety of initial conditions such as
depositional state and different fluid and gravitational forces due to variations
in size, shape and density. Also bed forms can have a significant influence on
threshold conditions.

In undirectional flow the relative importance of the threshold condition
depends very much on the sediment particle size. For coarse particles the
threshold condition will, for the majority of the time, be fairly constant, while
for fine sands it cannot be so precisely defined. A wide range of relationships
have been proposed by various investigators [6] and there is evidence to suggest
that Shields' curve, the most widely used [7] should be modified for both fine
materials [8] and coarse materials.[9]

The results of a number of investigations, relating to critical conditions for
threshold sediment movement under waves, have been compared [10] and
found to produce large differences in the results. It is evident that under waves,
while the symmetry of motions may not contribute to any sediment transport,

the instantaneous velocity may be great enough to overcome the threshold stress so that the sediment may be transported by a very weak superimposed current. Furthermore in an unsteady flow it may be expected that inertia forces in addition to drag and lift forces will contribute to the entrainment of sediment particles. Approximate analyses [11] have shown that in general the additional forces due to the unsteadiness of the motion are small when considering threshold conditions.

Experimental data have been used to show that Shields' criterion for the threshold of sediment movement in unidirectional steady flows serves as a reasonable general threshold criterion for movement under waves, when the entraining force is evaluated using Jonsson's wave friction factor relationship (see section 3.4.1). Figure 1.7 shows Shields' diagram for the initiation of sediment movement where the dimensionless bed shear stress is related to a Reynolds number where u_* is the shear velocity $(\tau_0/\rho)^{1/2}$ and τ_0 the shear stress at the bed. This result applies only to flat beds; threshold conditions for an initially rippled bed could be somewhat different.[12]

1.3.4 Models of Turbulence

The shear stress in a turbulent flow may be expressed as

$$\tau = -\rho \,\overline{u'w'} \tag{1.28}$$

where $\overline{u'w'}$ is the time average of the instantaneous velocity fluctuations in the fluid.

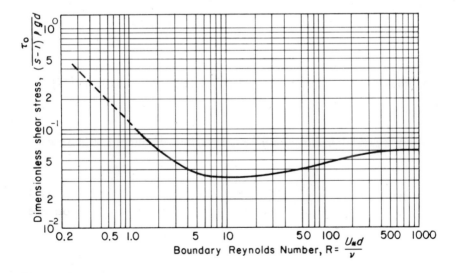

Figure 1.7 *Shields' diagram for the initiation of sediment movement*

By analogy to laminar flow and the parallel drawn by Boussinesq, equation 1.28 can be written as

$$\tau = \rho \epsilon \frac{du}{dz} \tag{1.29}$$

where ϵ is a coefficient of eddy viscosity analogous to laminar viscosity. Prandtl proposed that the turbulent viscosity or eddy viscosity coefficient be considered as the product of the fluid density, the magnitude of the velocity gradient and square of the characteristic length scale of turbulent motion so that

$$\tau = \rho l^2 \left| \frac{du}{dz} \right| \frac{du}{dz} \tag{1.30}$$

The physical interpretation of the length scale l or mixing length is the distance in the transverse direction that must be covered by an eddy in order to make the difference between its original velocity and the velocity of flow in its new position equal to the mean transverse fluctuation in the turbulent flow. The mixing length is not a property of the fluid, but a function of the flow itself.

For unidirectional flow von Kármán [13] introduced a similarity hypothesis. He suggested that the mixing length is proportional to the ratio of the first and second derivatives of mean velocity so that

$$l = \kappa \frac{du}{dz} \bigg/ \frac{d^2u}{dz^2} \tag{1.31}$$

where κ is known as von Kármán's constant and has a value of 0.4 for sediment-free fluid. However, in sediment-laden flow the value of κ may be at variance with this.

Equations 1.29, 1.30 and 1.31 are the fundamental relationships that are used to describe turbulent velocity distribution and to relate sediment transport to flow conditions.

The variation of mean horizontal velocity with depth may be derived from the turbulence model, that is, if shear stress varies linearly with depth [14]

$$\tau = \tau_0 (1 - z/h) \tag{1.32}$$

where $\tau_0 = \rho ghs$ for unidirectional flow. Thus, from equations 1.30, 1.31 and 1.32

$$gs (h - z) = \kappa^2 \left(\frac{du}{dz} \right)^4 \bigg/ \left(\frac{d^2u}{dz^2} \right)^2 \tag{1.33}$$

By integration

$$\frac{du}{dz} = \frac{u_*}{2 \kappa h \left[B - (1 - z/h)^{1/2} \right]} \tag{1.34}$$

where u_*, shear velocity, $= (ghs)^{1/2}$ and B is a constant of integration.

A second integration gives

$$u = \frac{u_*}{\kappa} \left\{ (1 - z/h)^{1/2} + B \ln \left[\frac{B - (1 - z/h)^{1/2}}{B} \right] \right\} + \text{const} \qquad (1.35)$$

For constant shear stress throughout the depth, equation 1.35 becomes

$$u = \frac{u_*}{\kappa} \ln (z/h) + \text{const} \qquad (1.36)$$

as in section 2.4.2.

In unidirectional flow sediment can be considered to be transported in two regions: bed load is transported in a layer adjacent to the stationary part of the bed, supported by inter-particle collision, and suspended load is transported in a region in which gravitational forces are overcome by fluid turbulence. Owing to observational difficulties the transition between the suspended load region and the bed load layer has, for a long time, remained undefined. Sediment transport under waves may be developed by methods parallel to unidirectional flow in that sediment can be considered to be transported as bed load and suspended load, treating the unsteady motion as a quasi-steady state over a long period.

1.3.5 Suspended Sediment

The simplest one-dimensional time-dependent suspended load distribution is given by the diffusion equation

$$\frac{\partial c}{\partial t} = \frac{\partial}{\partial z} \left(\epsilon_s \frac{\partial c}{\partial z} - cw' \right) \qquad (1.37)$$

where t is time, ϵ_s is a sediment diffusion coefficient and w' is the vertical velocity of the sediment.

In order to arrive at equation 1.37 it must be assumed that sediment diffusion in the horizontal direction is negligible compared to the vertical and that conditions are changing slowly enough to neglect lateral differences in advective transport of sediment and hence horizontal concentration gradients. In a quasi-steady state for which it can be assumed that $\partial c/\partial t = 0$, $w_s = -w'$ so that $\partial w'/\partial z = 0$ where w_s is the particle fall velocity, equation 1.37 can then be reduced to

$$\epsilon_s \frac{\partial c}{\partial z} + cw_s = 0 \qquad (1.38)$$

where c is sediment concentration.

Equation 1.38, which is identical to that for undirectional flow, can be solved by assuming that the diffusion of sediment is similar to momentum transfer of the fluid itself. As a consequence equation 1.29 is also applied to the sediment diffusion coefficient. This assumption implies that the presence of the sediment has no influence on the transfer mechanisms. A more complex form of equation 1.38 has been considered [14] for high concentrations which takes account of the volume occupied by the particles, as well as a sediment diffusion coefficient different from the eddy diffusion coefficient.

When applying equation 1.38 to oscillatory flow it is already assumed that the fall velocity of the particles is uniform and therefore unaffected by fluid acceleration. Furthermore when using linear wave theory the vertical distribution of the sediment diffusion coefficient cannot be related in any way to a shear stress distribution because the flow is, by definition, irrotational. It is therefore necessary to specify a vertical distribution of sediment diffusion coefficient as discussed in chapter 4.

The integration of equation 1.38 will only reveal the relative concentration distribution and is not valid in the region very close to the bed due to the neglect of governing forces in that region. Its complete solution requires the definition of boundary conditions at the bed.

1.3.6 Bed Load

Sediment transport near the sea bed may take the form of sliding or rolling or intermittent suspension, described as saltation. When the shear force acting on the bed increases to the extent that sediment is in motion, a rapid increase in the number of particle collisions occurs. As the result of a decrease in the velocity gradient, and hence of lift forces close to the bed, a collision layer of particles is formed known as the bed load. The point of distinction between the bed load and suspended load is not readily apparent either in the field or the laboratory.

Bagnold [15] presents an original and instructive approach to analysing the magnitude of bed movement, based fundamentally on the collisions between individual particles. The shear stress in excess of the threshold shear must be dispersed within the bed load layer, otherwise successive layers of material would be removed from the bed resulting in infinite scour. Bagnold suggests that the excess shear stress is dispersed by internal resisting forces in the bed load layer described by

$$\tau_d/p \approx \tan \alpha \tag{1.39}$$

where τ_d is the dispersed shear, p is the normal dispersive stress due to the submerged weight of the particles and α is a friction angle approximately equal to the angle of repose. Bagnold argued that, in the absence of grain suspension, the normal dispersive grain stress at the boundary must, under steady conditions, be equal to the normal immersed weight component of all the moving grains, no matter how they are dispersed and no matter what the flow conditions are.

The mobile bed consists of a sediment phase and a water phase. For high concentrations of sediment particles, shear stresses transmitted through the

water phase within the bed load may be ignored by comparison with the
forces in the sediment phase applied along the shear planes of the bed.
Consider a bed load layer of thickness z_0 with some concentration distribution
$c = \phi'(Z')$ where $Z' = z/z_0$. By assuming that the bed load thickness defines
the transition level between bed load and suspended load, equation 1.39 can
be used [16] to give the thickness by

$$z_0 = \frac{\tau_0 - \tau_c}{(\rho_s - \rho_w) g (\tan \alpha - \tan \beta) \cos \beta \int_0^1 \phi'(Z') \, dZ'} \qquad (1.40)$$

where τ_0 is the applied shear at the bed, τ_c is the threshold shear and β is the
angle of the bed to the horizontal.

The applied and resistive forces that lead to the derivation of equation 1.40
are shown in figure 1.8.

It is necessary to make some assumption with respect to the distribution
of concentration within the bed load layer. Concentration is often assumed
to be sensibly constant throughout the bed load layer but it would be more
plausible to assume [17] that there is an attenuation of concentration with
height above the bed, because the lower layers within the bed load are
supporting the particles in the upper layers.

The exact definition of the transition level between the bed load and the
suspended load should not be critical because the order of magnitude of
sediment flows above and below the transition level will be similar.
Continuity of fluid and sediment velocity and also of sediment concentration
at this level may be assumed. These considerations are somewhat easier to apply
to undirectional flow than to oscillatory flow, but they enable the reference
concentration to be defined empirically by calibration to field or laboratory
data [17] and hence a common boundary condition between the bed load and
suspended load.

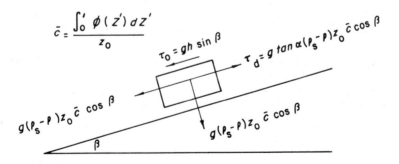

Figure 1.8 *Forces in the bed load*

1.3.7 Bed Forms and Effective Grain Shear Stress

At various stages of flow, the surface of a mobile bed acquires statistically periodic irregularities. In unidirectional flow these can generally by classified as ripples, dunes, bars, antidunes, shutes and pools.

Bed forms can have a significant influence on flow characteristics because they dominate the flow resistance of the bed. Much work has been directed towards the evaluation of friction factor in alluvial streams generally in order to determine stage discharge relationships.[18] The problem related to sediment transport is to determine, for given flow conditions, the residual shear force or energy that is available to transport the sediment. The total applied shear may be split up into components so that

$$\tau_0 = \tau_1 + \tau_2 + \tau_3 \tag{1.41}$$

where τ_1 is the equivalent flat bed shear, τ_2 is the shear resistance of the bed forms and τ_3 is the shear resistance in the suspended load. In most cases τ_3 can be neglected.

Expressions for τ_2 proposed for unidirectional flow do not easily apply to oscillatory flow because there are no equivalent stage discharge relationships. However, for the ripples that form under short-period waves in sand an equivalent roughness length can be related to the scale of the bed forms (see chapter 4).

1.3.8 Density Currents

In its simplest form a density current is caused by the motion of a fluid, underlying a fluid of lesser density, as it tends to restore a horizontal interface, in the absence of other external forces. A turbidity current represents a special case of a density current where the excess density of the lower fluid is caused by sediment in suspension.

If a sediment of terminal velocity w_s is considered to be in suspension in volumetric concentration c, in a turbidity layer of depth h, immediately above the bed, which is inclined to the horizontal at an angle β, and if the layer moves parallel to the bed at a mean steady velocity $\bar{u}$, the power per unit area (representing the rate of loss of potential energy) may be written [19]

$$p_1 = (\rho_s - \rho) gch\bar{u} \sin \beta \tag{1.42}$$

The power per unit area needed to maintain the suspension at a constant position relative to the bed, expended in the form of turbulence, must be

$$p_2 = (\rho_s - \rho) gchw_s \tag{1.43}$$

Neglecting losses at the upper boundary, a shear stress of τ_0 along the bed must account for loss of power per unit area

$$p_3 = \tau_0 \bar{u} \tag{1.44}$$

For the motion to be sustained $p_1 > (p_2 + p_3)$ and hence equations 1.42, 1.43 and 1.44 may be combined to give

$$(\rho_s - \rho) \, gch \left(\sin \beta - \frac{w_s}{\bar{u}} \right) > \tau_0 \qquad (1.45)$$

where $\bar{u} > w'/\sin \beta$. The bed shear stress may be evaluated from the turbulent velocity distribution so that the possibility of self-sustained turbidity currents may be investigated using the inequality of equation 1.45.

Turbidity currents have been of great interest to engineers where they have been encountered in the areas containing submarine cables. Heezen [20] provides evidence of turbidity currents derived from the breaking of such cables. The classic instance concerns the turbidity current provoked by large-scale slumping at the edge of the continental shelf by the Grand Banks earthquake, south of the Cabot Strait, in 1929. The precise time of failure of a number of cables in the area allowed the rate of progress of the turbidity currents to be established. This varied from about 50 km/h, on the slope of the shelf where the bed gradient was 1:10 to 1:30, to about 12 km/h on the abyssal plain where the bed slope was about 1:1500. The extent of the current, which covered an area about 150 km wide by about 600 km long, was subsequently proved by coring – the sediment had settled to a consolidated depth of about 1 m, with coarse sand present among the deep water sediments, as direct evidence of the flow.

It is believed that tsunamis are usually the result of slumping of underwater slopes set off by earthquakes rather than the direct result of the earthquake (some, however, are caused by submarine volcanic action such as that associated with Krakatoa in 1883). The initial slumping has been attributed to high pore pressures set up by closer particle packing of a loosely deposited sediment.[21]

References

1. J.S. McNown and J. Malaika, Effects of particle shape on settling velocity at low Reynolds numbers, *Trans. Am. Geophys. Un.*, **31** (1950)
2. C. Elata and A.T. Ippen, The dynamics of open channel flow with suspensions of neutrally bouyant particles, M.I.T. Department of Civil Engineering, Hydraulics Laboratory Technical Report No. 45 (1961)
3. H.A. Einstein, The bed-load function for sediment transport in open channel flows, *Tech. Bull. Soil Conserv. Serv. U.S. Dep. Agric.*, **1026** (1950)
4. G.K. Batchelor, *An Introduction to Fluid Dynamics* (Cambridge University Press, 1974)
5. S.G. Ward, Properties of well-defined suspensions of solids in liquids, *J. Oil Colour Chem Ass.*, **38**(g) (1955) 1–23
6. –, Sediment transport mechanics: initiation of motion, Progress Report of the Task Committee on the Preparation of Sediment Manual, *Proc. Am. Soc. civ. Engrs*, **92**, HY2 (1966)
7. A. Shields, Anwendung Ahnlichkeitsmechanik und der Turbulenzforschung auf die Gescheibebewegung, *Mitt. preuss. VersAnst. Wasserb Schiffb.*, **26** (1936) 1–36

8. A.J. Grass, Initial instability of fine bed sands, *Proc. Am. Soc. civ. Engrs*, **96**, HY3 (1970) 619-32

9. W.R. White, H. Mille and A.D. Crabbe, Sediment transport theories: a review, *Proc. Instn civ. Engrs*, **59** (2) (1975) 265-92; Discussion and reply, **61** (2) (1976) 207-28

10. R. Silvester and G.R. Mogridge, Reach of waves to the bed on the continental shelf, *Proceedings of the 12th Coastal Engineering Conference, Washington, 1970*, vol. II, 651-67

11. O.S. Madsen and W.D. Grant, Quantitative description of sediment transport by waves, *Proceedings of the 15th Coastal Engineering Conference, Hawaii, 1976*, 1093-112

12. P.D. Komar and M.C. Miller, The threshold of sediment movement under oscillatory water waves, *Proceedings of the 14th Coastal Engineering Conference, Copenhagen, 1974*,

13. T. von Kármán, Mechanische Ahnlichkeit und Turbulenz, *Nachr. Ges. Wiss. Göttingen*, **58** (1930) 58-76

14. J.N. Hunt, The turbulent transport of suspended sediment in open channels, *Proc. R. Soc. A*, **224** (1954) 322-35

15. R.A. Bagnold, The flow of cohesionless grains in fluids, *Phil. Trans. R. Soc. A*, **249** (1956) 235-97

16. C.A. Fleming and J.N. Hunt, A mathematical sediment transport model for unidirectional flow, *Proc. Instn civ. Engrs*, **61** (2) (1976) 297-310

17. C.A. Fleming, The development and application of a mathematical sediment transport model, Ph.D. Thesis, University of Reading, 1977

18. —, Sediment transport mechanics: F. Hydraulic relations for alluvial streams, Task Committee on the Preparation of Sedimentation Manual, *Proc. Am. Soc. civ. Engrs*, **97**, HY1 (1971) 101-41

19. R.A. Bagnold, Auto-suspension of transported sediment; turbidity currents, *Proc. R. Soc. A*, **265** (1962) 315-19

20. B.C. Heezen, Turbidity currents, in *The Sea*, vol. III, ed. M.N. Hill (Interscience, New York, 1963)

21. N.R. Morgenstern, Submarine slumping and the initiation of turbidity currents, *Marine Geotechnique* (University of Illinois, 1967) pp. 189-220

2

Tides and Currents

This chapter presents a brief account of tidal theory, indicating the causes of the most important features of tides and the steps involved in tidal analysis. Tides are subject to local sea changes which give rise to many oddities and apparent anomalies, especially close inshore. While a quantitative application of this theory may require a detailed mathematical analysis, the underlying causes can be described in relatively simple terms.

2.1 The Equilibrium Tide

2.1.1 Tangential and Normal Tractive Forces

The Mediterranean civilisations were substantially unaware of tidal phenomena because of the relatively small movement of the sea with which they were familiar. In places where appreciable diurnal tides (one cycle per day) and semi-diurnal tides (two cycles per day) occur, on the other hand, they have been associated with the passage of the moon for many centuries, even by primitive people. Only, however, when Sir Isaac Newton propounded his theory of gravitation was the first step taken in establishing a rational theory of causation.

Gravitational attraction of the Sun and the Moon exerts forces on the seas and oceans which cause a systematic rise and fall of water level, causing associated horizontal currents. The tide-producing forces are oscillatory but, on account of the complexity of the combined pattern of movement of the Sun and Moon, the resulting oscillatory force is predictable but irregular.

During the period of lunar orbit the Moon reaches positions of maximum declination to the north and south as well as maximum and minimum distances from the Earth (respectively apogee and perigee). The Moon's orbit causes semi-diurnal tides, the declination creating the diurnal tide. The Sun causes similar but lesser semi-diurnal and diurnal tides. The forces due to the Sun and Moon may act together or in opposition. At new and full Moon the combined forces reach a maximum, thus causing spring tides and large ranges at intervals of two weeks. Neap tides of minimum rise and fall occur when the forces are in opposition, that is, at first and last quarter of the Moon.

Newton calculated the tidal forces due to the gravitational pull of the Moon and the Sun along the following lines. Figure 2.1 represents a plane containing the Earth and the Moon.

The Moon's gravitational pull on a particle of unit mass at X is

$$\frac{gMe^2}{Ex^2} \quad \text{towards O}'$$

where e and E are the radius and mass of the Earth, M is the mass of the Moon, x the distance to the centre of the Moon and g the acceleration due to gravity at the surface of the Earth. Tides are caused by the departures of the magnitudes of these forces acting on particles of the sea from their mean value for the Earth as a whole. This is itself approximately the same as the Moon's gravitational pull at the centroid of the Earth. But the pull of the Moon on a unit mass at the centre of the Earth is

$$\frac{gMe^2}{Er^2} \quad \text{along OO}'$$

where r is the distance between the centres of the Earth and Moon.

With θ and ϕ defined as in figure 2.1, the normal components of these two forces along OX are

$$\frac{gMe^2}{Ex^2} \cos(\theta + \phi) \text{ and } \frac{gMe^2}{Er^2} \cos\theta$$

respectively. The normal component P_n of the differential tractive force is then

$$P_n = g\,\frac{M}{E}\left[\frac{e^2}{x^2}\cos(\theta + \phi) - \frac{e^2}{r^2}\cos\theta\right]$$

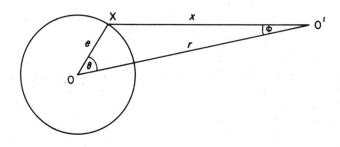

Figure 2.1 *Lunar tidal forces*

from figure 2.1, which may be simplified by approximation to

$$P_n \approx g \, \frac{M}{E} \, \frac{e^3}{r^3} \, (3 \cos^2 \theta - 1) \tag{2.1}$$

Similarly, the tangential differential tractive force at X

$$P_t = g \, \frac{M}{E} \left[\frac{e^2}{x^2} \sin(\theta + \phi) - \frac{e^2}{r^2} \sin \theta \right]$$

$$\approx \frac{3}{2} \, g \, \frac{M}{E} \, \frac{e^3}{r^3} \sin 2\theta \tag{2.2}$$

Clearly P_n is a maximum when $\theta = 0$ or π, when, from equation 2.1, $P_n \approx 1.12 \, g$ x 10^{-7} for $E/M \approx 81.5$ and $r/e \approx 60.3$. Likewise P_n has a minimum value of $\sim -0.56 \, g$ x 10^{-7} when $\theta = \pi/2$ or $3\pi/2$. This normal component is evidently negligible by comparison with g which acts in the same direction.

From equation 2.2, P_t is seen to have maxima and minima of $\sim \pm 0.84 \, g$ x 10^{-7} when $\theta = \pi/4, 3\pi/4$, etc., and is zero intermediately at $\theta = 0, \pi/2$, etc.

Similar relationships may be established for tractive forces due to the Sun, which are equivalent to the numerical values obtained from equations 2.1 and 2.2, multiplied by a factor of about 0.46 to take account of the different values, for the Sun, of the ratios corresponding to M/E and e^3/r^3.

2.1.2 Levels of the Equilibrium Tide

For the equilibrium tide, (that is, ignoring all dynamic considerations) the slope of the sea at any point on the surface of the Earth (considered to be entirely covered by the sea) is given by the ratio of $P_t : g$. From equation 2.2

slope $= k \sin 2\theta$

where k represents

$$\frac{3}{2} \, \frac{M}{E} \, \frac{e^3}{r^3}$$

Figure 2.2 represents a quadrant of the Earth between two planes, passing through O and O', containing an angle λ. Let the mean sea level from P to Q (see figure 2.2) be h above the geoid, that is, the sea surface with no tide. Then

change in level from P to X $= - \int_0^\theta k \sin 2\theta \, e \, d\theta = \frac{ke}{2} (\cos 2\theta - 1)$

that is, amplitude or half-height of the tide $= ke/2$.

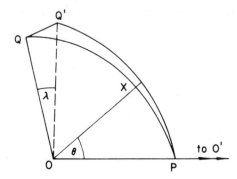

Figure 2.2 *Reference diagram*

Equating the volume of the tidal wave from P to Q with the volume of the sea in this quadrant with no tide, gives

$$\int_0^{\pi/2} ke^3 \lambda \cos 2\theta \sin \theta \, d\theta + \int_0^{\pi/2} h\lambda e^2 \sin \theta \, d\theta = 0$$

that is

$$ke \int_0^{\pi/2} \frac{(\sin 3\theta - \sin \theta)}{2} \, d\theta = -h \int_0^{\pi/2} \sin \theta \, d\theta$$

or

$$h = ke \, \frac{\left[\frac{\cos 3\theta}{6} + \frac{1}{2} \cos \theta \right]_0^{\pi/2}}{\left[\cos \theta \right]_0^{\pi/2}}$$

$$= \frac{1}{6} ke \text{ or } \frac{1}{3} \text{ amplitude} \tag{2.3}$$

Hence with respect to the geoid, the tide will vary in the range $\pm ke/2 + ke/6$, that is, between $\frac{2}{3} ke$ and $-\frac{1}{3} ke$.

2.1.3 Tractive Forces in Three Dimensions

Figure 2.3 indicates the shell of the northern hemisphere, where

O and O' represent centres of Earth and Moon
U and U', points where OO' cuts surface of Earth
X, a point on the Earth's surface through which is drawn a great circle, UXU'
C: $\angle$XOO'
P: North Pole

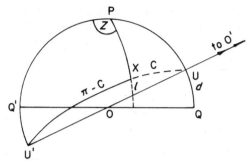

Figure 2.3 *Reference diagram for equilibrium tide*

Q and Q': points on equator in the plane of O,O', and P
d, north declination of Moon, that is, $\angle UOQ$
l, north latitude of X
Z, longitude of X east of meridian PQ'U'

Then, $\angle POX = \pi/2 - l$ and $\angle POU = \pi/2 - d$, $\angle XOU = \theta$ (see figure 2.1). The tangential tractive force $= kg \sin 2\theta$ from equation 2.2 where

$$k = \frac{3}{2} \frac{M}{E} \frac{e^3}{r^3}$$

and

P_{tn} (north component) $= kg \sin 2\theta \cos PXU$ (2.4)

P_{te} (east component) $= kg \sin 2\theta \sin PXU$ (2.5)

But, from the properties of spherical triangles formed from intersections of great circles

$$\cos \theta = \cos (\pi/2 - l) \cos (\pi/2 - d)$$
$$+ \sin (\pi/2 - l) \sin (\pi/2 - d) \cos (\pi - Z) \quad (2.6)$$

$$\cos (\pi/2 - d) = \cos (\pi/2 - l) \cos \theta + \sin (\pi/2 - l) \sin \theta \cos PXU \quad (2.7)$$

and

$$\sin \theta \sin PXU = \sin (\pi/2 - d) \sin (\pi - Z) \quad (2.8)$$

Equations 2.4, 2.5, 2.6, 2.7, and 2.8 simplify to give

$$P_{tn} = kg[- \tfrac{1}{2} \sin 2l(1 - 3 \sin^2 d)$$
$$- \cos 2l \sin 2d \cos Z - \tfrac{1}{2} \sin 2l \cos d \cos 2Z] \quad (2.9)$$

and

$$P_{te} = kg[\sin l \sin 2d \sin Z - \cos l \cos^2 d \sin 2Z] \quad (2.10)$$

It will be seen that P_{tn} has a component which is a constant (long period component) for given values of l and d, a diurnal component $f(Z)$, and a semi-diurnal component, $f(2Z)$. P_{te} has diurnal and semi-diurnal components only. As will be indicated below, d has a maximum value of about 30°; for a given latitude, the diurnal component of P_{tn} and of P_{te} increases with increasing d, while the semi-diurnal component decreases somewhat with increasing d. When $d = 0$, there is no diurnal component.

For a given value of d, the constant term for P_{tn} is a maximum for $2l = \pm\pi/2$, that is, $l = \pm \pi/4$, while the diurnal component of P_{tn} is a maximum for $2l = 0$ or π, that is, $l = 0°$ or $\pi/2$, representing a point on the equator or close to the North or South Pole; the diurnal component of P_{te} is a maximum for $l = \pm \pi/2$, that is, close to the North or South Pole. In the same way, the semi-diurnal components of P_{tn} and P_{te} are seen to be maxima for $l = \pm \pi/4$ and $l = 0°$ respectively. It is evident that the maximum values of the factors for each component are of the same order.

2.1.4 The Equilibrium Tide over the Earth's Surface

The slope of the surface following a line of latitude will be given by

$$\frac{P_{te}}{g} = k[\sin l \sin 2d \sin Z - \cos l \cos^2 d \sin 2Z]$$

from equation 2.10. Hence the change in sea level between X and a point on the same latitude on PUQ is

$$k \int_{\pi}^{Z} (\sin l \sin 2d \sin Z - \cos l \cos^2 d \sin 2Z) e \cos l \, dZ$$

$$= ke\left[- \sin l \cos l \sin 2d \cos Z + \frac{1}{2} \cos^2 l \cos^2 d \cos 2Z \right]_{\pi}^{Z}$$

$$= -\frac{ke}{2}\left[(1 + \cos Z) \sin 2l \sin 2d + (1 - \cos 2Z) \cos^2 l \cos^2 d\right]$$

but the level on PUQ at latitude l may be derived from equation 2.3 substituting $l - d$ for θ, as

$$ke/2\left[\cos 2(l - d) + \frac{1}{3}\right]$$

Hence the sea level at any point X on figure 1.3 is given by

$$\frac{ke}{2}\left[\frac{1}{3} + \cos 2\,(l - d) - \sin 2l \sin 2d\,(1 + \cos Z)\right.$$
$$\left. - \cos^2 l \cos^2 d\,(1 - \cos 2Z)\right]$$

$$= \frac{ke}{2} \left[\frac{1}{3} + \cos 2\,(l-d) - \sin 2l \sin 2d - \cos^2 l \cos^2 d \right.$$

$$\left. - \sin 2l \sin 2d \cos Z + \cos^2 l \cos^2 d \cos 2Z \right]$$

$$= \frac{ke}{2} \left[3 \left(\sin^2 l - \frac{1}{3} \right) \left(\sin^2 d - \frac{1}{3} \right) - \sin 2l \sin 2d \cos Z \right.$$

$$\left. + \cos^2 l \cos^2 d \cos 2Z \right] \tag{2.11}$$

and this represents the general equation for the equilibrium tide due to the Moon. A similar expression may be derived for the equilibrium tide due to the Sun and summation of the two will give that for the combined effects of Sun and Moon (disregarding in each instance the secondary gravitational effects of the shape of the tidal wave itself and other approximations of small order). Equation 2.11 contains a constant term for the particular latitude and declination, a diurnal and a semi-diurnal term.

2.1.5 Harmonic Analysis of Equilibrium Tides

In applying a relationship such as equation 2.11 to the computation of the equilibrium tide, at a certain time and a certain position on the Earth's surface, it is necessary to introduce terms that will take account of the relative motion of the Moon and Sun in these respects

(1) angular orbit around the Earth
(2) distance from the Earth
(3) angular velocity around the Earth [a function of (2)].

The problem is complicated by the relative motions and differing cyclical periods of the Moon and Sun. Thus, while the ecliptic of the Sun makes a constant angle of 23°27' with a plane through the equator and completes a cycle of rotation of the ecliptic about the Earth in about 365¼ days (the Julian year), the Moon's motion is compounded of an orbit around the Earth and an oscillation relative to the ecliptic; the completion of an integral number of cycles of each type of motion occupies about 18.6 (Julian) years.

The mean lunar day is about 24.84 h but, as an added complication, the distance of the Moon from the Earth varies with a period a little longer than that of the orbit, or of the superimposed oscillation referred to above. For a comprehensive analysis, all these considerations have to be taken into account. The total tide-raising force may be expressed as the sum of a number of cosine curves of different amplitude and frequency. If tides were caused by a single celestial body orbiting the Earth above the equator a simple harmonic tidal force would result, of the form

$$h = A \cos (nt + k)$$

where A is the amplitude, n the angular velocity and k the phase lag. Account may be taken of the complexities of the combined relative motions of Sun and Moon by representing the tidal force as a sum of a number of harmonic

TABLE 2.1 *Major harmonic constituents*

Name	Description	Hourly Speed (°)	Relative Magnitude
	Semi-diurnal Constituents		
M_2	Principal lunar constituent, moving at twice the speed of the mean Moon.	28.98	1.00
S_2	Principal solar constituent, moving at twice the speed of the mean Sun.	30.00	0.46
N_2 L_2	These two constituents between them allow for the changes in the Moon's distance due to its elliptic orbit round the Earth.	28.44 29.53	0.20 0.03
K_2 T_2	These two constituents between them allow for the effect of the declination of the Sun and Moon and of changes in the Sun's distance	30.08 29.96	0.13 0.03
μ_2 $2N_2$ ν_2 λ_2	These four constituents allow for perturbations of the Moon's orbit by the Sun's attraction for the Moon.	29.97 27.90 28.51 29.46	0.02 0.03 0.04 0.01
$2MS_2$	A semi-diurnal shallow water constituent of the same speed as μ_2 produced by interaction of M_2 and S_2.	27.97	—
	Diurnal Constituents		
K_1 O_1	O_1 and part of K_1 allow for the effect of the Moon's declination.	15.04 13.94	0.58 0.42
K_1 P_1	P_1 and part of K_1 allow for the effect of the Sun's declination.	14.96	0.20
Q_1 M_1 J_1	These three constituents between them allow for the effect of changes in the Moon's distance on K_1 and O_1.	13.40 14.49 15.59	0.08 0.02 0.03
	Quarter-diurnal Constituents		
M_4	The first shallow water harmonic of M_2, with a speed twice that of M_2.	57.98	—
MS_4	The shallow water constituent produced by the interaction of M_2 and S_2, with speed equal to sum of speeds of M_2 and S_2.	58.98	—

components. The amplitude and phase of the contributory factors to tidal motion are known as tidal constituents, the most common of which are listed in table 2.1. The principal tidal constituents are called M_2 and S_2, relating to synodic tides of the Moon and Sun respectively; the subscript '2' indicates that they are both semi-diurnal (thus, subscript '1' relates to diurnal and '4', '6', etc., to quarter, sixth and higher diurnal constituents). Un-numbered constituents relate to longer-term harmonics with periods of two weeks or more, associated with the combined effects of Sun and Moon.

On account of variation of the Moon's orbit the mean amplitude of each constituent is modified by a factor f and its phase increased by u° for any particular point in time. In theory similar modifications should be made for the Sun's constituents but these are sufficiently small to be neglected.

The phase of any tide-raising force E may be calculated for any time on the Greenwich meridian. Applying the nodal correction described above, the true theoretical phase of a constituent is $E + u$, the values of which are published annually in the Admiralty Tide Table Vol.2 Table VIII for 0 hours GMT. Values at any other time are formed by adding the product of the speed of the constituent (in degrees per hour) and the time (in hours GMT). If the phase of a particular constituent at Greenwich at hour t GMT is $E + u$, the phase of the corresponding tidal constituent at any place at hour t (local time, calculated from longitude, 1 hour = 15° longitude) will be $(E + u) - g$ where g is known as the phase lag constant for that place. Summarising the above, the contribution of every tidal constituent may be expressed as

$$h = fA \cos [(E + u) - g]$$

where h is the height relative to mean sea level. The quantities A and g form the tidal constants for a particular location. The tidal level at any particular time and location is given by the sum of the above expressions derived for each tidal constituent.

In addition to constituents related to astronomical events, shallow water constituents may also be applied. These account for the inertia, friction and resonance of a particular shallow body of water and are expressed as higher harmonics as a matter of convenience; these factors account for the 1 to 2 days which elapse between the phase of the Moon and its associated spring or neap tide.

For most parts of the world, known values of amplitude constants will serve to indicate whether a tide is predominantly diurnal or semi-diurnal. Thus, if $\pi (A_{s2}) > 2 (A_{k1} + A_{o1})$, tide is predominantly semi-diurnal and if $\pi (A_{s2}) < 2 (A_{k1} + A_{o1})$, tide has a strong diurnal component (where the subscript relates to the constituent). In the latter case it is more useful to differentiate between the two ranges of tide that occur each day rather than between spring and neap periods (see table 2.2).

2.2 Dynamic Modifications of the Equilibrium Tide

2.2.1 Progress of the Tidal Wave

From equation 3.14 the rate of advance C of a tidal wave, being a long wave in water shallow with respect to wave length, is given by $C = [gh]^{1/2}$ where the depth of water, h, is large by comparison with the wave height.

For the equilibrium tide in a boundless ocean, since e, the Earth's radius, is of the order of 6370 km, section 2.1.2 indicates that the lunar equilibrium tide would be only $0.84 \times 10^{-7} \times 6370 \times 10^{6}$ mm = 530 mm. However, when the tidal wave in a deep ocean strikes the continental shelf, consideration of continuity of flow indicates that there will be an increase in tidal currents. The reduction in C on account of shoaling also leads to an increase in height of the tide; this aspect is discussed in greater detail in section 3.1.4 and illustrated by figure 3.23.

For an enclosed sea or an estuary, resonance is likely to lead to the generation of a standing oscillation where the length of the enclosed sea, in the direction of the tidal wave, approaches an integral number of half wave lengths for the appropriate 'root mean square' depth of water. For a semi-diurnal tide, for example, the minimum length of sea for resonance would be about 6 x 3600 x C or 21600 x 22 m, that is, about 480 km (260 nautical miles) for a depth of 50 m (27 fathoms). Convergence of the coasts of the sea will lead to an increase in height of the tidal wave as the width of channel decreases and the two factors of resonance and convergence are responsible to varying degrees for the particularly high semi-diurnal tidal ranges experienced in certain gulfs and estuaries such as the Bay of Fundy, the Bay of St. Malo and the estuary of the River Severn.[1]

It may be noted that, in its simplest form, a wave progressing in the x-direction may be considered to represent a forced oscillation of the form

$$\frac{d^2x}{dt^2} + C^2x = A \cos nt$$

where $A \cos nt$ is an applied periodic force, yielding a wave of amplitude

$$\frac{A}{C^2 - n^2}$$

which is in phase with the equilibrium tide where $C > n$ but half a wave length out of phase where $C < n$, that is, where the celerity of the wave is less than the rate of passage of the tide inducing force. Where $C \sim n$, the amplitude becomes very great in the absence of damping forces.

2.2.2 Coriolis Forces

Tidal currents, and hence the advance of tidal waves, may be considerably modified in direction by the rotation of the Earth.

Consider a vector **AB** of length r and inclined at angle θ to the x-axis and use the Argand diagram notation, that is, for a complex function the real part is parallel to the x-axis and the imaginary part parallel to the y-axis. Then vector

$$D = r(\cos\theta + i\sin\theta) = r\, e^{i\theta}$$

where $i = (-1)^{1/2}$

$$\text{velocity } V = \frac{dD}{dt} = ri\,\frac{d\theta}{dt}\,e^{i\theta} + \frac{dr}{dt}\,e^{i\theta}$$

and

$$\text{acceleration} = \frac{dV}{dt}$$

$$= \left[-r\left(\frac{d\theta}{dt}\right)^2 + 2i\,\frac{dr}{dt}\,\frac{d\theta}{dt} + ir\,\frac{d^2\theta}{dt^2} + \frac{d^2r}{dt^2} \right] e^{i\theta}$$

Where $\dfrac{d\theta}{dt}$ is constant, this reduces to

$$\left[-r\left(\frac{d\theta}{dt}\right)^2 + 2i\,\frac{dr}{dt}\,\frac{d\theta}{dt} + \frac{d^2r}{dt^2} \right] e^{i\theta} \qquad\qquad (2.12)$$

where the first and third terms are centripetal and linear accelerations directed along the vector D. The second term represents an acceleration of magnitude $2V\omega$ transverse to r, where V is velocity and ω angular velocity. The component of the Earth's angular velocity of spin, Ω, resolved in the plane of the surface of the Earth at latitude l is $\Omega \sin l$ and hence the transverse component of acceler-

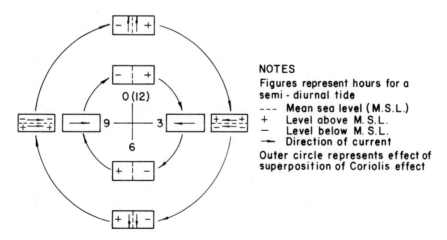

NOTES
Figures represent hours for a semi-diurnal tide
--- Mean sea level (M.S.L.)
+ Level above M.S.L.
− Level below M.S.L.
→ Direction of current
Outer circle represents effect of superposition of Coriolis effect

Figure 2.4 *Diagram of effect of Coriolis force*

ation, known as the Coriolis effect, is $2V\Omega \sin l$. In the northern hemisphere it
will be seen that this is always inclined to the right of the direction of the
velocity vector V. In an enclosed sea the effect of this term is to tend to build
up the level of water to the right of the flow caused by a standing oscillation, as
indicated diagrammatically in figure 2.4.

It is apparent from figure 2.4 that the Coriolis effect causes the location of
high and low water to rotate anti-clockwise around the perimeter of this idealised
sea (in the northern hemisphere), and from this tendency is derived the complex
amphidromal system of tides with high water apparently rotating about points
of no tidal amplitude, associated with rotary systems of tidal streams as
illustrated in figure 2.5 for the North Sea.

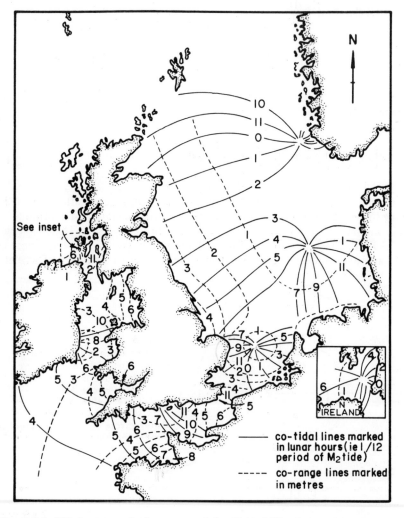

Figure 2.5 *Tidal range and phase around the United Kingdom*

Equations 2.9 and 2.10 on the other hand indicate a generally clockwise rotation of the semi-diurnal equilibrium tide for the northern hemisphere. In general terms, for a large shallow sea where tidal currents are high in relation to the tidal range, Coriolis forces will predominate; for a small deep sea the equilibrium tidal forces will predominate and this is found to occur, for example, in the Caspian and Black Seas.

Where the tidal currents are approximately in phase with the tidal wave, that is, maximum currents occur in opposed directions near the times of high water and low water, then a tide confined to a channel (away from the equator where Coriolis effects are not experienced since sin l = 0) will be found to have a different range along the two sides of the channel. To take an example, the flood tide current travelling with the crest of the tidal wave in the Irish Sea raises the height of high water along the Welsh coast and depresses the height along the Irish coast. The ebb tide current at low water has the opposite effect and as a result the tidal range along the Welsh coast is 2 to 4 m greater than that on the opposite Irish coast.

2.2.3 Shallow Water Effects

Consider a tidal wave travelling in relatively shallow water of depth h as indicated in figure 2.6. A uniform distribution of particle velocity with depth is assumed (see section 3.1.1). If we consider the diagram of figure 2.6 as having a velocity of $-C$ superimposed on the particle velocities u indicated, then the wave would appear to be motionless and, by Bernoulli, for no loss of energy along streamlines

$$(u - C)^2 + 2gz = \left(u - C + \frac{du}{dx}\, \delta x\right)^2 + 2g\left(z + \frac{dz}{dx}\, \delta x\right)$$

(if $|C| > |u|$) or

$$2g\,\frac{dz}{dx} = -2(u - C)\,\frac{du}{dx} \qquad\qquad (2.13)$$

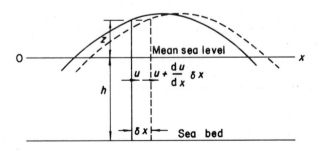

Figure 2.6 *Shallow water distortion of tidal wave*

but, by continuity

$$(u - C)(h + z) = \left(u - C + \frac{du}{dx}\, \delta x\right)\left(h + z + \frac{dz}{dx}\, \delta x\right)$$

or

$$(h + z)\frac{du}{dx} = -(u - C)\frac{dz}{dx} \tag{2.14}$$

Substituting for du/dx and dz/dx from equations 2.13 and 2.14 gives

$$2(u - C)^2 = 2g(h + z) \text{ or } C = u + [gh(1 + z/h)]^{1/2} \tag{2.15}$$

But mean transport per unit width is $-Ch$ and hence

$$(h + z)(u - C) = -Ch \text{ or } \frac{u}{C} = \frac{z}{h + z} \tag{2.16}$$

and, substituting for u in equation 2.15 gives

$$C = \left[gh\left(1 + \frac{z}{h}\right)\right]^{1/2}\left(1 + \frac{z}{h}\right)$$

which, for fairly small values of z/h, gives

$$C \approx \left(1 + \frac{3}{2}\frac{z}{h}\right)[gh]^{1/2}$$

Thus, as the tidal wave advances in shallow water, its form becomes distorted by the crest tending to overtake the trough since

$$\frac{C}{\bar{C}} = 1 + \frac{3}{2}\frac{z}{h} \tag{2.17}$$

where $\bar{C}$ is mean celerity (that is, that applicable to $z = 0$). Where, for example, $z = 0.2h$, $C = 1.3\bar{C}$, this will lead to the steepening of the rising tide and flattening of the falling tide curves, that is the period of flow is reduced and the period of ebb is increased.

If a wave of initial form $z = H/2 \cos x$ is considered to be advancing through shallow water (but $H \ll h$) of mean depth h then, after a short period T, the advance of any part of its profile will be CT where

$$C = \left(1 + \frac{3}{2}\frac{z}{h}\right)\bar{C}$$

$$= \left(1 + \frac{3}{4}\frac{H}{h}\cos x\right)\bar{C}$$

If the new wave profile is considered as shifted by a distance $\bar{C}T$ towards the origin, then the distorted wave profile is shown by the broken line in figure 2.6 and its equation is

$$z = \frac{H}{2} \cos k(x + \Delta X)$$

where $k = 2\pi/L$ and where

$$x + \Delta X = x + \frac{3H}{4h} \bar{C}T \cos kx$$

For small values of $k\Delta X$, $\sin k\Delta X$ and $\cos k\Delta X$ can be expanded in the first few terms of the series

$$\sin k\Delta X = k\Delta X - \frac{(k\Delta X)^3}{3!} + \cdots, \cos k\Delta X = 1 - \frac{(k\Delta X)^2}{2!} + \cdots$$

and thus

$$z \approx \frac{H}{2} \cos kx \left[1 - \frac{3kH}{4h} \ (\bar{C}T \sin kx) \right.$$

$$\left. - \left(\frac{3kH\bar{C}T}{4h} \right)^2 \cos^2 kx \left(\frac{1}{2!} - \frac{3kH\bar{C}}{3!4h} T \sin kx \right) + \cdots \right]$$

and, by further approximations, the difference between the original wave form and the distorted wave form may be related to the wave height H in terms of the first, second and third . . . harmonics, that is, the M_4 (quarter-), M_6 (sixth-), M_8 (eighth-diurnal) constituent (see section 2.1.5) if the original wave form is considered to represent a semi-diurnal (M_2) wave. These constituents are found to be approximately proportional to H^2, H^3, H^4 . . . respectively indicating the relative importance of the tidal amplitude in creating these tidal harmonics. The ratio between the ranges of semi-diurnal spring and neap tides is generally about 2, and thus the M_4, M_6 and M_8 constituents will be approximately 2, 4 and 8 times as pronounced, respectively, for a spring tide as for a neap tide, neglecting questions of resonance.

A point of some importance is that combination of M_2 and S_2 waves (see section 2.1.5) may produce several shallow water oscillations of the various harmonics, including long-period terms arising from the difference between the periods of the M_2 and S_2 terms (see figure 3.5). The relative predominance of any one constituent depends on local conditions and in particular on resonance. Qualitatively, if not quantitatively, the curious shapes of certain estuarial and coastal tide curves may be explained by the action of shallow water effects on the deep water tidal constituents.

A case of special interest occurs along the south coast of England between Portland and Southampton. At Southampton there are two distinct peaks to high water while at Portland there are two troughs to low water. These phenomena are due to the presence of a marked quarter-diurnal constituent in conjunction with the semi-diurnal wave. Consider the two wave forms $x_1 = A \sin nt$ and $x_2 = B \sin (2nt + \alpha)$. These equations represent standing waves, that is, waves with periodic variation of form which remain in the same position. The first may be considered as a semi-diurnal wave and the second as a quarter-diurnal wave with a phase lead of α. When $\alpha = \pi/2$

$$x = x_1 + x_2 = A \sin nt + B \cos 2nt$$

$$\frac{\mathrm{d}x}{\mathrm{d}t} = An \cos nt - 2Bn \sin 2nt$$

and hence, where $\mathrm{d}x/\mathrm{d}t = 0$, either $\cos nt = 0$ and maxima or minima occur at $nt = \pi/2, 3\pi/2 \ldots$ (as for the semi-diurnal wave) or $4B \sin nt = A$, that is, $nt = \sin^{-1} A/4B$ and this gives the phase angle of two peaks symmetrically placed about $\pi/2$. If $A > 4B$ evidently the angle is imaginary and hence for the two-peaked tide the quarter-diurnal constituent must have an amplitude at least a quarter that of the semi-diurnal wave. If the phase lead α approaches $3\pi/2$, then the combined wave form will have two troughs, again provided that $A < 4B$. Similar conditions may be derived for sixth-diurnal waves and shorter period constituents; these may promote or oppose the action of the quarter-diurnal wave in causing multiple crests or troughs.

The semi-diurnal lunar tides in the English Channel correspond approximately to a standing oscillation with the node displaced by Coriolis effect and friction, to give an imaginary 'amphidromal point', that is, a point of no tidal amplitude, for the M_2 constituent inland from Christchurch Bay. Thus the semi-diurnal constituent is small from Portland to Southampton and conditions of shallow water here are also favourable for strong quarter-diurnal and higher harmonics.

2.2.4 Tidal Prediction

While Doodson [2] records a rudimentary tide table (in the British Museum) for London Bridge in the year 1213, the preparation of regular tide tables for the main ports of Britain was started during the seventeenth and eighteenth centuries and based, presumably, on a simple method of application of direct observation; the actual processes were not divulged and remain unknown. The first Admiralty tide tables were issued in 1833. At the present date, these tables provide (Part 1) times and levels of high and low water at standard ports in Britain and overseas, together with notes of the extent of the observations on which the predictions are based, which allow their accuracy to be estimated. There are also approximate corrections in time and level for secondary ports, relative to the standard ports, tables for attaching chart datum, on which tidal predictions are based, to ordnance datum in the locality, and other tables (which should be treated with caution for areas close inshore where the tide curve may be distorted) to allow prediction of the intermediate times and heights for simple harmonic tide curves. Special tide curves are also provided for Liverpool and Southampton. Part II of the Admiralty tide tables provides data for the principal tidal constituents used in tidal prediction by the Admiralty method.

The tidal constituents for a particular location may be derived from a period of observations. Table 2.1 indicates that the speeds of M_2 and S_2, M_2 and N_2 differ by only 1° and ½° respectively. If these constituents are to be separately evaluated it is recommended that a period of hourly observation should extend over 30 days. The period of observation should be a year if S_2 and K_2 are to be accurately separated. Meteorological variations and inaccuracies in reading a tide gauge have to be allowed for; a longer period, even with gaps, will yield better results than a shorter period.

Admiralty Tidal Handbook No.1 provides a semi-graphical method of harmonic tidal analysis for a 30-day record. Where only a few days of tidal records are available, *Admiralty Tidal Handbook No.3* describes a method of analysis of short period observations. Table 2.2 sets out definitions of the most important parameters used to describe tidal ranges and levels.

Tidal computations for a comprehensive harmonic analysis based on hourly tide readings used to be a most laborious occupation when carried out manually. The first tide-predicting machine, once tidal constants had been evaluated for certain ports, was devised by Lord Kelvin and used a long wire fixed at one end and reeved in a vertical plane around a series of pulleys whose vertical positions were controlled by cranks. The wire carried a recording pen at its free end which was constrained to move vertically. The cranks were geared together and with the recording drum, so that each crank represented a harmonic constituent in range, speed and phase, while the drum rotated at a predetermined steady rate representing the passage of time. A high degree of precision was necessary in order to obtain the requisite accuracy, with a careful selection of gear trains to approximate to the relative periods of lunar and solar constituents. An accuracy of two minutes was expected throughout a year's operation with the most advanced machines.

The best methods of tidal analysis using desk calculating machines are those developed and described by Doodson.[2] Cartwright [3] describes a computer method based on Fourier series and illustrates its application in the evaluation of selected tidal constituents from analysis of hourly data over periods of 29 days and of ½-hourly data over 24 hours. A method of relaxation is described that is used to separate out the contribution of different components of approximately similar 'speed number' (see section 2.1.5).

Analog computers are used for prediction of tides. Hydraulic models (a special form of analogue) are also used but, unless these are confined to represent small areas, they must incorporate means for reproducing Coriolis effects by being mounted on a rotating turntable. One such model has been used to examine a proposed tidal power scheme at Mont St. Michel; the investigation indicated that the proposed barrage would considerably reduce the tidal range and hence impair the economics of the scheme. Section 2.7 touches on numerical methods currently used for tidal analysis and prediction.

2.3 Modification of Tidal Pattern

An inherent difficulty in tidal prediction arises from the susceptibility of the tide to variable interference by other factors, usually those relating to the

TABLE 2.2 *Definition of Tidal Terms*

Term	Abbreviation	Definition	Comment
Mean sea level	MSL	Time-averaged level of sea	Reasonably predicted from 30-day hourly readings. Precise definition requires readings for full lunar cycle (18.6 years see section 2.1.5)
Mean tide level	MTL	Average of high water and low water levels	MTL not usually equal to MSL
Mean high water springs	MHWS	Average of two successive highest high water levels in 24 h	For semi-diurnal tide. From records of each period of spring tides during one year
Mean low water springs	MLWS	Average of two successive lowest low water levels in 24 h	For semi-diurnal tide. From records of each period of spring tides during one year
Mean high water neaps	MHWN	Average of two successive highest high water levels in 24 h	For semi-diurnal tide. From records of each period of neap tides during one year
Mean low water neaps	MLWN	Average of two successive lowest low water levels in 24 h	For semi-diurnal tide. From records of each period of neap tides during one year
Mean high high water	MHHW	Average of higher (of two) daily high water levels	For tides with strong diurnal component, from daily records during one year
Mean low high water	MLHW	Average of lower (of two) daily high water levels	For tides with strong diurnal component, from daily records during one year
Mean low low water	MLLW	Average of lower (of two) daily low water levels	For tides with strong diurnal component, from daily records during one year
Mean high low water	MHLW	Average of higher (of two) daily low water levels	For tides with strong diurnal component. from daily records during one year
Lowest astronomical tide	LAT	Lowest predicted tide under average meteorological conditions	From calculations of harmonic constants where adequate long-term records (Admiralty Chart Datum). No predicted tide > 0.1 m below LAT
Highest astronomical tide	HAT	Highest predicted tide under average meteorological conditions	From calculations of harmonic constants where adequate long-term records. May be exceeded once or twice per year

weather. The principal factors are described below, together with a brief note on 'tidal waves' or tsunamis as they are currently termed; these, although rare events, cause waves of period intermediate between tides and wind-waves.

2.3.1 Barometic Pressure

A static area of low pressure over an area of the sea, neglecting for the present the effects of geostrophic winds that are associated with atmospheric pressure systems (see section 3.3.4) will set up a barometric slope, by causing a relative raising of the sea surface by about 10 mm per mb (1 mb corresponding to a pressure of 10^2 N/m^2). In fact, appreciable surges are only likely to develop on this account when a progressive wave is built up by the resonance which results from a cyclone advancing at a speed approaching $[gh]^{1/2}$, the natural celerity of a long wave in water of depth h.

2.3.2 Storm Surge and Wind Set-up

Several factors may contribute to surges in water level. Most commonly, storm surges are caused by the meteorological conditions associated with large barometric depressions and hence with strong winds. The water level rise will be in part directly due to the pressure gradient (section 2.3.1) and in part due to wind set-up. Amplitudes of surges will only be small in deep water but will become magnified on account of the shoaling effect (section 3.4.2) on entering shallow water.

The basic equations of motion and of continuity that may be used to describe storm surges are given in chapter 1. The generative forces are those due to barometric pressure, wind stress and Coriolis effect. The dissipative forces are those due to bottom stress (that is, friction) and gravity. Generally vertical acceleration, the Earth's curvature and interaction with surface waves may be neglected. Several modern numerical techniques have been derived for solving the basic hydrodynamic equations.[4, 5, 6]

These only differ from the methods used for pure tidal models in the addition of extra terms to represent surface wind stress. Wind patterns may be complex and variable; an accurate knowledge of the wind structure is required for a reliable result. Hurricanes provide an exception to this general statement in that the wind structure is relatively well ordered and estimated.

The lack of detailed wind information leads to design water levels being generally based on historical records, statistically analysed [7] to yield extreme water levels for particular return periods.

Simplified techniques will provide approximate values of wind set-up in the quasi-steady state. Thus, when wind blows over the sea, apart from the creation of waves (see chapter 3), the shear stress at the sea surface causes a 'wind-slope' of the sea surface. Thus, if a wind blows for a long enough period to establish steady conditions

$$\tau_s + \tau_0 = S\rho h \qquad (2.18)$$

where τ_s is the surface shear stress, τ_0 the shear stress between the returning current and the sea bed, S the surface gradient caused by wind set-up where h is the mean sea depth.

$$\tau_s = C\rho_a\, U^2 \tag{2.19}$$

where C is a friction coefficient, ρ_a air density and U wind velocity at a specified height. If $n = 1 + \tau_0/\tau_s$, equations 2.18 and 2.19 may be combined as

$$S = \frac{Cn\rho_a\, U^2}{\rho h} \tag{2.20}$$

(where $\rho_a/\rho \sim 1.25 \times 10^{-3}$). Wind speed is usually measured at a height of 10 m above sea level, and $1.15 \leqslant n \leqslant 1.30$. If the wind blows at an angle θ to the coastline, the component $U \sin \theta$ gives rise to the set-up while the component $U \cos \theta$ creates a current parallel to the coast, which on account of Coriolis force may contribute to set-up.

Thus, for a given wind speed, the wind-slope is inversely proportional to the sea depth. Francis [8] describes three methods for determining C.

(1) By direct measurement of S by measuring water levels at each side of a lake, care being necessary to ensure that the conditions entail adequate mixing between water layers.

(2) By measurement of τ in the air, by determining change of wind speed with respect to height in the boundary layer.

(3) (Only applicable to a relatively constant wind blowing over an extensive ocean) by measuring the change in direction and magnitude of the wind with altitude, clear of surface waves, such change being attributable to the surface shear and to geostrophic forces.

Kullenberg [19] describes determination of the shear friction velocity u_* $= (\tau_0/\rho_w)^{1/2}$ by measuring wind speeds and current distribution. C is shown to be of the order of 1.0 to 1.35×10^{-3} applied to U_{10} measured at a height of 10 m.

As explained in section 3.3.4 the direction of the wind over the sea is approximately transverse to the barometric gradient and the wind speed at a given latitude is approximately proportional to the barometric gradient (unless the isobars are strongly curved). The wind-slope is not only at right angles to the direction of barometric surface slope, as derived from section 2.3.1, but usually considerably greater in magnitude for depths of water of interest to the coastal engineer.

2.3.3 Seiches

A seiche is a surge generated within an enclosed or partially enclosed body of water which has a period of resonance similar to that of the disturbing force. Theoretical expressions for the resonant periods of simple shapes of the body of water are given in section 3.9. Numerical methods are required for more complex geometry.

2.3.4 Tsunamis

Tsunamis (popularly, but incorrectly, called tidal waves) usually have a seismic origin (but see section 1.3.8) and will thus be propagated from a faulted or orogenic area. The maximum height of wave at any point will be related to its distance from the origin, the energy content and area of the initial disturbance, and to energy losses in transit—these will generally be small except in the immediate locality of the disturbance.

Lamb [10] obtains the solution for surface waves in deep water travelling from a disturbance caused by an initial impulse, for the one-dimensional case. At a distance X (clear of the immediate source of disturbance), he demonstrates that maximum wave height $\propto 1/X^{3/2}$ and that, on account of steadily increasing wave length, wave celerity and group velocity (see section 3.1.2) are each $\propto X^{1/2}$.

Penney [11] provides a solution for the two-dimensional case of a system of circular surface waves in deep water diverging from a disturbance, caused by an underwater or above-water explosion. Where the initial disturbance is considered as being confined within a radius r, the nth crest at radius R from the epicentre will be the greatest where n is the nearest integer to $(R/2r + 1)/2$. The group velocity, corresponding to the rate of travel of the region of maximum wave height is $(gh/2)^{1/2}$ and the maximum wave height will be inversely proportional to R.

This analysis assumes that the depth of water is at least $0.2L$ where L is the effective wave length (see section 3.1.1).

In areas subject to tsunamis, statistical data on their frequency and magnitude will help economic assessment of the sufficiency of alternative schemes or structures. While the effects of refraction and shoaling may be assessed by methods applicable to short-period water waves (chapter 3) and run-up calculated on the same basis, there is no proven way of estimating the wave height at the centre of the disturbance.[12, 13]

Coastal engineers are usually concerned with tsunamis that have degenerated into trains of shallow water waves advancing at a rate $(gh)^{1/2}$ where h is the depth of water (see section 3.1.4). On account of their relative infrequency and unpredictability much remains to be learned of their fundamental characteristics. Tsurata [14] for example describes an analysis for tsunamis entering Ofunato Harbour, considering waves with sinusoidal wave form of height 0.5 m and various periods between 10 and 60 minutes, limits which include recorded periods of most tsunamis encountered at coastal regions.

2.4 Tidal Streams

Records of tidal streams may be analysed by a method similar to that used for tide levels, on the basis of rates of flow and direction at hourly intervals. If the

tidal stream is rectilinear for the majority of the time, one set of harmonic
constants may be used to analyse the flow. However, if the tidal stream is rotary,
the current vectors must be expressed as components in x and y-directions,
choosing x to correspond with axis of major flow. The true components are
analysed separately, yielding two sets of harmonic constants. A semigraphical
analysis of tidal streams is also described in *Admiralty Manual of Hydrographic
Surveying* (Vol. 2, Chapter 2) 1969. From predictions of tidal streams at one or
more localities, numerical methods of applying the Eulerian equations permit
predictions of tide levels and tidal streams over large areas of sea, as described in
section 2.7.

2.4.1 Variation of Velocity with the Stage of the Tide

A tide at any point is considered as comprising elements of progressive and
reflected sinusoidal waves of varying amplitude and period. The tide stream may
be computed as the sum of the streams due to the several elements. Figure 2.7
indicates that, in a progressive wave, the maximum stream occurs in the direction
of advance of the wave at high water and contrary to the direction of advance
at low water, with slack water occurring at mean tide levels.

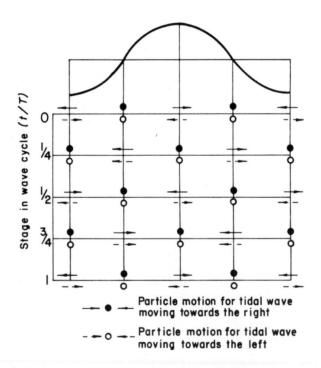

Figure 2.7 *Diagram of tidal streams associated with tidal wave*

A standing wave, on the other hand, may be considered to represent the sum of a progressive and reflected (or retrogressive) wave of equal period and amplitude.

The variations of the tide stream observe the same periodical laws as those derived for the tidal amplitudes. For a progressive wave (see section 3.1.1), the mean velocity $\bar{u}$ on a vertical section, in the direction of advance of the wave, is given by $\bar{u} = Cz/h$ where C is the wave celerity, z the height of water surface above mean level and h the mean depth. Thus, where $C = (gh)^{1/2}$ and the tidal amplitude is $H/2$ (that is, tidal height = H)

$$|\bar{u}_{max}| = \frac{H}{2} \left(\frac{g}{h}\right)^{1/2} \tag{2.21}$$

The profile of a progressive wave of wave length L and period L/C may be represented at

$$z = \frac{H}{2} \cos \frac{2\pi}{L} (x - Ct) \tag{2.22}$$

and that of a standing wave, the sum of the progressive and reflected wave of equivalent period and height, by

$$z = \frac{H}{2} \left[\cos \frac{2\pi}{L} (x - Ct) + \cos \frac{2\pi}{L} (x + Ct) \right]$$

$$= H \cos \frac{2\pi x}{L} \cos \frac{2\pi Ct}{L} \tag{2.23}$$

that is, a standing wave of height $2H$ with nodes at $x = L/4, 3L/4$, etc., with extreme values at $t = 0, t = L/2C$, etc. In a similar way, since $\bar{u} = Cz/h$, the velocity for the standing wave may be represented by

$$\bar{u} = \frac{C}{h} \frac{H}{2} \left[\cos \frac{2\pi}{L} (x - Ct) - \cos \frac{2\pi}{L} (x + Ct) \right]$$

$$= \frac{C}{h} H \sin \frac{2\pi x}{L} \sin \frac{2\pi Ct}{L} \tag{2.24}$$

The velocity nodes therefore occur, as indicated in figure 2.7, at crest and trough of the standing wave, that is, at $x = 0, L$, etc., while velocity at the nodal points of equation 2.23 fluctuates with the tide to extreme values of $\bar{u}_{max} = CH/h$ when $t = L/4C, 3L/4C$, etc., that is, when $z = 0$ everywhere from equation 2.23. Where, at the mouth of an estuary or inlet, the passage of a progressive wave in the open sea sets up a tide in the enclosed area approximately in phase, the resulting current vector will appear in consequence to rotate, clockwise where the coastline is to the left of the direction of a progressive wave, anti-clock-wise for a coastline to the right, as shown diagrammatically in figure 2.8.

The extreme value of the tidal stream for a standing wave and a progressive wave of the same height is seen to be the same, that is, for a tidal height (or range) of H, $|\bar{u}_{max}| = CH/2h$ or, where h is large by comparison with H, $C = (gh)^{1/2}$ and

$$|\bar{u}_{max}| = \frac{H}{2}\left(\frac{g}{h}\right)^{1/2} \tag{2.25}$$

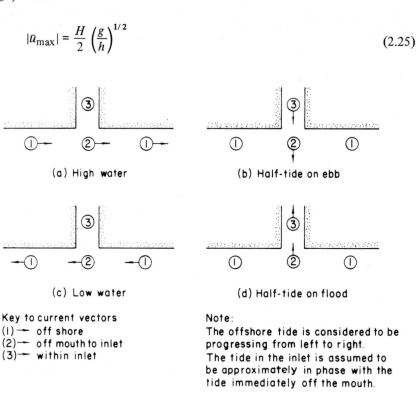

(a) High water   (b) Half-tide on ebb

(c) Low water   (d) Half-tide on flood

Key to current vectors
(1) → off shore
(2) → off mouth to inlet
(3) → within inlet

Note:
The offshore tide is considered to be progressing from left to right.
The tide in the inlet is assumed to be approximately in phase with the tide immediately off the mouth.

Figure 2.8 *Diagram of rotary tidal current at mouth of inlet*

2.4.2 Variation of Velocity with Respect to Depth

The theory of long low waves in shallow water (see section 3.1.1) leads to a constant value of u on a vertical section, the associated horizontal component of velocity. In fact, bottom friction, surface shear and eddy viscosity (the turbulent mixing of a fluid) cause a variation of u with depth, and current profiles determined at sea, in the absence of significant surface currents driven by winds, usually provide a fairly good fit to a curve of the form

$$u = k(z')^{1/n} \tag{2.26}$$

where z' is measured upwards from the sea bed and k and n are constants. Van Veen [15] recommended a value of 5 for n in the Dover Strait while Cartwright [3] considered such a value to be somewhat low; a figure of about 7 has also been suggested as applicable to tidal streams off the east coast of Great Britain. Such a relationship as equation 2.26 implies that maximum currents occur at the surface. In fact, the top 1 m is affected not only by wind but by the super-position of orbital currents associated with waves, so that for practical reasons surface velocities are usually measured 1.5 m or so below surface. For a depth of water h, mean current $\bar{u}$ is given, from equation 2.26 by

$$\bar{u} = \frac{1}{h} \int_0^h u \; dz' = \frac{k}{h} \int_0^h (z')^{1/n} \; dz' =$$

$$= \frac{n}{(n+1)} \; kh^{1/n}$$

But u_s at the surface, where $z' = h$, is $kh^{1/n}$ and hence

$$\bar{u} = \frac{n}{n+1} u_s \tag{2.27}$$

which is a relationship of value in determining the best fit for n. In the Dover Strait, values of 5 or 7 would give a ratio of $u_s/\bar{u}$ of 1.2 and 1.14 respectively; $\bar{u}$ occurs at a height $[n/(n+1)]^n h \sim 0.4h$ above sea bed. Flux per unit width, or integrated flow, may be represented as

$$F = \int_0^h u \; dz' = \bar{u}h \tag{2.28}$$

It is of interest to consider the implications of equation 2.26 with respect to the variation with depth of the coefficient of eddy viscosity ϵ which relates shear forces set up by interchange in momentum, on account of turbulent mixing, to the velocity gradient. For steady flow ϵ is defined by

$$\tau = \rho\epsilon \; \frac{du}{dz'} \tag{2.29}$$

where τ is the horizontal shear stress and, for a constant surface gradient in the direction of x and u

$$u \; \frac{d\tau}{dz'} = \text{const.} \tag{2.30}$$

Substituting in equations 2.29 and 2.30 for du/dz' and u respectively from equation 2.26

$$\tau = \frac{k\rho\epsilon z'^{(1-n)/n}}{n}$$

(2.31)

and

$$\frac{d\tau}{dz'} \propto (z')^{-1/n}$$

(2.32)

Thus, from equations 2.31 and 2.32

$$\frac{d}{dz'} \left[\epsilon (z')^{(1-n)/n} \right] \propto (z')^{-1/n}$$

or

$$\epsilon \propto (z')^{2(n-1)/n}$$

(2.33)

For a value of $n = 5$, equation 2.33 indicates $\epsilon \propto (z')^{1.6}$. As discussed by Johns and Odd [16] ϵ at $z' \to 0$ is related to the surface roughness of the bed; it is close to the sea bed, in fact, that the greatest departures are observed from the assumed form of equation 2.26 (see also chapter 4).

Mass transport due to a tidal stream is determined by integrating instantaneous values of the flux F across the breadth of the tidal stream. The residual mass transport requires determination of mass transport at regular intervals throughout one or more tidal cycles. As the period of slack water approaches, since the velocities at all levels are affected by the same gradient, reversal of flow tends to occur earlier towards the sea bed than at the surface; where stratification due to salinity or temperature variation occurs, this effect will be accentuated. Turbulence tends to mask such an effect and, in addition, accentuates the difficulty in measuring effective velocities close to the sea bed. McDowell [17] indicates the effect of the Strouhal number (see section 6.4.2) on the phasing of flow reversal related to depth.

Tidal races, overtides or overfalls, are formed where the tide stream is constricted or caused to change violently in direction. The most pronounced tide races occur where two tidal systems differing in phase or in range are connected by a narrow strait and a compensation flow therefore occurs. One such example is found off Hurst Castle at the west end of the Solent where, on the rising tide, a difference of 0.6 m or more may be found between tide curves at each side of the point, causing an eastward tide stream of 2.5 to 3 m/s at spring tides. Pillsbury [18] provides a simplified analysis of overtides and their effect on distortion of the local tidal curves.

2.5 Sea Surface as a Levelling Datum

Hydrographic surveys should preferably be related to chart datum (LAT — see table 2.2) if this is locally known, which may be transferred to the survey site by taking simultaneous tidal observations at the two sites over an adequate period, following procedures recommended by the *Admiralty Handbook of Hydrographic Surveying*.

For a semi-diurnal tide (see section 2.1.5), observed mean low and high water at points 1 and 2 are assessed as

$$OMLW = (l_1 + 3l_2 + 3l_3 + l_4)/8$$

$$OMHW = (h_1 + 2h_2 + h_3)/4$$

where l_1, l_2, l_3 and l_4 are four consecutive levels of low water and h_1, h_2 and h_3 the intermediate high water levels. Then observed mean range OMR = OMHW – OMLW and observed mean tide level OMTL = ½ (OMHW + OMLW). If complete sets of hourly data are available, observed mean sea level (OMSL) will be preferred for accuracy, to OMTL. True mean tide level (TMTL) at gauge 1 is known from tide predictions, as the mean of MHWS and MLWS for example. Then sounding datum at gauge 2

$$d_2 = (OMTL)_2 - (OMTL - TMTL)_1 - [TMTL_1(OMR)_2/(OMR)_1]$$

or where $(TMTL)_1$ not known, $d_2 = (OMTL)_2 - (OMTL)_1 (OMR)_2/(OMR)_1$. For a diurnal tide it is necessary to determine the major harmonic constituents preferably over a period of 29 days. This will not always be practical and two or more series of 25 hour observations, preferably at spring tides, will suffice. The results may be analysed in accordance with *Admiralty Tidal Handbook No.3: Tidal Analysis* for short-period observations. The chart sounding datum at the new gauge may then be obtained from

$$d_2 = (OMTL)_2 + (OMTL - TMTL)_1 - \frac{(TMSL)_1 \Sigma A_2}{\Sigma A_1}$$

where ΣA_1 and ΣA_2 are the sums of the amplitudes of the four major constituents.

For construction work or surveys at sea, levels have to be related to the local surface of the sea and it is then necessary to calculate the surface level in order to determine heights in relation to a fixed datum. Where tidal variation is small and the site is close inshore it is frequently adequate to make use of a tide curve from a tide recorder at a point on the coast in close proximity.

Alternatively the tide offshore may be computed if the approximate shape of the co-range and co-tidal lines is known for the locality for the principal tide constituent (or constituents for a complex tide curve), possibly M_2, S_2, K_1 and O_1 for a predominantly semi-diurnal tide. The M_2 constituent will serve to make a rough correction only of range and phase. It will be found that corrections for phase are more important than corrections of range, because of the high rates of change near mean tide level.

Figure 2.9 indicates co-range and co-tidal lines for the M_2 constituent for the Dover Strait. For investigations for the Channel Tunnel, the area was subdivided

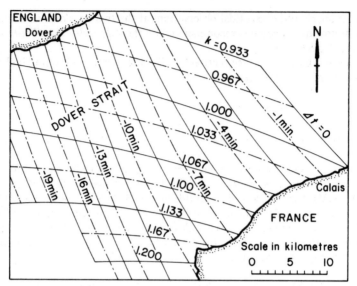

Figure 2.9 *Co-tidal and co-range lines for the Dover Straits*

by these lines into zones which allowed the sea level Z_1 at any point within a zone x, y to be estimated, with respect to the level at a coastal tide recorder, by the formula

$$Z_t = k\, Z_{p(t+\Delta t)} \tag{2.34}$$

where k is the ratio of range at x, y to the range at the tide recorder. The subscript p relates to the level at the recorder and the subscript Δt to the difference in phase between x, y and the tide recorder. The calculation was repeated for tide recorders at Dover and Calais, using appropriate values of k and Δt in each instance, with the results providing an assured error in level at x, y of less than 200 mm across the width of the Strait.

The sea surface may also be used to a higher degree of accuracy to relate levelling datums for separated land areas. As an example, Cartwright and Crease [19] describe how this has been carried out to compare reference levels in France and Britain. The mean sea level over a period of two years was calculated from tide curves obtained on each coast (Ramsgate and Dunkirk in this instance) and corrections applied for various dynamic factors affecting the slope of the sea surface between the two points. The factors considered were

(1) Coriolis force
(2) wind shear and bottom shear
(3) atmospheric pressure
(4) dynamic head at the recorder (negligible in this case)
(5) acceleration of the sea currents.

In order to estimate the contribution due to Coriolis effect it is necessary to be able to estimate the residual mass transport, caused mainly by the prevailing westerly wind. This is achieved by the relationship established between mass transport in the Strait and the resulting potential difference set up, and continuously monitored by the Post Office Engineering Department, in a cross-channel cable between St. Margaret's Bay and Sangatte, the seawater constituting a moving conductor in the Earth's magnetic field. The mean total correction for wind, atmospheric pressure and acceleration amounted to about 25 mm, that for Coriolis effect to about 55 mm.

2.6 Tidal Bores

The complexities of tidal movement in estuaries, where frictional and density effects assume importance, are beyond the range of this book and the reader is directed initially to Rossiter and Lennon [20] and McDowell and O'Connor. [21] The phenomenon of the tidal bore or eagre requires brief explanation, however, since it is closely related to the development of the breaking wave.

Referring to figure 2.10 for a steady flow u at point x along a bed of slope s, with water depth h, by Bernoulli

$$\tfrac{1}{2}u^2 + gh = gsx \tag{2.35}$$

and hence

$$u\,\frac{du}{dx} + g\,\frac{dh}{dx} = gs \tag{2.36}$$

but, by continuity, where s is small

$$(u + du)(h + dh) = uh \text{ or } h\,du = -u\,dh \tag{2.37}$$

Hence, since

$$\frac{du}{dx} = \frac{du}{dh}\frac{dh}{dx}$$

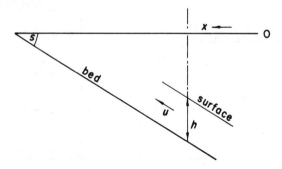

Figure 2.10 *Flow on a slope*

Equations 2.36 and 2.37 give

$$\frac{dh}{dx} = \frac{s}{\left(1 - \dfrac{u^2}{gh}\right)} \tag{2.38}$$

and this implies a rapid increase in depth where u approaches $(gh)^{1/2}$, the rate of travel of a long-period wave of small amplitude, with the effect accentuated for a steep bed gradient.

Consider a bore propagated at velocity C up a parallel-sided river channel, where u_1 and u_2 represent current velocities behind and ahead of the bore respectively (figure 2.11). By considerations of continuity

$$h_1(u_1 - C) = h_2(u_2 - C) = q \tag{2.39}$$

and the forces causing changes in momentum

$$\tfrac{1}{2}g(h_1{}^2 - h_2{}^2) = -q(u_1 - C - u_2 + C) \tag{2.40}$$

on a section reduced to rest by superimposing a velocity $-C$. For $C > |u_2|$

$$C = u_1 + \left[\frac{gh_2(h_1 + h_2)}{2h_1}\right]^{1/2}$$

or

$$C = u_2 + \left[\frac{gh_1(h_1 + h_2)}{2h_2}\right]^{1/2} \tag{2.41}$$

from equations 2.39 and 2.40, and the height of the bore B ($= h_1 - h_2$) is given by

$$B = -\frac{3}{2}h_2 + \left[\frac{h_2{}^2}{4} + \frac{2h_2(u_2 - C)^2}{g}\right]^{1/2} \tag{2.42}$$

which is the expression for the hydraulic jump.

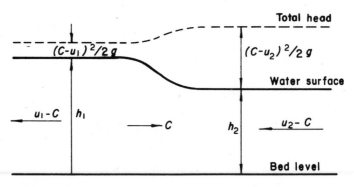

Figure 2.11 *Reference diagram for a tidal bore*

Peregrine [22] shows that when $B/h < 0.28$ the bore consists of a series of undulations. When $0.75 > B/h > 0.28$, the leading wave of the series at least is bound to break. For greater values of B/h the bore consists of a single wave front. From equation 2.42 $B = 0$ where

$$C = u_2 + (gh_2)^{1/2} \ [\text{or } u_1 + (gh_1)^{1/2}]$$

being the upstream rate of advance of a long low wave ahead of, or behind the bore respectively, and generally

$$C \approx \frac{u_1 + u_2}{2} + \frac{[(gh_1)^{1/2} + (gh_2)^{1/2}]}{2}$$

Dronkers [23] traces the development of a bore by the method of characteristics (see section 1.2). Systems of characteristic lines are found to converge and intersect, indicating a discontinuity, at a point where a bore will be formed. The method can nevertheless be used to predict the water levels and flows associated with propagation of the bore. The method of characteristics may also be applied to three-dimensional problems of propagation of long (tidal) waves, in which case cones of characteristics have to be considered in the (x, y, t) space system.[24]

2.7 Methods of Numerical Analysis for Tidal Phenomena

Numerical tidal models are based on the shallow water equations. For two dimensions in plan they are written as follows.

Momentum equations

$$\frac{\delta u}{\delta t} + \underbrace{(u \frac{\delta u}{\delta x} + v \frac{\delta u}{\delta y})}_{\text{convective terms}} + g \frac{\delta \eta}{\delta x} - fv + \tau u = \psi_x$$

$$\frac{\delta v}{\delta t} + (u \frac{\delta v}{\delta x} + v \frac{\delta v}{\delta y}) + g \frac{\delta \eta}{\delta y} + fu + \tau v = \psi_y$$

Continuity equation

$$\frac{\delta \eta}{\delta t} + \frac{\delta(hu)}{\delta x} + \frac{\delta(hv)}{\delta y} = 0$$

where

u, v	=	velocity in x, y-directions
η	=	water surface elevation above MSL
h	=	total depth of water
f	=	Coriolis parameter $2\Omega \sin \theta$
Ω	=	angular velocity of Earth
θ	=	latitude
τ	=	$g\dfrac{(u^2 + v^2)^{1/2}}{Ch^2 h}$
g	=	gravitational acceleration
Ch	=	Chezy coefficient
ψ_x, ψ_y	=	wind stress and atmospheric pressure terms in x, y-directions

The equations are usually simplified for particular applications by reducing the number of dimensions or by neglecting certain terms in the momentum equations. The equations are averaged over the breadth in regular estuaries and over the depth where the flow is well mixed vertically. While three-dimensional models have been developed [25] estuaries are generally modelled in one dimension, or two dimensions in side elevation where there is significant stratification of flow, while large bodies of water are represented by two dimensions in plan. The wind stress and atmospheric pressure terms of the momentum equations are only sometimes included.[26, 27] When the equations are averaged over the breadth the Coriolis term drops out and the convective (non-linear) terms are usually neglected. Some models, two-dimensional in plan, also neglect the convective terms, largely because of the difficulty of representing them numerically.

Models are classified by their numerical solution technique, the method of characteristics, finite difference or finite element. The method of characteristics (section 1.2) follows the propagation of a series of small disturbances in the boundary conditions from the initial state and is unconditionally stable. The path of the characteristics in real situations is rather arbitrary which makes the method difficult to apply beyond one-dimensional models.

Finite difference models approximate the partial differential equations by using finite, rather than infinitesimal, differences.[28] Models of this type can be explicit (one unknown per equation) or implicit (many unknowns per equation). In the case of the former, stability considerations limit the time step whereas in the latter this restraint is relaxed but at the price of greatly increased computational complexity. For models two-dimensional in plan the alternating direction implicit method (explicit in one direction, implicit in the other, alternating with each time step) has proved to be very successful.

Finite element models approximate the solution over a small area (element) and by using a mesh of interconnected elements cover the area of interest. They find the best solution for the mesh and approximating functions used. Though finite elements are sometimes used throughout a model, most use finite elements only for the space discretisation and finite differences to advance in time [29]; harmonic functions in time have also been used to take advantage of the periodic nature of the flow. Finite element models have yet to win the wide acceptance given to finite difference models.

Glossary of Terms

Amphidromal	:	having no (semi-diurnal) tidal amplitude
Co-range	:	having the same range or amplitude (of a tide)
Co-tidal	:	having the same phase of tidal movement
Declination	:	angular distance with respect to celestial equator
Ecliptic	:	the path of the Sun's annual motion as seen from the Earth
Geoid	:	mean sea level considered as a continuous surface across land and sea
Geostrophic	:	caused by forces due to rotation of the Earth
Orogenic	:	relating to folding and faulting of the Earth's crust
Overfall	:	rapid tide race
Seiche	:	periodical motion of a lake or sea not attributable to tidal forces
Synodic	:	interval of time between two similar positions of the Moon relative to the Earth
Tsunami	:	wave caused by sudden underwater movement, usually of seismic origin

Example 2.1

What will be the difference in sea level at opposite points on the two sides of a straight parallel channel 37 km (20 nautical miles) wide, at latitude 45°, through which a steady 2 m/s (4 knot) current is flowing?

Coriolis effect sets up an acceleration force of $2V\Omega \sin l$ (section 2.2.2) transverse to a current V.

$$\Omega = \frac{2\pi}{24 \times 3600} = 7.25 \times 10^{-5} \text{ rad/s}$$

and hence

$$2V\Omega \sin l = 2 \times 2 \times 7.25 \times 10^{-5} \times 1/(2)^{1/2}$$

$$= 2.05 \times 10^{-4} \text{ m/s}^2$$

This accelerating force will establish a transverse surface slope

$$= 2.05 \times 10^{-4}/g = 2.05 \times 10^{-4}/9.81 = 2.1 \times 10^{-5}$$

and hence the difference in level between opposite points 37 km apart

$$= 2.1 \times 10^{-5} \times 37 \times 10^2 = 0.78 \text{ m}$$

(If the course of the current was curved towards the right in the northern hemisphere to a radius R, then for no surface slope transverse to the current, Coriolis forces would be balanced if $V^2/R = 2.05 \times 10^{-4}$ m/s^2, that is

$$R = 2 \times 2 \times 10^4/2.05 \sim 20 \text{ km})$$

Example 2.2

A system of straight parallel isobars has 5 mb intervals spaced 110 km apart. What is the resulting slope of the surface of the sea of depth 20 m at latitude 45° (a) transverse to the isobars (b) parallel to the isobars? The sea and air temperatures are the same.

There are two components of slope caused by the weather system, the barometric slope transverse to the isobars and the wind slope in the direction of the wind.

$$\text{barometer slope} = \frac{5 \times 100}{1020 \times 110 \times 1000 \times 9.81}$$

for seawater of density 1020 kg/m^3.

Hence barometric slope (transverse to isobars) $= 4.5 \times 10^{-7}$. The wind slope (by equation 2.20) is $S = C\rho_a U^2/\rho gh$ where C is, 3×10^{-3}, $\rho_a = 1.2$ kg/m^3 and $h = 20$ m. Hence

$$S = \frac{3 \times 10^{-3} \times 1.2 \, U^2}{(1020 \times 9.81 \times 20)}$$

$$= 1.8 \times 10^{-8} \times U^2$$

From figure 3.16 $U = 0.63 \, U_g$ while from equation 3.63

$$U_g = \frac{500 \times 10^4}{2 \times 0.73 \times 1.2 \times 0.707 \times 110 \times 1000} = 36.7 \text{ m/s}$$

Hence

$$U = 23 \text{ m/s}$$

and

$$S = 1.8 \times 10^{-8} \times (23)^2 = 9.5 \times 10^{-6}$$

If we assume that the wind direction is 15° from the line of the isobar in the direction of the pressure gradient (section 3.3.3), then parallel to the isobars

$$\text{sea slope} = 9.5 \times 10^{-6} \cos 15° = 0.92 \times 10^{-6}$$

transverse to the isobars

$$\text{sea slope} = 9.5 \times 10^{-6} \sin 15° + 4.5 \times 10^{-7}$$

$$= 2.46 \times 10^{-6} + 4.5 \times 10^{-7} \approx 2.9 \times 10^{-6}$$

Example 2.3

What is the probable magnitude of the surface current associated with a semi-diurnal tide of 6 m height in 30 m mean depth of water, ignoring wind and Coriolis effects?

By equation 2.25, the mean value of the maximum current on a vertical section

$$\bar{u}_{max} \sim H/2 \, (g/h)^{1/2}$$

$$= \frac{6}{2} \left(\frac{9.81}{30} \right)^{1/2}$$

$$= 1.71 \text{ m/s}$$

If a velocity distribution $u = kz^{1/n}$ be assumed by equation 2.26, then equation 2.27 indicates that maximum surface current $= (n + 1)/n. \, \bar{u}_{max} \sim 2 \text{ m/s} \, (\sim 4$ knots) for $n = 5$.

Example 2.4

Given the following data for observed tide levels (semi-diurnal) at an established gauge and a new survey site, calculate the sounding datum for the new site.

	Established Gauge (m) 1	New Site (m) 2
LW	0.5	1.2
HW	3.7	3.6
LW	0.8	1.4
HW	3.6	3.3
LW	0.4	1.0
HW	3.9	3.9
LW	0.7	1.3
MHWS	3.5	—
MLWS	0.5	—

The working below follows the steps outlined in section 2.5.

$$(OMLW)_1 = (0.5 + 3 \times 0.8 + 3 \times 0.4 + 0.7)/8 = 0.51$$
$$(OMHW)_1 = (3.7 + 2 \times 3.6 + 3.9)/4 = 3.70$$

$$
\begin{aligned}
(OMR)_1 &= 3.70 - 0.51 &&= 3.19 \\
(OMTL)_1 &= (3.70 + 0.51)/2 &&= 2.10 \\
(TMTL)_1 &= (3.5 + 0.5)/2 &&= 2.00 \\
(OMLW)_2 &= (1.2 + 3 \times 1.4 + 3 \times 1.0 + 1.3)/8 &&= 1.21 \\
(OMHW)_2 &= (3.6 + 2 \times 3.3 + 3.9)/4 &&= 3.52 \\
(OMR)_2 &= 2.31 \\
(OMTL)_2 &= 2.36
\end{aligned}
$$

The correct sounding datum at the new site should be

$$
2.36 - (2.10 - 2.0) - \frac{2.0 \times 2.31}{3.19} = 0.81 \text{ m}
$$

If $(TMTL)_1$ were unknown the next best estimate would be

$$
2.36 - \frac{2.10 \times 2.31}{3.19} = 0.84 \text{ m}
$$

Example 2.5

Given a set of tidal constituents for Jabal al Ali (United Arab Emirates) in time zone −4h G.M.T., (1) determine the nature of the tide at Jabal al Ali; (2) predict the tide level at 1600 h. on 14 August 1979.

		M_2	S_2	K_1	O_1
(a)	g	003	053	155	101
(b)	A	0.42	0.15	0.24	0.18
(c)	Speed	28.98°/h	30.00	15.04	13.94

MSL = 1.09 m

Seasonal correction for August 1979 = +0.1 m (from A.T.T. vol. II) therefore

MSL (Aug.79) = 1.19 m

$\pi A_{S2} = 0.47$ and $2(A_{K1} + A_{O1}) = 0.84$

therefore tides have a strong diurnal component resulting in inequalities between successive tides.

		M_2	S_2	K_1	O_1
(d)	$(E + u)$ at 0000 h GMT, 14/8/79	216	360	228	350 (from A.T.T. table VIII*)
(e)	$(E + u) - g$, time zone −4 (d) − (a)	213	307	73	249

*Table VIII provides values specifically for use with the Admiralty method as described in pamphlet NP159.

		M_2	S_2	K_1	O_1
(f)	Increment for 16 h (c) × 16	104	120	241	223
(g)	$(E + u) - g$ at 1600 h 14/8/79, (e) + (f)	317	67	314	112
(h)	f (Aug. 79)	1.04	1.0	0.89	0.82 (from A.T.T. table VIII)
(i)	$fA \cos [(E + u) - g]$	0.32	0.06	0.14	-0.06

Predicted tide level at 1600 h = 1.19 + 0.32 + 0.06 + 0.14 - 0.06
= 1.65 m

Note that the use of only four tidal constituents will not produce a particularly good prediction. In the above case the predicted tide using M_2, S_2, N_2, K_2, K_1, O_1 and P_1 was 1.57 m.

Reference

1. A. Owen and N.S. Heaps, Some recent model studies for tidal barrages in the Bristol Channel, *Record of the Colston Society Symposium, Bristol, 1978,* pp. 85-92
2. A.T. Doodson, The analysis of tidal observations for 29 days, *Int. hydrogr. Rev.,* **XXXI** (1954) 63-91
3. D.E. Cartwright, A study of currents in the Straits of Dover, *J. Inst. Navig.,* **XIV** (1961) 130-51
4. A. Damsgaard and A.F. Dinsmore, Numerical simulation of storm surges in bays, Symposium on Modelling Techniques, *2nd Annual Symposium of ASCE Waterways, Harbors and Coastal Engineering Division, San Francisco, 1975,* vol. II, pp. 1535-51
5. N.S. Heaps, Three dimensional modelling of the Irish Sea, *Proceedings of the 16th Coastal Engineering Conference, Hamburg, 1978,* vol. III, pp. 2671-86
6. A.M. Davies, Role of 2D and 3D models in JONSDAP 76, *Proceedings of the 16th Coastal Engineering Conference, Hamburg, 1978,* vol. I, pp. 1085-103
7. A. Fuhrboter, Frequencies and probabilities of extreme storm surges, *Proceedings of the 16th Coastal Engineering Conference, Hamburg, 1978,* vol. I, pp. 949-64
8. J.R.D. Francis, Wind action on a water surface, *Proc. Instn civ. Engrs.,* **12** (1959) 197-216
9. G. Kullenberg, An experimental and theoretical investigation of the turbulent diffusion in the upper layer of the sea, Institute of Physics and Oceanography, University of Copenhagen, Report No. 25 (1974) p. 288
10. H. Lamb, *Hydrodynamics,* 6th edn (Cambridge University Press, 1945)
11. W.G. Penney, Gravity waves produced by surface and underwater explosions, *Underwat. Explos. Res.,* **II** (1943) 679-93
12. G.H. Keulegan and J. Harrison, Tsunami refraction diagrams by digital computer, *Proc. Am. Soc. civ. Engrs.,* **96**, WW2 (1970) 219-33

13. K.L. Heitner and G.W. Hansner, Numerical model for tsunami run up, *Proc. Am. Soc. civ. Engrs.*, **96**, WW3 (1970) 701-19
14. S. Tsurata, Application of electronic computers to the analysis of anti-tsunami breakwaters, Modern Trends in Hydraulic Engineering, Central Water and Power Research Station, Poona, *Symposia*, **II** (1966) 38-42
15. J. Van Veen, Onderzoekingen in de Hoofden (Measurements in the Straits of Dover and their relation to the Netherlands Coasts, 1936)
16. B. Johns and N. Odd, On the vertical structure of tidal flow in river estuaries, *Geophys. J. R. astro. Soc.*, **12** (1966) 103-10
17. D.M. McDowell, Scale effect in hydraulic models with distorted vertical scale, Modern Trends in Hydraulic Engineering, Central Water and Power Research Station, Poona, *Symposia*, **II** (1966) 15-25
18. G.B. Pillsbury, *Tidal Hydraulics* (U.S. Army Corps of Engineers, 1956)
19. D.E. Cartwright and J. Crease, A comparison of the geodetic reference levels of England and France by means of the sea surface, *Proc. R. Soc. A*, **273** (1963) 558-80
20. J.R. Rossiter and G.W. Lennon, Computation of tidal conditions in the Thames Estuary by the initial value method, *Proc. Instn civ. Engrs.*, **31** (1965) 25-56
21. D.M. McDowell and B.A. O'Connor, *Hydraulic Behaviour of Estuaries*, (Macmillan, London and Basingstoke, 1977)
22. D.H. Peregrine, Calculations of the development of an undular bore, *J. Fluid Mech.*, **25** (1966) 321-30
23. J.J. Dronkers, *Tidal Computations in Rivers and Coastal Waters* (North Holland, Amsterdam, 1964)
24. A. Daubert and O. Graffe, Quelques aspects des écoulements presque horizontaux à deux dimensions en plan et non permanents. Applications aux estuaires, *Houille blanche*, **8** (1965) 841-59
25. J.J. Leendertse, R.C. Alexander and Shiao-Kung, A three dimensional model for estuaries and coastal seas, Rand Corporation, Rand Memorandum R-1417-OWRR (1973)
26. M.B. Abbott, A. Damsgaard and Robenhuis, System 21, Jupiter, a design system for two dimensional flows, *J. Hydraul. Res.*, **11** (1973)
27. T.J. Weare, The third London Airport study, *J. Hydraul. Res.*, **15** (1977) 55-72
28. J.B. Hinwood and I.G. Wallis, Review of Models of Tidal Waters, *J. Hydraul. Div. Am. Soc. civ. Engrs.*, **101** (1975) 1405-21
29. W.G. Gray and D.R. Lynch, On the control of noise in finite element tidal computations: a semi-implicit approach, *Computers and Fluids*, **7** (1979) 47-67
30. T.J. Weare, Instability in tidal flow computation schemes, *Proc. Am. Soc. civ. Engrs.*, **102** HY5 (1976) 569-80

3

Waves

In Chapter 3 we considered waves of periods measured in minutes, hours or days. In this chapter we are concerned with waves of, say, 1–30 s, which are predominantly those caused by wind.

Only forty years ago, the civil engineer's oceanological tool kit comprised little more than Stevenson's empirical formula, which predicted maximum wave height, in feet, as 1.5 (fetch in miles)$^{1/2}$. The Second World War saw great advances, not only in the prediction of waves by oceanographers, but also in the application of the results by engineers to the design and construction of maritime works.

Wave theories discussed here normally assume trains of long, smooth, regular waves. The surface of a smooth wave follows a continuous sinuous line; regular waves belong to a parallel train of constant wavelength. Waves met at sea are more frequently short-crested, random and irregular: irregular and short-crested because of the intersections of waves which are travelling in different directions, and random because of the perpetually varying profile resulting from superposition of waves of different heights and lengths.

In this chapter some of the more simple mathematical formulae concerning sea waves are derived briefly, and their limitations, caused by the simplifying assumptions involved, are indicated. For problems outside the range of the simple theories, references are included to authorities on the characteristics of waves of greater complexity. A brief account is also provided of the prediction of waves, the interpretation of wave records, the reflection, refraction and diffraction of waves, ship waves, currents generated by waves and, finally, a note on questions of resonance.

3.1 The Linear Theory of Waves

3.1.1 Solution for Airy Waves

The original theory of smooth low waves in two dimensions is attributed to Airy.[1] The theory assumes that there is a velocity potential ϕ satisfying Laplace's equation (derived in chapter 1)

$$\frac{\partial^2 \phi}{\partial x^2} + \frac{\partial^2 \phi}{\partial z^2} = 0 \tag{3.1}$$

where x is a horizontal axis, z the vertical axis, (positive upwards), the origin being at the level of the equilibrium surface (figure 3.1). $q = -$ grad ϕ, where q is a velocity vector with components u ($= \partial\phi/\partial x$) and w ($= \partial\phi/\partial z$) (see section 1.1) in the horizontal and vertical directions respectively. For an incompressible fluid in a gravitational field, Bernoulli's full equation is

$$\frac{p}{\rho} + \tfrac{1}{2}q^2 + gz + \frac{\partial\phi}{\partial t} = 0$$

This equation may be reduced to

$$\frac{p}{\rho} + \frac{\partial\phi}{\partial t} + gz \approx 0 \tag{3.2}$$

by the linear theory which neglects terms involving the square of the velocity. Thus, η, the elevation of the surface, where $p = 0$, may be written

$$\eta \approx -\frac{1}{g}\left[\frac{\partial\phi}{\partial t}\right]_{z=\eta} \tag{3.3}$$

or

$$\eta \approx -\frac{1}{g}\left[\frac{\partial\phi}{\partial t}\right]_{z=0} \tag{3.4}$$

since η is a small quantity. But since the normal to the surface is very nearly vertical

$$\frac{\partial\eta}{\partial t} \approx \left[\frac{\partial\phi}{\partial z}\right]_{z=0} \tag{3.5}$$

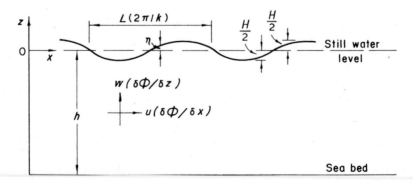

Figure 3.1 *Reference diagram for Airy wave*

Hence, from equations 3.4 and 3.5

$$\frac{\partial^2 \phi}{\partial t^2} + \frac{g\partial \phi}{\partial z} = 0 \qquad (3.6)$$

where $z = 0$. A solution of this equation for a progressive wave may be found in the form

$$\phi = P e^{i(\sigma t - kx)} \qquad (3.7)$$

where P is a function of z only, yielding from equation 3.6 a solution for

$$\eta = \frac{H}{2} \cos (kx - \sigma t) \qquad (3.8)$$

or

$$\eta = \frac{H}{2} \cos 2\pi \left(\frac{x}{L} - \frac{t}{T}\right) \qquad (3.9)$$

where $L \ (= 2\pi/k)$ is the wave length and $T \ (= 2\pi/\sigma)$ is the wave period in seconds. Using the fact that $w \ (= \partial \phi/\partial z)$ must be zero at $z = -h$, that is, at the sea bed, the velocity potential may then be derived as

$$\phi = \frac{HC}{2} \frac{\cosh 2\pi(z + h)/L}{\sinh 2\pi h/L} \sin 2\pi \left(\frac{x}{L} - \frac{t}{T}\right) \qquad (3.10)$$

where wave celerity or rate of progress is

$$C = g\frac{T}{2\pi} \tanh \frac{2\pi h}{L} \qquad (3.11)$$

or, since $C = L/T$

$$C = \left(\frac{gL}{2\pi} \tanh \frac{2\pi h}{L}\right)^{1/2} \qquad (3.12)$$

Where $h/L \geqslant 0.5$, the expression

$$C_0 = \left(\frac{gL_0}{2\pi}\right)^{1/2} = \frac{gT}{2\pi} \qquad (3.13)$$

(that is, $L_0 = 1.56T^2$ m or $5.12T^2$ ft) involves an error in C_0 (subscript 0 relating to deep water) of less than 0.5 per cent since $\tanh 2\pi h/L \approx 1$.

Where $h/L \leqslant 0.04$, the expression

$$C_s = (gh)^{1/2} \tag{3.14}$$

(subscript s relating to shallow water) involves an error of less than 5 per cent, since $\tanh 2\pi h/L \approx 2\pi h/L$.

From equations 3.12 and 3.13 since $C = L/T$

$$\frac{C}{C_0} = \frac{L}{L_0} = \tanh \frac{2\pi h}{L} \tag{3.15}$$

Tanh $2\pi h/L$, h/L and $2\pi h/L$ are plotted in figure 3.2 against h/L_0 to permit the determination of C and L in a wave of length L_0 in deep water, and to indicate the errors involved in the approximations of equations 3.14 or 3.15 for any intermediate depth of water.

According to this linearised theory the particles move in closed orbits, that is there is no mass transport. The displacements of the particles are given by

horizontally

$$X = \frac{H}{2} \frac{\cosh 2\pi (z + h)/L}{\sinh 2\pi h/L} \sin 2\pi \left(\frac{x}{L} - \frac{t}{T} \right)$$

and vertically $\hspace{4cm} (3.16)$

$$Z = \frac{H}{2} \frac{\sinh 2\pi (z + h)/L}{\sinh 2\pi h/L} \cos 2\pi \left(\frac{x}{L} - \frac{t}{T} \right)$$

where (x, z) is the mean position; $z = -h$ corresponds to the bed.

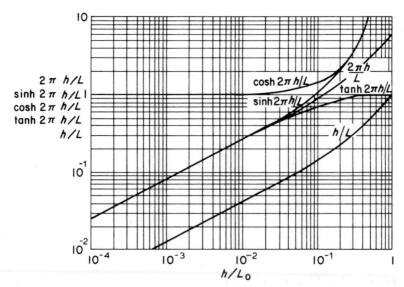

Figure 3.2 *Relationship between h/L_0 and functions of h/L*

From equation 3.16 it is evident that the particle orbits are elliptical, the horizontal and vertical excursions being respectively

$$\xi = \pm \frac{H}{2} \frac{\cosh 2\pi (z + h)/L}{\sinh 2\pi h/L} \quad \text{and} \quad \zeta = \pm \frac{H}{2} \frac{\sinh 2\pi (z + h)/L}{\sinh 2\pi h/L}$$

For deep water ($h/L \geqslant 0.5$) the orbits are approximately circular with the water motion at $z = L/2$ only 4 per cent of its value at the water surface ($z = 0$). For shallow water ($h/L \leqslant 0.04$) the horizontal motion varies little between the surface and the bed (figure 3.3).

For many purposes including the calculation of wave forces on structures (chapter 7), the determination of tidal currents (chapter 2) and the estimation of sediment transport (chapter 4), it is necessary to know the particle velocities and accelerations. These can be obtained by differentiating the particle displacements with respect to time. The horizontal and vertical velocities respectively are

$$u = \frac{\pi H}{T} \frac{\cosh 2\pi (z + h)/L}{\sinh 2\pi h/L} \cos 2\pi \left(\frac{x}{L} - \frac{t}{T}\right)$$

and   (3.17)

$$w = \frac{\pi H}{T} \frac{\sinh 2\pi (z + h)/L}{\sinh 2\pi h/L} \sin 2\pi \left(\frac{x}{L} - \frac{t}{T}\right)$$

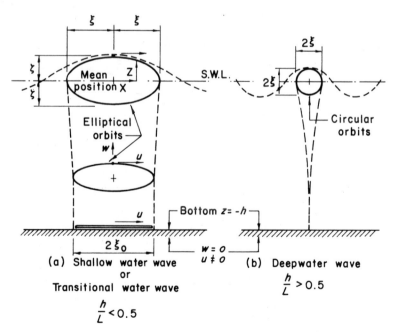

Figure 3.3 *Water particle orbits for deep water and shallow water waves*

Where $h/L \geqslant 0.5$ these expressions for the velocities may be simplified to

$$u = \pi \frac{H}{T} e^{2\pi z/L} \cos 2\pi \left(\frac{x}{L} - \frac{t}{T}\right) \text{ with maximum } \hat{u} = \pi \frac{H}{T} e^{2\pi z/L} \quad (3.18)$$

and

$$w = \pi \frac{H}{T} e^{2\pi z/L} \sin 2\pi \left(\frac{x}{L} - \frac{t}{T}\right) \text{ with maximum } \hat{w} = \pi \frac{H}{T} e^{2\pi z/L} \quad (3.19)$$

These approximations assume that $\tanh 2\pi h/L = 1$. The error involved in making such an assumption for values of h/L down to about 0.2 is small (see figure 3.2). Values of $\hat{u}$ and $\hat{w}$ may be derived by the use of figure 3.4. The oscillatory motion at bed level is obtained by the substitution $z = -h$ in equations 3.17.

Equations 3.18 and 3.19 indicate circular orbits for the water particles with constant angular velocity, from equation 3.13, of

$$\sigma = \left(\frac{2\pi g}{L_0}\right)^{1/2} \text{ and radius} = \frac{H e^{2\pi z/L}}{2} \quad (3.20)$$

(with z measured upwards from the surface, figure 3.3). At the water surface, the orbital radius corresponds to half the wave height with

$$|\hat{u}| = \frac{\pi H}{T} = \frac{gH}{2C_0} \quad (3.21)$$

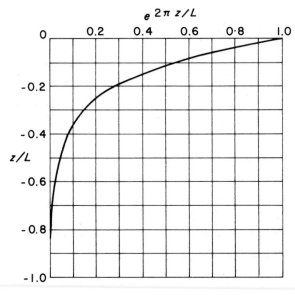

Figure 3.4 *Variations of $e^{2\pi z/L}$ with $-z/L$*

(from equation 3.13). In shallow water ($h/L \geqslant 0.04$) we may make the following approximations

$$\sinh \frac{2\pi h}{L} \sim \frac{2\pi h}{L}, \quad \sinh \frac{2\pi z}{L} \sim \frac{2\pi z}{L}, \quad \cosh \frac{2\pi h}{L} \sim \cosh \frac{2\pi z}{L} \sim 1$$

whence it is found from equation 3.17 that the horizontal velocity u varies between $\pm HL/2hT$. By comparison between equation 3.8 and equation 3.17 in which the above approximations have been made, the horizontal velocity is seen to be

$$u = C\eta/h$$

that is, directly proportional to the surface elevation, η, at the vertical section considered.

The horizontal and vertical accelerations respectively are

$$\frac{\partial u}{\partial t} = \frac{2\pi^2 H}{T^2} \frac{\cosh 2\pi (z + h)/L}{\sinh 2\pi h/L} \sin 2\pi \left(\frac{x}{L} - \frac{t}{T} \right)$$

$$\frac{\partial w}{\partial t} = \frac{2\pi^2 H}{T^2} \frac{\sinh 2\pi (z + h)/L}{\sinh 2\pi h/L} \cos 2\pi \left(\frac{x}{L} - \frac{t}{T} \right)$$

(3.22)

The subsurface pressure is

$$p = -\rho g z + \frac{\rho g H}{2} \frac{\cosh 2\pi (z + h)/L}{\cosh 2\pi h/L} \cos 2\pi \left(\frac{x}{L} - \frac{t}{T} \right) \qquad (3.23)$$

= hydrostatic less dynamic pressure (in pressure terms)

The energy of a wave is composed of two parts: potential energy exists due to the deviation of its profile from still water level; kinetic energy is in the form of oscillatory motion of the water particles. The kinetic energy per unit width is obtained from

$$E_k = \int_0^L \int_0^h \rho \frac{u^2 + w^2}{2} \, dx \, dz$$

which from equation 3.17 reduces to

$$E_k = \rho g \frac{H^2 L}{16} \qquad (3.24)$$

where ρ is unit mass of water.

In a similar manner, the potential energy of a wave per unit width is

$$E_p = \int_0^L \int_0^h g \rho z \eta^2 \, dx \, dz$$

and substituting for η from equation 3.9 we have

$$E_\mathrm{p} = \rho g \, \frac{H^2 L}{16} \tag{3.25}$$

so that the total energy of the wave per unit area is

$$E = \frac{E_\mathrm{k} + E_\mathrm{p}}{L} = \frac{E_\mathrm{t}}{L} = \frac{\rho g H^2}{8} \tag{3.26}$$

In the linear wave theory only, the kinetic and potential energies are thus equal, but this is not true in general. It so also interesting to note that over 99 per cent of the energy in a wave is in a depth less than $L/2$ below the mean water level.

3.1.2 Group Velocity and Energy Transfer

A fundamental concept relating to a wave train in deep water is that of group velocity. When a train of waves moves through a calm area, the leading ones have to set up the necessary oscillatory motion and consequently lose height; in fact each leading crest may be seen gradually to disappear. The rate of advance of the leading fully developed wave is in consequence less than that of the individual waves of the fully formed train that follows. Lamb [2] describes the phenomenon in these words, 'If attention be fixed on a particular wave, it is seen to advance through a group, gradually dying out as it approaches the front, while its former place in the group is occupied in succession by other waves which have come forward from the rear'.

Consider the sum of two wave forms, illustrated in figure 3.5

$$\eta = \frac{H}{2} \cos (kx - \sigma t) + \frac{H}{2} \cos (k'x - \sigma't)$$

$$= H \cos \left[\frac{(k + k')x}{2} - \frac{(\sigma + \sigma')t}{2} \right] \cos \left[\frac{(k - k')x}{2} - \frac{(\sigma - \sigma')t}{2} \right]$$

where $k - k'$ and $\sigma - \sigma'$ are each small, representing a series of waves whose amplitude varies between 0 and H. The pitch between points of corresponding amplitude is $2\pi/(k - k')$. The amplitude of the combined wave form is seen to

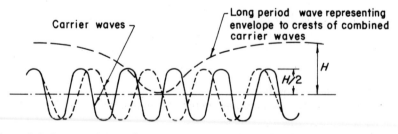

Figure 3.5 *Superposition of two wave trains with small difference in wave length*

vary in the profile of a longer wave. The combined waves may thus be said to constitute carriers to this longer type, analogous to amplitude–modulated radio waves. The time required for the long period wave to advance by one complete wave length is $2\pi/(\sigma - \sigma')$. In the limit, group velocity

$$C_g = \frac{d\sigma}{dk} = \frac{d(kC)}{dk} = C + \frac{k\,dC}{dk} \tag{3.27}$$

and from equation 3.12, substituting for $L = 2\pi/k$

$$C_g = \tfrac{1}{2}C\left(1 + \frac{4\pi h/L}{\sinh 4\pi h/L}\right) = C_n C \tag{3.28}$$

Where $h/L > 0.5$ this reduces to

$$C_g \approx \tfrac{1}{2}C_0 \tag{3.29}$$

while in shallow water

$$C_g \approx C_s \tag{3.30}$$

It is of considerable interest to consider the average rate of transmission of power in the direction of a wave.[3] This may be expressed

$$P = \frac{1}{T}\int_0^T \int_0^{-h} (p + \rho g z)\,u\,dt\,dz$$

which, from equations 3.2 and 3.10, integrating and reducing, simplifies to

$$P = \rho g\,\frac{H^2}{8}\,\frac{C}{2}\left(1 + \frac{4\pi h/L}{\sinh 4\pi h/L}\right) = C_n\,\rho g\,\frac{H^2 C}{8} \tag{3.31}$$

and

$$P = \frac{E_t}{T}\,\frac{C_g}{C} = EC_g \tag{3.32}$$

from equations 3.28, 3.25 and 3.26.

3.1.3 Standing Waves

Standing waves are those whose form varies periodically but which remain in the same position. The equation of velocity potential may be derived from first principles through equations 3.1 to 3.6. Alternatively it may be derived from equation 3.10 since a standing wave may be considered to represent the super-position of a progressive wave on an equivalent one travelling in the opposite direction. When this effect is due to the reflection of a progressive wave train from a vertical wall it is often called 'clapotis'; the height is then double that of the original wave train (see chapter 7).

The velocity potential for a standing wave of height H may be written

$$\phi = \frac{HC}{2} \frac{\cosh 2\pi (z + h)/L}{\sinh 2\pi h/L} \sin \frac{2\pi x}{L} \cos \frac{2\pi t}{T} \tag{3.33}$$

where T is period, L wave length and h depth of water (see figure 3.1). The elevation of the surface is then

$$\eta = \frac{H}{2} \sin \frac{2\pi x}{L} \sin \frac{2\pi t}{T} \tag{3.34}$$

(cf. equation 3.9) where $C = (gT/2\pi) \tanh (2\pi h/L)$ from equation 3.12. The particle motions are given by

$$X = \frac{H}{2} \frac{\cosh 2\pi (z + h)/L}{\sinh 2\pi h/L} \cos 2\pi x/L \sin 2\pi t/T$$

$$\tag{3.35}$$

$$Z = \frac{H}{2} \frac{\sinh 2\pi (z + h)/L}{\sinh 2\pi h/L} \sin 2\pi x/L \sin 2\pi t/T$$

The particles move up and down vertically beneath the troughs and crests and move horizontally beneath the nodes. The particle velocities u and w may be derived, as for the progressive wave, as

$$u = \frac{\pi H}{T} \frac{\cosh 2\pi (z + h)/L}{\sinh 2\pi h/L} \cos \frac{2\pi x}{L} \cos \frac{2\pi t}{T} \tag{3.36}$$

and

$$w = \frac{\pi H}{T} \frac{\sinh 2\pi (z + h)/L}{\sinh 2\pi h/L} \sin \frac{2\pi x}{L} \cos \frac{2\pi t}{T} \tag{3.37}$$

Evidently, by comparing equations 3.36 and 3.37 at a given depth of water, u varies between a maximum value at a node, ($x/L = 0, \frac{1}{2}, 1$, etc.) at time $t/T = 0, \frac{1}{2}, 1$, etc., and zero at all times at a point of maximum amplitude ($x/L = \frac{1}{4}, \frac{3}{4}$, etc.)

The velocities and magnitudes of the oscillations and their variation with depth are therefore identical to those of a progressive wave of the same height and period, given by equations 3.16 and 3.17. In addition, the same approximations for waves in deep or shallow water may be applied.

By a process of integration similar to that of equations 3.24 and 3.25 the sum of the potential and kinetic energy of a standing wave per unit width of wave is found to be

$$E_t = E_p + E_k = \rho g \frac{H^2 L}{16} \tag{3.38}$$

There is a periodic transformation of potential and kinetic energies, that is, $E_p \doteqdot E_k$. These relationships could be derived by summing the energies of a progressive and an equivalent reflected wave, each of height $H/2$, to yield a standing wave of height H. By the symmetry of the motion, no horizontal transmission of power occurs with a standing wave. This might be established by deriving the relationship for standing waves, which corresponds to equation 3.31 for progressive waves. Table 3.1 summarises the principal properties of Airy waves.

3.2 Waves of Finite Height

Up to this point it has been assumed, for both standing waves and progressive waves, that the height is small not only by comparison with the length but also by comparison with the depth of water through which the wave is being propagated. Clearly, except for swell and the long-period waves associated for example with tsunamis, seiches and tides, the validity of the assumptions made must be examined in terms of the accuracy of the available wave height and period data and the engineering significance of the errors involved. The prediction of maximum wave crest elevation can be of particular importance in this respect.

Non-linear wave theories have been developed for various surface profiles. These generally assume the wave to be broad crested and to travel at constant celerity in a uniform depth of water without changing shape. The two-dimensional model shown in figure 3.6 summarises the basic parameters used.

3.2.1 Stokes Waves

Stokes [4] developed the theory of Airy waves for waves of somewhat greater amplitude. The form was expressed as a series of terms of $\cos 2\pi n\, (x/L - t/T)$ where $n = 0, 1, 2, 3, \ldots$. Such waves are irrotational, that is to say

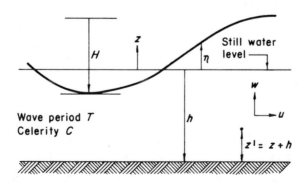

Figure 3.6 *Reference diagram for broad-crested periodic waves*

TABLE 3.1 *Summary of principal characteristics of Airy waves*

Water Depth Wave Characteristic	1. Shallow $\left(\dfrac{h}{L} \le \dfrac{1}{25}\right)$	2. Intermediate $\left(\dfrac{1}{25} < \dfrac{h}{L} < \dfrac{1}{2}\right)$	3. Deep $\left(\dfrac{h}{L} > \dfrac{1}{2}\right)$
Surface profile	As 2	$\eta = \dfrac{H}{2}\cos\left(\dfrac{2\pi x}{L} - \dfrac{2\pi t}{T}\right) = \dfrac{H}{2}\cos\theta$	As 2
Celerity	$C = L/T = (gh)^{1/2}$	$C = \dfrac{L}{T} = \dfrac{gT}{2\pi}\tanh\left(\dfrac{2\pi h}{L}\right)$	$C = C_0 = \dfrac{L}{T} = \dfrac{gT}{2\pi}$
Group velocity	$C_g = C$	$C_g = CnC = \dfrac{1}{2}\left(1 + \dfrac{4\pi\,h/L}{\sinh(4\pi\,h/L)}\right)C$	$C_g = C/2$
Particle velocity horizontal	$u = \dfrac{H}{2}(g/h)^{1/2}\cos\theta$	$u = \dfrac{\pi H}{t}\,\dfrac{\cosh\left[2\pi\,(z+h)/L\right]}{\sinh(2\pi h/L)}\cos\theta$	$u = \dfrac{\pi H}{T}\,e^{2\pi z/L}\cos\theta$
Particle velocity vertical	$w = \dfrac{\pi H}{T}\left(1 + \dfrac{z}{h}\right)\sin\theta$	$w = \dfrac{\pi H}{t}\,\dfrac{\sinh\left[2\pi(z+h)/L\right]}{\sinh(2\pi h/L)}\sin\theta$	$w = \dfrac{\pi H}{T}\,e^{2\pi z/L}\sin\theta$
Particle acceleration horizontal	$\dot u = \dfrac{2\pi}{T}\,u\tan\theta$	$\dot u = \dfrac{2\pi}{T}\,u\tan\theta$	$\dot u = \dfrac{2\pi}{T}\,u\tan\theta$
Particle acceleration vertical	$\dot w = \dfrac{-2\pi}{T}\,w\cot\theta$	$\dot w = \dfrac{-2\pi}{T}\,w\cot\theta$	$\dot w = \dfrac{-2\pi}{T}\,w\cot\theta$
Subsurface pressure	$p = \rho g(\eta - z)$	$p = \rho g\eta\,\dfrac{\cosh\left[2\pi\,(z+h)/L\right]}{\cosh(2\pi h/L)} - \rho gz$	$p = \rho g\eta\,e^{2\pi z/L} - \rho gz$

$\partial u/\partial z - \partial w/\partial x = 0$. In deep water, if terms involving $(H/L)^3$ and higher powers are neglected from the Fourier series relating to such an analysis

$$C_0 = \left[\frac{gL_0}{2\pi} \left(1 + \frac{\pi^2 H_0{}^2}{L_0{}^2} \right) \right]^{1/2} \tag{3.39}$$

where C is wave celerity, H wave height and L wave length. As the ratio H/L increases, the crest becomes steeper and the trough flatter than the Airy wave. This has the effect of raising the median height relative to the still water level. The particle orbital velocities have a superimposed forward drift or mass transport, which is given for a second-order wave by

$$\bar{U} = \frac{1}{2} \frac{\pi^2 H^2}{LT} \frac{\cosh 4\pi (z+h)/L}{\sinh^2 2\pi h/L} \tag{3.40}$$

which reduces to $\bar{U} = (\pi^2 H^2{}_0/L_0 T) \, e^{4\pi z/L_0}$ for deep water.

Relationships for particle velocities and the wave forms become complex as the number of terms retained increase. The use of digital computers has enabled rapid solutions to be obtained for the higher-order formulations. In practice the the fifth-order Stokes wave is frequently used in estimating wave forces on structures since many of the experimental constants derived from field measurements have been correlated with this theory.

3.2.2 Gerstner Trochoidal Wave

The surface form of a Gerstner wave is a trochoid, that is, the path of a point on a disc whose circumference rotates along a straight line. Referring to figure 3.7 the disc, of radius k^{-1}, which is equal to $L/2\pi$ by definition (see equation 3.9) rolls along a horizontal line, and the wave surface is the locus of a point at radius

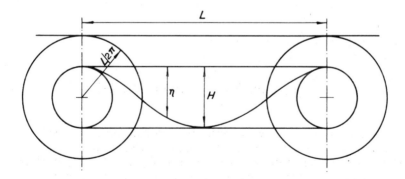

Figure 3.7 *Reference diagram for Gerstner wave*

$H/2$, where H is wave height. For an angle of rotation θ, the surface depression below crest level is

$$\eta = \frac{H}{2} \, (1 - \cos \theta) \tag{3.41}$$

while the horizontal distance of the surface from the origin at a crest is given by

$$x = L \left(1 - \frac{\theta}{2\pi} + \frac{H}{2L} \, \sin \theta \right) \tag{3.42}$$

Where H is small, the form tends towards a sine wave and hence in the limit the wave corresponds to a deep water Airy wave.

3.2.3 Stream Function Waves

Although the Stokes waves satisfy the basic Laplace equation and the sea bed boundary conditions, the free surface boundary conditions are not fully satisfied. The components of flow at the surface are not necessarily in accordance with the shape of the surface and its motions, nor is a restriction placed on the pressure immediately below the free surface. The dynamic free surface boundary condition is

$$\eta + \frac{1}{2g} \, [(u - C)^2 + w^2] - \frac{C^2}{2g} = \text{const} \tag{3.43}$$

The stream function solution may be expressed as

$$\psi \, (x,z) = \frac{L}{T} \, z + \sum_{n=1}^{N} X \, (n) \sinh \left[\frac{2\pi n}{L} \, (h + \eta) \right] \cos \left(\frac{2\pi n}{L} \, x \right) \tag{3.44}$$

and evaluated by setting $z = \eta$ to give a surface

$$\eta = \frac{T}{L} \, \psi_n - \frac{T}{L} \sum_{n=1}^{N} X \, (n) \sinh \left[\frac{2\pi n}{L} \, (h + \eta) \right] \cos \left(\frac{2\pi n}{L} \, x \right) \tag{3.45}$$

For a particular water depth, wave height and period the function exactly satisfies the Laplace equation, the sea bed and the surface flow boundary conditions for arbitrary values of the constants L, ψ_n and $X(n)$. These values can be obtained numerically so that the dynamic free surface boundary condition is best satisfied for a specific wave height. Fifth-order solutions have been published by Dean.[5]

3.2.4 Solitary Waves

A solitary wave is a progressive wave, relative to the body of water, whose motion is unaffected by preceding or following crests, that is, it is theoretically a single very long wave. It might be, for example, a tsunami generating by seismic disturbance; also the theory can be used to represent the effect of swell running up a gradually sloping beach with the crests distantly spaced. In the solitary wave theory the surface profile is entirely above the still water level. The wave is therefore not periodic and has no definite wave length. Boussinesq [6] derived the characteristics of the solitary wave, in shallow water of depth h, directly from the general equation for steady flow

$$\phi + i\psi = F(x + iz) = e^{izD} F(x) \tag{3.46}$$

where D is the operator d/dx and $F(x)$ is real. Expansion and separation of real and imaginary terms, neglecting fourth and higher derivatives of x and including the boundary conditions at the surface and the sea bed lead to a relationship

$$\left(\frac{dz}{dx}\right)^2 = \frac{3(z-h)^2}{h^2}\left(1 - \frac{gz}{C^2}\right) \tag{3.47}$$

where the origin is taken on the sea bed immediately beneath the crest, x is measured horizontally, z vertically upwards, and C is the velocity at some distance from the crest.

The general equation of the surface of the solitary wave, of crest height H above still water level, is then

$$\eta(= z - h) = H \operatorname{sech}^2 \frac{x}{2b} \tag{3.48}$$

where a horizontal velocity $-C$ is superimposed on the conditions assumed initially, thus bringing the water remote from the crest to rest and making the wave a progressive wave with celerity C (see figure 3.8). In equation 3.48

$$b = h\left(\frac{h+H}{3H}\right)^{1/2} \tag{3.49}$$

also

$$C = g^{1/2}(h+H)^{1/2} \tag{3.50}$$

and the relationship between H/h and b/h is indicated in figure 3.9.

McCowan [7] developed the theory further by deriving a more complex expression of the conformal transformation $(\phi + i\psi) = F(x + iz)$ of which the Boussinesq expression (equation 3.48) represents a first approximation. The mathematics of McCowan's form become very tedious and it is fortunate that, for most engineering purposes, equations 3.48, 3.49 and 3.50 suffice as a definition of the wave form and characteristics. Where it is necessary to know

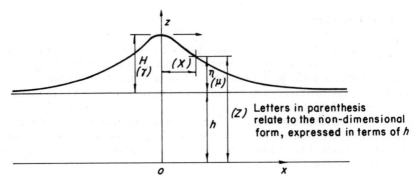

Figure 3.8 *Reference diagram for solitary wave*

with greater precision the velocity distribution in the solitary wave, it is simpler
to consider it as a special case of the cnoidal wave (see section 3.2.5) rather than
embark on solutions of McCowan's equation, but useful information on this
subject is provided by Wiegel and Beebe [8] together with experimental results
for comparison with theory.

It is helpful, in considering the field of application of the solitary wave, to
express the equation in non-dimensional form. Where $X = x/h$, $Z = z/h$, $\mu = \eta/h$
and $\gamma = H/b$, $Z = 0$ at sea bed, and $Z = 1 + \gamma$ at crest, then equations 3.48, 3.49
and 3.50 may be rewritten as

$$\mu = \gamma \, \text{sech}^2 \left[X \left(\frac{3\gamma}{4(1 + \gamma)} \right)^{1/2} \right] \approx \gamma \, \text{sech}^2 \left[X \left(\frac{3\gamma}{4} \right)^{1/2} \right] \qquad (3.51)$$

$$b = \frac{h(1 + \gamma)^{1/2}}{(3\gamma)^{1/2}} \approx \frac{h}{(3\gamma)^{1/2}} \qquad (3.52)$$

and

$$C = (gh)^{1/2} \, (1 + \gamma)^{1/2} \approx (gh)^{1/2} \qquad (3.53)$$

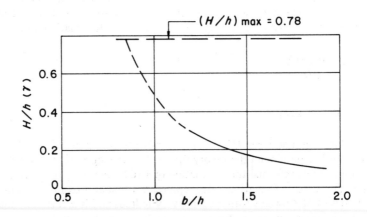

Figure 3.9 *Relationship between H/h and b/h for solitary wave*

the approximate forms to equations 3.51, 3.52 and 3.53 being adequate for use when $\gamma(= H/h)$ is less than about $\frac{1}{3}$.

The Boussinesq theory assumes that horizontal velocity on a vertical section beneath the wave is uniform for $0 \leqslant z \leqslant (h + \eta)$. Figure 3.10, based on Munk [9] indicates the departure from this assumption by the adoption of McCowan's wave form. It is apparent that for values of γ up to about $\frac{1}{3}$ no great error is involved in the Boussinesq approximation but, for values greater than this, the assumption leads to considerable overestimates of velocities at lower levels.

The volume of a solitary wave per unit length above still water level is given in non-dimensional form between points $\pm X$ on the x-axis by

$$\varDelta = \int_{-X}^{X} \mu h \, dX$$

$$= \int_{-X}^{X} \gamma h^2 \operatorname{sech}^2 \left[\left(\frac{3\gamma}{4} \right)^{1/2} X \right] \, dX \qquad (3.54)$$

(using the approximate form of equation 3.51) so

$$\varDelta = \left[\gamma h^2 \left(\frac{4}{3\gamma} \right)^{1/2} \tanh \left\{ \left(\frac{3\gamma}{4} \right)^{1/2} X \right\} \right]_{-X}^{X} \qquad (3.55)$$

and

$$\varDelta = \frac{4h^2 \gamma^{1/2} \left(1 - \dfrac{\mu_x}{\gamma} \right)^{1/2}}{3^{1/2}} \qquad (3.56)$$

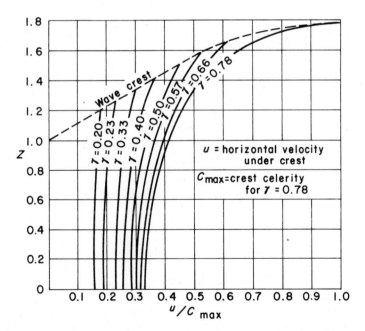

Figure 3.10 *Horizontal velocities beneath crest of solitary wave; after Munk [9]*

where μ_x relates to height at $\pm X$.

For widely spaced wave crests equation 3.56 becomes

$$\Delta = \int_{-\infty}^{\infty} \mu\Delta \, \mathrm{d}X = 4h^2 \left(\frac{\gamma}{3}\right)^{1/2} \tag{3.57}$$

Where crests are spaced at distance L, then the 'period' of the solitary wave is

$$T_{\text{sol}} = \frac{L_{\text{sol}}}{C} \approx \frac{L_{\text{sol}}}{(gh)^{1/2}} \tag{3.58}$$

Where a train of solitary waves approaches a beach or similar barrier there can be no over-all transport of water. There is therefore a return flow of water to balance the volume contained in each crest. This gives rise to a superimposed horizontal velocity $\bar{u}$ considered as uniformly distributed on a vertical plane. Evidently, away from the crest, from equation 3.56

$$\bar{u} = \frac{\Delta}{hT_{\text{sol}}} = \frac{4h}{T_{\text{sol}}} \left(\frac{\gamma - \mu}{3}\right)^{1/2} \tag{3.59}$$

Because of the relationship of equation 3.53, the kinetic energy of a solitary wave, for small values of γ, is found to be equal to the potential energy and so the total energy

$$E_{\text{sol}} = \frac{8}{3} \rho g h^3 \gamma \left(\frac{\gamma}{3}\right)^{1/2} \tag{3.60}$$

using the approximate form of equations 3.51 and 3.53. Table 3.2 indicates the values of X to ensure that 90 per cent of Δ and of E_{sol} are contained between $\pm X$.

TABLE 3.2 *Minimum values of X to contain 90 per cent of Δ and E_{sol}*

γ	0.2	0.4	0.78
X for 90% Δ	3.9	2.7	2.0
X for 90% E_{sol}	2.4	1.7	1.2
$\pi/(3\gamma)^{1/2}$ i.e. (π/M)	4.0	2.85	2.05

McCowan's form of the solitary wave introduces a factor M ($= h/b \approx (3\gamma)^{1/2}$ from equation 3.52) and it has been widely stated (see for example Bagnold [10]) that the spacing of crests of solitary waves expressed in non-dimensional form must be at least $2\pi/M$ apart for the theory to be applicable. Such a value of L/h corresponds to $|X| = \pi/(3\gamma)^{1/2}$ and it is of interest to note from table 3.2 that such a criterion gives much the same values for $|X|$ as does the requirement for 90 per cent Δ.

The vertical displacement of a particle at a height z_0 in still water is $z_0 \eta/h$; for small values of γ, the motion is approximately parabolic, with the maximum horizontal velocity $H(g/h)^{1/2}$.

At the moment of breaking, it can be shown [2] that the limiting crest angle of $120°$ of the wave determines a theoretical ratio of (H/h) of 0.78 or $h = 1.28H$, and this relationship is of great importance, but see sections 7.1 and 3.2.6.

3.2.5 Cnoidal Waves

Sections 3.2.1 to 3.2.4 have treated briefly the simpler forms of finite waves. Waves of finite height in relatively shallow water, say $L \geqslant 10h$, which cannot be considered as solitary waves, require a more complex treatment. McCowan's form of the solitary wave has been mentioned briefly in section 3.2.4 where it was stated that a more tractable method of analysis was by the alternative theory of cnoidal waves. The theory of cnoidal waves was first described by Korteweg and de Vries [11] in 1895 but it has only recently found favour with engineers. The name comes from the fact that the wave profile is expressed in terms of the Jacobian elliptic function $cn(u)$, hence the adjective 'cnoidal'. The first-order approximation for the surface elevation is

$$\eta = H \, cn^2 \left[2K(k) \left(\frac{x}{L} - \frac{t}{T} \right), k \right] \tag{3.61}$$

where $K(k)$ is the complete elliptic integral of the first kind of modulus k, and k is a real number such that $0 \leqslant k \leqslant 1$. The equation may also be written as

$$\eta = H \, cn^2 \left[2K \left(\frac{x}{L} - \frac{t}{T} \right) \right] \tag{3.62}$$

with only one argument, with the modulus understood. The origin is situated at the level of the water trough (cf. the wave illustrated in figure 3.6); η and x are the vertical and horizontal coordinates of the water surface; H is the vertical height of the crest above the trough since $cn(0) = 1$. The period of the cn^2 function is $4K(k)$; compare this with the period 2π of the trigonometric function in equation 3.9. When $k = 0$, $4K(k) = 2\pi$ and the cnoidal wave becomes the sinusoidal wave of the linear Airy wave theory. When $k = 1$ the period is 'infinite' and we have the solitary wave. When $k = 0.9999$ the period $4K$ is about 7π hence the solitary wave regarded as a limiting case of the cnoidal wave can be considered as having a finite period for many practical purposes. Wiegel [12] and the Shore Protection Manual [13] give formulae and charts showing the principal properties of cnoidal waves for given values of k.

3.2.6 Limitations on the Use of Wave Theories

Comparison between wave theories and laboratory measurements, as shown for example in figures 3.11 and 3.12 demonstrates the wide divergence of results which can arise from the various assumptions made in the wave theories that have been described. Furthermore, in reality wind generated waves are seldom

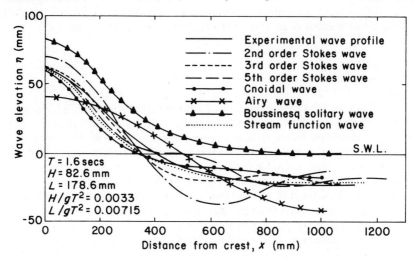

Figure 3.11 *Comparison between surface profile; after Dean [5]*

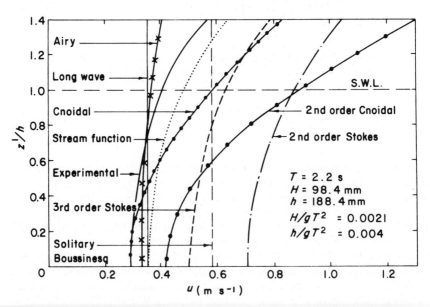

Figure 3.12 *Comparison between horizontal velocity profiles under the wave crest; after Dean [5]*

long crested, truly periodic or unchanging. Reference to photographs will only too readily demonstrate that the surface boundary conditions under extreme conditions are rarely smooth or stable. Because much of the irregularity is of fairly high frequency the adoption of a particular wave theory as an analytical model can be a valuable design tool provided the limitations of the model are appreciated.

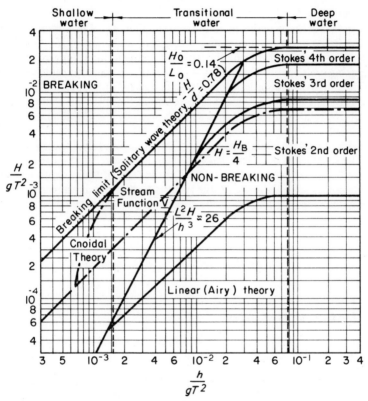

Figure 3.13 *Regions of validity for various wave theories; after Méhauté [14]*

Swart and Loubser [15] describe the basis and application of a number of wave theories, in particular considering the degree to which each satisfies conditions of continuity, kinetic (that is, energy conservation) boundary condition at bed and surface, also dynamic (that is, particle velocity parallel to surface) boundary condition, at free surface. Furthermore they summarise thus all the assumptions made by all such theories of water waves

(1) non-breaking waves
(2) water movement is two dimensional
(3) water depth is constant (that is, bed horizontal)
(4) frictionless flow
(5) invariant density
(6) surface tension is neglected

(7) wave motion periodic (except solitary waves)

(8) wave propagates with a constant velocity.

There is a wide range of opinion as to the applicability of particular wave theories to particular purposes. Several attempts have been made to rationalise the problem in terms of the water depth, wave height and period. Figure 3.13 shows the regions of validity for the various wave theories as described in the *Shore Protection Manual.* [13]

The breaking limits derive directly from the theoretical maximum solitary wave $H = 0.78h$ and a maximum deep water wave steepness of $H_0 = 0.14L_0$. An analytical justification for using the fifth-order stream function wave close to the breaking limit has been backed up with laboratory measurements by Dean.[5] The availability of fifth-order Stokes wave computer programs to engineers frequently leads to its use in place of lower-order theories. The shallow water boundary of validity for the Stokes waves is given by the Ursell number $Ur = L^2 H/h^3$.

For shallow water conditions $h/gT^2 < 0.0155$, the cnoidal theory may be used. The theory has the merit that for a very long wave length it reduces to the Boussinesq solitary wave theory and that as the ratio of water depth to wave height becomes large the wave profile reduces to that of a linear wave. An approximate range of validity for the cnoidal theory has been determined by Laitone and others as $h/L < \frac{1}{8}$ and the Ursell number $Ur < 26$.

It is expected that the results of experiments currently being undertaken may well lead to better understanding of the anatomy of wind-generated waves.

3.3 Wind Waves

3.3.1 The Generation of Waves

The development of the theory of generation of wind waves is at present at an interesting stage. Although the mechanism is not yet fully understood, certain generalisations can be made concerning the generation of waves in deep water.

(1) A minimum wind velocity is required to cause surface waves [1 m/s (3 ft/s) measured at a height of about 2 m (6 ft) above still water level].

(2) A spectrum of maximum levels of wave energy in specified narrow ranges of wave period will be associated with a given wind velocity, the wave period and height tending to increase with increasing wind.

(3) The 'fully developed' condition of point (2) requires the wind to blow over the area of sea of the developing waves for a certain minimum period; the stronger the wind, the longer is the period. Full development may be prevented on account of the limited duration of exposure of the wave to the wind and this may be caused by a limited travel of the developing wave, that is, the fetch.

Kinsman [16] presents the mathematician's approach to the calculation of wind waves. Essentially, this is a statistical account with a partial acceptance of several theories of the formation of waves but with no single self-sufficient theory. Kinsman, in fact, quotes with approval Lord Rayleigh's statement that 'The basic law of the seaway is the apparent lack of any law'.

Wind blowing over a calm sea will transmit a certain amount of energy to the sea by virtue of the shear force at the surface. What is required is an explanation of the initial instability necessary for the transformation into wave energy. This has been partly related to the formation of capillary waves [and hence the minimum wind velocity quoted in point (1)] and, partly, particularly for strong winds, to the existence of air turbulence causing gusts to travel along the water surface. Once wave crests have begun to form, the energy transfer from the wind is partly responsible for increased wave celerity — and hence increased wave length — and partly for increased wave height.

The energy is believed to be transferred partly by pressure variation at the surface which leads, due to viscosity of the air, to maximum and minimum air pressures slightly down-wind of wave trough and crest respectively and, hence, promotes a forced oscillation of the surface. Another means of transfer of energy is caused by the greater exposure of the sea to the wind at the crest of the wave; this leads to a forward water current at this point, in the same direction as the orbital velocity in the crest of the wave.

In fact, the disorganised form of a stormy sea does not readily lend itself to a complete explanation in terms of mathematical formulae. It is not possible to derive a comprehensive set of empirical formulae based directly on model tests, because of the differential scale effects of the several parameters. Development of existing knowledge is therefore largely a matter of collecting data of winds and waves at sea and comparing the actual wave characteristics with those deduced by hindcasting from the knowledge of the winds, thus allowing empirical constants to be attributed to the theoretical equations. This process is attended by a number of complicating factors including: first, the fact that the wind is constantly varying in strength and direction and hence a great amount of information is required before a specific wave spectrum can be presented as a function of fetch, F (or duration of wind) and wind speed, U; second, because of the fact that the rate of energy transfer for an average wind speed U, measured at a specified height above the sea, is dependent on the degree of temperature stability of the air. A cold wind blowing over a warm sea will set up convection currents and cause a large measure of transfer of energy to the lower levels of the air stream. In addition, real waves are relatively short crested and this introduces third-dimensional complications to two-dimensional theory.

The depth of water affects the growth of the waves, initially because of the modification to wave celerity in shallow water, subsequently because of increased energy losses and, ultimately, by virtue of the limitation on maximum wave height. For example, Bretschneider [17] indicates that, for Lake Okeechobee, Florida, with a fetch of 16 km (10 miles), the significant wave height for wind speeds between 55 to 125 km/h was only about 60 to 65 per cent of its deep water value in a water depth of 3.5 m reducing to about 40 per cent in a water depth of 2 m.

3.3.2 The Decay and Attenuation of Waves

When waves leave the area of their generation, several factors contribute to their decay.

(1) Because of the disparity between wave velocity and group velocity, a dispersion of energy occurs in the direction of propagation of the wave.

(2) There is an over-all loss in wave energy by friction and turbulence, causing most rapid decay of the shorter steeper waves where the velocities are higher (see section 3.4.1).

(3) There is a transfer of energy from waves of shorter period to those of longer period, leading to an over-all shift in the wave energy spectrum (see section 3.8).

(4) A dissipation of energy occurs transverse to the principal direction of propagation.

It is interesting to note that the first three factors mentioned above tend towards the suppression of the shorter waves and hence to the greater preponderance of long swell at a distance from the area of generation.

Snodgrass [18] describes the results of a study of the changes in characteristics of wave trains, from storms in the Southern Pacific traced along a great circle between New Zealand and Alaska. Six wave-recording stations were established for the purpose, covering a line about 10 000 km long. Once or twice each week it was possible to trace an identifiable event across the ocean. The study of the energy peak on a wave frequency/time diagram confirmed that there was a slight increase in low-frequency wave energy and a reduction in high-frequency wave energy, most of such interchange occurring near to the storm centre (within the 'storm diameter'); wave scattering appeared to account for most of this effect (see section 3.3.3). Very slight interaction was found to occur between swell and local storm waves; this effect was less than anticipated. Attenuation of waves of period greater than 13 s was found to be negligible.

The tracing of the 'ridge lines' on the frequency/time diagrams permitted the 'slope' of the ridge, relating frequency to distance along the line of recorder stations, to be obtained and, in consequence, the time and position of the storm source of the waves in question.

Bretschneider [19] has considered the contribution of two factors to the damping of waves: bottom friction and bottom percolation. It is apparent that neither factor will affect the height of the wave unless significant orbital motion occurs near the sea bed and the effects will become increasingly marked as the ratio of water depth to wave length decreases. Bretschneider and Reid [20] provide graphical relationships between the reduction in wave height and bottom roughness and permeability. For a bottom of sand or finer material, percolation is negligible by comparison with bed friction. For shoaling water the effect has to be studied by a numerical step by step basis which could readily be built into a computer program for studying wave refraction (section 3.4.2). To give a numerical example, a 10 s period wave, initially 5 m high, in water 20 m deep, would be expected to be reduced to a height of about 4.5 m after travelling 1000 m.

3.3.3 The Prediction of Waves

Wave predictions for a particular location may be derived either from wind records for the area or from wave records. Provided the wave records have been obtained with a suitable recorder for a sufficiently long period and at a location appropriate to the project, the predictions obtained therefrom are generally more reliable than those from wind records which depend on an appreciation of wind climates, the fetch, depth variations and swell caused by remote storms.

In exposed coastal conditions the limiting effects of water depth can often be the controlling mechanism for extreme wave conditions, in which case it may only be necessary to determine whether conditions can be sufficiently severe to develop the limiting wave condition. Where storm surges can be associated with severe wind conditions, as in the case for beaches exposed to the south-west in the English Channel, the return period for extreme conditions may be directly related to the return period for maximum water levels.

3.3.4 Wave Records: Forecasting and Hindcasting Techniques

Wave forecasting and hindcasting techniques are essentially based on a knowledge of the wind speed, over a period of time, in the total area of generation and of any intermediate decay of the waves before they reach the location. Empirical formulae, presented in tabular or graphical form, are then used to relate the wave characteristics to the wind.

Wiegel [12] has assembled data on fetch F, wind velocity U, significant wave height H_s, wave period T and celerity C, and has plotted the dimensionless factors gT/U, C/U and gH_s/U^2 against gF/U^2. A widely used method for the prediction of deep water waves is presented by Bretschneider [21] and is of more direct use to the engineer for elementary problems than those for wave spectra prepared by Pierson et al. [22] The Shore Protection Manual [13] sets out the relevant figures in a readily applied form.

As will be described later, the coastal engineer often assumes a train of regular waves for the solution of problems, applying correction factors, in certain instances, in recognition of the departure from nature introduced by such an assumption. Analysis based on wave spectra, however, presents maximum and significant wave heights related to wave periods. Spectral methods should be used for design problems, such as those entailing resonance, where the wave period may be critical. The wave spectrum may be used with advantage for model testing, often accompanied by a simulated wind. There can be no doubt that spectral analysis gives results far closer to nature than the regular wave height and period method; only rarely can the full spectrum be used in subsequent calculations in this book, however, and only in those of an advanced nature (see section 3.3.6).

A graphical relationship relating significant wave height, H_s, peak energy period, T_p, and wind duration to fetch length and wind speed is shown in figure 3.14. This is based on the original relationships due to Darbyshire and Draper [23] which were derived from observations around Britain and provides a means of estimating wave parameters from wind data for coastal waters (30 to 45 m deep). The significant wave height and associated peak energy period may be determined by the fetch or the duration of the wind depending on which limiting criterion is first encountered by the ordinate representing wind speed.

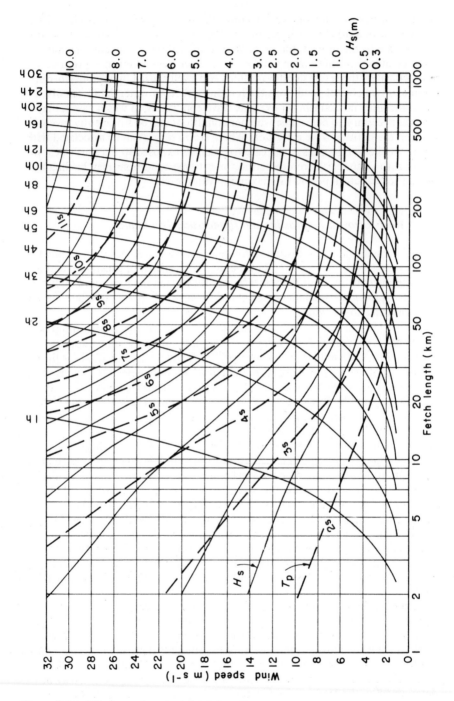

Figure 3.14 *Wind speed against fetch length*

The zero crossing period may be determined from the approximate relationship $T_z \approx T_p/1.4$.

It must be stressed that as the data accumulates, the empirical formulae will continue to evolve. No theory has yet reached a final state but the simpler relationships will continue to be used for all but the most intricate or large-scale design problems.

Wind speed, U, is a fundamental factor for any wave prediction. Unless otherwise stated, it should be assumed that measured values of U relate to a height of 10 m above sea level. The uncertainties due to temperature stability of the air may introduce errors greater than those arising from the use of wind velocities at a level other than 10 m, provided that these are obtained from between, say, 5 and 15 m above sea level. [24]

The fetch may be simple to determine for a land-locked sea with a stable pressure system. In the extreme case, however, of a moving pressure system in an extensive ocean, the question becomes complex. The *Shore Protection Manual* [13] provides a method, based on Bretschneider's tables, for evaluation of design waves in such cicumstances. Bretschneider [25] considers the particular case of hurricane waves caused by a moving cyclone; for a speed of advance of about 12 m/s at which the greatest cumulative effect occurs, the maximum height of wave is increased by about 50 per cent.

In view of the scatter in the direction of the divergence of waves from a storm centre, the maximum fetch to be considered is not necessarily that in the direct line of the direction of the wind. One procedure in current use, where F is the fetch in any direction and θ the angle between the fetch and the wind, is to take the greatest value of

$$F \text{ where } |\theta| \leqslant 30°$$

and

$$F \cos |\theta| \text{ where } |\theta| \leqslant 45°$$

Since a certain proportion of the total wave energy is attributable to waves not travelling precisely in the direction of the wind, the effective length of fetch, F_e needs to be adjusted where the width, W, over which the wind is blowing, is confined. Figure 3.15 indicates a simplified graphical analysis due to Saville [26] and the adjustment factor for varying ratios of W/F, based on the latter of the above criteria, that is, $F_e = F \cos \theta$. From figure 3.15a, rays such as OA (at intervals from 0 to 5 or 10°) are superimposed on a plan of the seaway or other bounded water surface representing the fetch, and measured as l to a predetermined scale. When subscript 0 relates to unlimited width of fetch, the effective fetch is

$$F_e = F \, \frac{\displaystyle\sum_{\theta=\theta_2}^{\theta=\theta_1} kl}{\displaystyle\sum_{\theta=\theta_2}^{\theta=\theta_1} kl_0}$$

where k and limits θ_1 and θ_2 depend on initial assumptions.

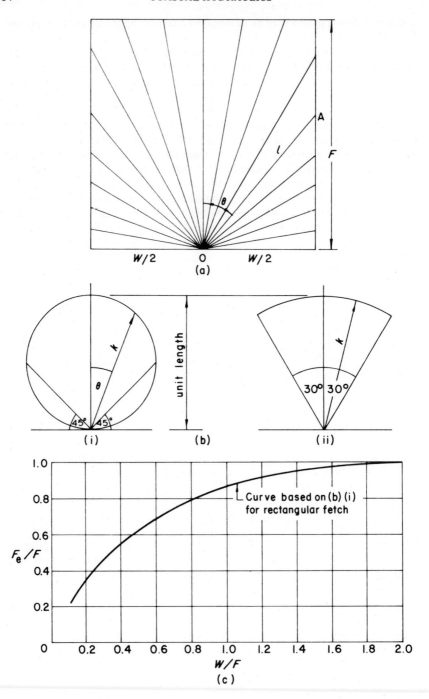

Figure 3.15 *Effective fetch for limiting width of seaway; after Saville [26]*

For the cases shown in figure 3.15b

(i) $k = \cos\theta$, $\theta_1 = 45°$, $\theta_2 = -45°$
(ii) $k = 1$, $\theta_1 = 30°$, $\theta_2 = -30°$

Figure 3.15c indicates the ratio F_e/F for a rectangular fetch of width W, adopting the hypotheses of figure 3.15b(i).

Empirical tables have been prepared by Wiegel [12] for evaluating the effect of the decay length on wave period and significant height. The divergence of wave direction from the direction of the wind also leads to the familiar confused interference pattern of short-crested waves, with properties slightly different from long-crested waves, including a somewhat greater celerity.

It is possible to base calculations of waves on the 'gradient' wind, that is, the wind related to the barometric pressure gradient. Where the isobars are straight and parallel, from equation 2.12 the 'geostrophic' wind speed

$$U_g = \frac{1}{2\Omega\rho_a \sin\phi} \frac{dp}{dx} \text{ m/s} \quad \text{or} \quad \frac{3 \times 10^3}{X \sin\phi} \text{ knots} \tag{3.63}$$

where Ω is the angular velocity of rotation of the Earth (0.73×10^{-4} rad/s), ϕ is the latitude, ρ_a the air density (1.2 kg/m^3 at N.T.P.), dp/dx is the pressure gradient in N/m^2/m and X is the distance in nautical miles between isobars at intervals of 5 mb (1 mb $= 10^2$ N/m^2). Alternatively, Bretschneider's tables [12, 13] may be used for the same purpose. Computer methods have also been developed for direct wave prediction from isobaric charts.[27]

The direction of the wind close to the surface is, because of friction, turned 10 to 15° to the left of the isobaric lines (up to 40° over land) in the northern hemisphere. Figure 3.16 indicates the correction to be made to derive surface wind from U_g for different degrees of curvature of the isobars (expressed in terms of degrees of latitude) and for a range of temperature differences between sea and air. Further refinements in the technique have been developed.[13]

Where it is necessary to allow for the effect of swell the wave heights should not be combined by direct superposition. Instead a reasonable estimate of the combined wave height may be obtained by summing squares $H = (H_1^2 + H_2^2)^{1/2}$ where H_1 is predicted locally generated wave and H_2 is predicted swell height.

3.3.5 Wave Records: Analysis

The successful development and application of wave recorders (see section 7.2) has considerably extended the possibility for wave prediction to be based on the statistical evaluation of previous measurements of waves. The use of digital recording and computer programs have further extended the potential of this method.

The analysis of such wave records and the extension of this analysis to arrive at the concept of a 'design wave' are described in the companion papers by Draper [28] and Tucker.[29] Essentially, the method involves the acquisition of

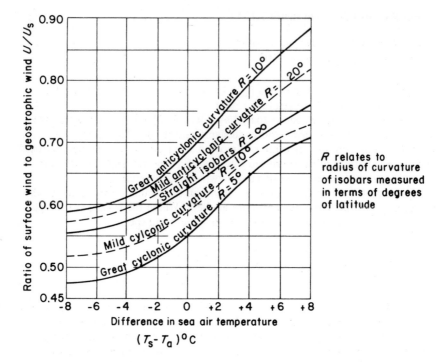

Figure 3.16 *Relationship between surface wind and geostrophic wind; after*
Bretschneider [25]

intermittent wave records, each of a few minutes duration, representing, say, 10
per cent of the total period covered by the records. The total number of crests
and zero crossings (that is, passage of the records across mean water level, at the
time of the record, in an upward direction) are counted, together with associated
periods and amplitudes of the highest crests and lowest troughs. From such data,
it is possible to establish for each record

> H_{max}, the greatest height from trough to adjacent crest
> H_{rms}, the equivalent root mean square wave height
> H_s the significant wave height, that is, the mean height of the one-third
> highest waves (Tucker [29] provides a rather more precise definition)
> $\bar{H}$, the mean wave height
> T_c and T_z, the mean periods between adjacent crests and adjacent zero
> crossings respectively
> T_s, the period associated with H_s (not recommended as statistically valid)
> $H_{1/10}$, the mean height of the highest 10 per cent of all waves
> $H_{1/100}$, the mean height of the highest 1 per cent of all waves
> T_p, the period corresponding to the peak of the wave energy spectrum
> ϵ, the spectral width: a measure of the range of frequencies present relative
> to the mean wave frequency

The factor ϵ is related to the shape of the probability distribution of the height of the wave crests, being estimated from

$$\epsilon^2 = 1 - \left(\frac{T_c}{T_z}\right)^2 \tag{3.64}$$

If the wave components cover a wide range of frequencies, T_c will be much smaller than T_z so that ϵ will approach unity. Conversely, for a simple swell or narrow-banded spectrum ϵ will approach zero.

The heights of waves on wave records are often found to correspond approximately to a Rayleigh distribution function for which the probability of heights exceeding a given wave height H is

$$p(H) = \exp[-2(H/H_s)^2] \tag{3.65}$$

If a record contains N waves and n ($\leqslant N$) exceed a given wave height H, the probability of exceedance is n/N so that using equation 3.65

$$H_s = \frac{H}{(\frac{1}{2}\ln N/n)^{1/2}}$$

The special case of $n = 1$ will give the probable extreme height of a wave in a record of N waves so that

$$H_{max} = H_s \left(\frac{\ln N}{2}\right)^{1/2}$$

The following approximations may also be made

$$H_s \approx (2)^{1/2} H_{rms}$$

$$H_{1/10} \approx 1.27 H_s \approx 1.8 H_{rms}$$

$$H_{1/100} \approx 1.67 H_s \approx 2.36 H_{rms}$$

Wave records can be prepared in digital form for analysis by computer. Alternatively Draper [30] describes a simple method of making an elementary analysis where a graphical trace only is available. On a representative wave trace of, say, 20 min, if A be the highest wave crest and C the lowest trough (figure 3.17), then $H_1 = A + C$. The time length of the trace divided by the number of zero crossing (N_z) yields T_z. Table 3.3 provide values of a factor F_s ($H_s = F_s \times H_1$) for different values of N_z. If F_1 corresponds to the number of waves in a record and F_2 is the number of waves in an arbitrary period (figure 3.18), then H_{max} for this period is given by

$$H_{max} = H_1 \frac{F_2}{F_1} \tag{3.66}$$

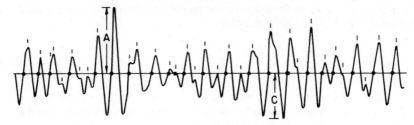

The points marked with a dash are wave crests.
The points marked with a dot are zero upward crossings.

Figure 3.17 *Section of a wave record; after Draper [30]*

In using such a simple method it is necessary to emphasise that the record must be truly representative of the longer period to which it is applied.

Draper [31] recommends that standard data analysis should comprise the following

   (1) wave height exceedance — one for each season
   (2) zero crossing period histogram — one for each season
   (3) spectral width parameter — annual
   (4) scatter diagram $(T_z\text{-}H_s)$ — annual
   (5) persistence of storms — annual
   (6) persistence of calms — annual
   (7) extreme waves (calculated by one of several methods) — annual
   (8) wave spectra (directional) — if available
   (9) sea bed wave spectra — if available
  (10) sea bed particle speed exceedence — if (9) available.

The return periods of waves of a given height may be estimated by the extrapolation of a plot of wave height frequency diagram, for which the

TABLE 3.3 *Factor F_s relating H_1 to H_s*

No. of Zero-crossings, N_z, in a Record	Factor F_s	No. of Zero-crossings, N_z, in a Record	Factor F_s
20–21	0.77	64–73	0.65
22–23	0.76	74–85	0.64
24–25	0.75	86–100	0.63
26–27	0.74	101–118	0.62
28–29	0.73	119–139	0.61
30–32	0.72	140–166	0.60
33–35	0.71	167–202	0.59
36–39	0.70	203–253	0.58
40–44	0.69	254–315	0.57
45–49	0.68	316–390	0.56
50–55	0.67	391–488	0.55
56–63	0.66	489–615	0.54

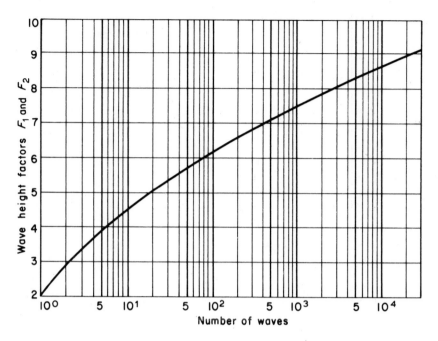

Figure 3.18 *Wave height factors F_1 and F_2 in relation to number of waves; after Draper [30]*

Weibull distribution, plotting $\log_{10}(H_s)$ against $\log_{10}\left[\log_{10}(1-p)^{-1}\right]$ where p, cumulative probability is given by

$$p = (2R - 1)/2N \tag{3.67}$$

where R is the cumulative occurrence of the wave height $\geqslant H_s$ and N is the total number of readings. The significant wave height, H_s, for a return period of y years is found by the 'best fit' straight line by reading off H_s corresponding to $(1-p)^{-1} = N'y$ (figure 3.19) (and hence $H_{1/100}$ etc. may be estimated), where N' is the number of readings in a year (that is, if records obtained every 3 hours, $N' = 2920$). An example is shown in figure 3.19.

When making a simplified analysis of wave records for a particular location it is often helpful to construct a frequency diagram of H_s against T_z. Such a plot will serve to indicate the most characteristic wave steepnesses for the locality.

3.3.6 Probabilistic Description of Waves

In general, it is a radical simplification to describe waves in the open sea as being long crested and as having a discrete period and height. In reality, the variation in sea elevation at a point is random in character, as can be seen from the simplified record of surface displacement against time, shown in figure 3.17.

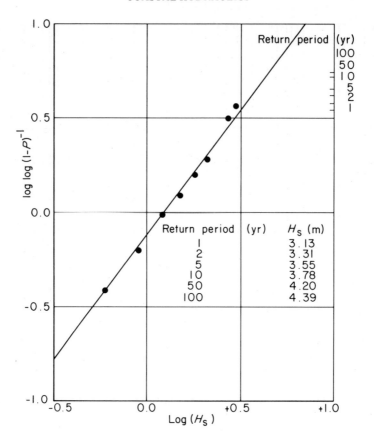

Figure 3.19 *Weibull distribution and return period of* H_s

For some engineering purposes it is useful to regard the wave environment as a sea state that persists for a finite period of time, generally a few hours. Over this time the statistical properties of surface elevation variation are then considered (but see section 7.5).

The sea surface elevation may be considered as the superposition of an infinite number of sinusoidal frequency components of different amplitude. Wave spectra are usually represented by a curve plotted as spectral density against frequency. Spectral density has units m^2 s and is a measure of energy density of a wave spectrum. Omitting the constant factor g from the expression for wave energy (see equation 3.26) the spectral density is $f_i = \frac{1}{8} H_i^2 / \delta f$ where δf is the frequency band over which the quantity is calculated that is, it represents the mean value over the interval.

The standard deviation of sea elevation σ_η is the square root of the area under the spectral density function curve. For most sea conditions it is reasonable to assume that the process is narrow band Gaussian, in which case a close approximation to the significant wave height is $4\sigma_\eta$.[32]

Various formulations of spectral density functions have been developed from field data. The Pierson–Moskowitz (PM) spectrum is often used as a model and is given as a function of frequency (f) in its general form by

$$S^{\eta\eta}\,(f)_{PM} = \alpha g^2 (2\pi)^{-4} f^{-5} \exp\left[-\frac{5}{4}\left(\frac{f_p}{f}\right)^4 \right] \tag{3.68}$$

where α is a constant relating H_s to the peak energy frequency f_p ($= 1/T_p = 1/1.4T_z$). The value of α is usually taken to be 0.0081.

In the specific case of a fully arisen sea generated by a constant wind of sufficient duration equation 3.68 may be written

$$S^{\eta\eta}\,(f) = \frac{\alpha g^2}{(2\pi)^4 f^5} \exp\left[-0.74 \left(\frac{g}{2\pi U_{19.5} f}\right)^4 \right]$$

where $U_{19.5}$ is the wind speed in m/s at an elevation of 19.5 m above mean sea level.

Figure 3.20 shows the PM spectrum evaluated for significant wave heights of 1, 2 and 3 m. It can be seen that the effective bandwidth (given by a rectangle of height $S^{\eta\eta}(f_p)$ and with area equal to the area under the curve) is small, which support the narrow bandwidth assumption.

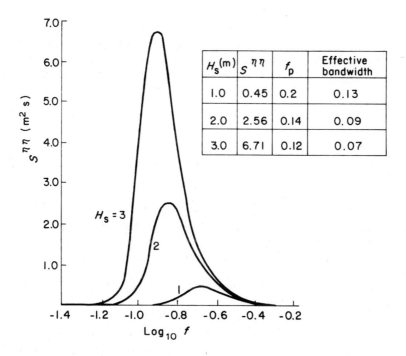

H_s(m)	$S^{\eta\eta}$	f_p	Effective bandwidth
1.0	0.45	0.2	0.13
2.0	2.56	0.14	0.09
3.0	6.71	0.12	0.07

Figure 3.20 *Pierson–Moskowitz wave spectra*

It has been observed that the sea spectrum in the growing phase has a much sharper peak than the PM spectrum. To allow for this the JONSWAP spectrum applies a 'peak enhancement' function to the PM spectrum so that

$$S^{\eta\eta}(f) = \alpha g^2 \, (2\pi)^{-4} f^{-5} \, \exp\left[-\frac{5}{4}\left(\frac{f_p}{f}\right)^4\right] \gamma^{\left[\exp \; -(f-f_p)^2/2B^2 f_p^2\right]}$$

(3.69)

$$B = B_A = 0.07 \quad f \leqslant f_p$$
$$ = B_B = 0.09 \quad f > f_p$$

where γ is a constant and is the ratio of the maximum JONSWAP spectral energy to that of the corresponding PM spectrum. By appropriate choice of α, γ, B_A and B_B the spectrum has a high degree of generality for which γ, B_A and B_B control the 'peakiness' of the spectrum.

Wave spectra formulations can be extended to account for directional properties. The general form of a directional spectrum is

$$S^{\eta\eta}(f,\theta) = S^{\eta\eta}(f)F(\theta)$$

and

$$\int_{-\pi}^{\pi} F(\theta) \, d\theta = 1$$

where $F(\theta)$ is a function describing the directional distribution of wave energy often assumed to be a cosine squared function for $|\theta| \leqslant \pi/2$ and otherwise zero. However, wave data has not as yet been comprehensive enough to allow for definitive correlations to be made.

3.4 Waves in Shoaling Water

Real sea waves undergo considerable variation as they enter shallow water. The principal factors may be listed as

(1) wave attenuation due to friction (section 3.4.1)
(2) distortion of the wave profile (section 2.3) which may, where the sea bed gradient is very gentle, lead to such steep-fronted waves that each degenerates into a number of waves of shorter period, as with the tidal bore (section 2.6)
(3) transfer of energy in the wave spectrum, usually towards waves of longer period (section 3.3.2)
(4) wave attenuation due to reflection, especially where the wave encounters a steep bed slope
(5) differential refraction of waves of different periods (section 3.4.2) which may lead to areas of relative predominance of specific periods.

As a consequence of such factors, inshore wave spectra may vary appreciably from those from records of the corresponding waves in deep water. Where

possible, engineering designs should be based on wave records in the immediate
locality of the proposed works.

3.4.1 Wave Damping and Bottom Friction

The dissipation of wave energy by any means such as bottom percolation or
bottom friction will cause a corresponding reduction in wave height. From the
work of many researchers it is evident that bottom friction, percolation and
viscous dissipation are in many cases significant mechanisms of energy
dissipation.

Isaacson [34, 35] considered viscous damping, using a second-order approx-
mation to cnoidal wave theory. His results indicate a significantly greater
damping for shallow water than that predicted by linear theory but slightly less
damping for intermediate depths ($0.5 < h/L < 0.04$).

When dealing with inshore areas the oscillatory flow at the bed is, under most
circumstances, rough turbulent [36] and the effects of bottom roughness
are more significant than viscosity. Much theoretical work has been carried out
on wave damping due to percolation through a porous bed. Experimental work
[37] on smooth permeable and smooth impermeable and rippled surfaces has
confirmed that the effects of percolation can be ignored for sand sizes less than
about 2.0 mm.

The bottom friction and hence the value of bottom stress in wave-induced
turbulent boundary layers is of outstanding importance in relation to sediment
transport. Bagnold [38] gave one of the earliest empirical formulae for a
friction coefficient based on a quadratic friction law. He found that the friction
coefficient decreases with increasing wave period and increasing near bottom
orbital velocities.

Jonsson [40] carried out experiments in an oscillating water tunnel with
artifical roughness. In this theoretical considerations he assumed that the shear
stress at the bed (τ_0) could be found from the turbulent velocity profile.[36]
The wave friction factor f_W was defined by

$$\hat{\tau}_0 = \frac{1}{2} f_W \rho \hat{u}_0{}^2 \tag{3.70}$$

where $\hat{\tau}_0$ is the maximum shear stress at the bed and $\hat{u}_0$ is the maximum orbital
velocity at the bed. Integrating the boundary layer equations and fitting unknown
constants empirically to experimental data, a relationship for f_W is given
approximately as [39]

$$\ln f_W = -5.977 + 5.213 \left(\frac{\hat{\xi}_0}{k_N}\right)^{-0.914} \tag{3.71}$$

where $\hat{\xi}_0$ is the horizontal amplitude of oscillation at the bed and k_N the
(Nikuradse) roughness parameter. A limiting value of $f_W = 0.3$ is found for

$\hat{\xi}_0/k_N < 1.57$. In this equation the phase shift between maximum shear and maximum velocity is neglected.

Relationships due to Jonsson, [40] Kajiura [41] and Kamphius [42] are shown in figure 3.21. The agreement between them is quite good.

The value of friction factor f_w gives an estimate of the maximum bottom shear required for the threshold of sediment movement. For time-dependent problems a wave energy factor reflecting the loss of wave energy should be used.

The mean dissipation of energy per unit area of the bed may be expressed as

$$E_t = \overline{u_0 \tau_0} \tag{3.72}$$

where u_0 and τ_0 are simultaneous values. Assuming that the shear stress varies as a cosine function Kajiura found that

$$f_w = \frac{8}{3\pi \cos \phi_0} f_e \tag{3.73}$$

where ϕ_0 is the phase lead of the maximum shear stress over the maximum free stream particle velocity; the value of phase lead has been found experimentally [36] and theoretically [43] to be approximately 30° so that the ratio between f_w and f_e should be about 0.98. Experimentally f_w has been found to be slightly greater than f_e and equality can be assumed.

For practical applications, equation 3.71 provides a convenient method of estimating bed shear stress via equation 3.70. The estimation of roughness lengths is discussed in chapters 4 and 5.

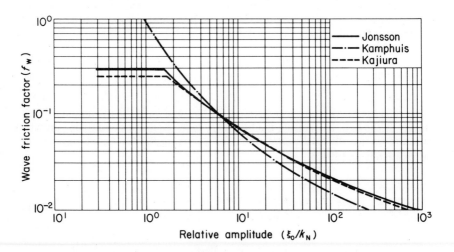

Figure 3.21 *Relationships for wave friction factors*

3.4.2 Wave Refraction

The transformation of waves in shoaling water involves a change of wave height, length and velocity with depth. When waves move shoreward from deep water and approach the shoreline obliquely, the wave crests tend to conform to the bottom contours. This is because the inshore portion of the wave travels at a lower velocity than the portion in deeper water. The extent of wave refraction depends on the relative magnitudes of water depth to wavelength. The criterion for 'deep water' is generally taken as $h > L_0/2$. At shallower depths, refraction occurs for waves oblique to sea bed contours.

Wave refraction theory has been developed from solutions for light wave optics and in the following discussion Airy wave theory is assumed. Furthermore it is assumed that the wave can everywhere be described by expressions derived for a horizontal bottom. The physical situation required to satisfy this condition is that the horizontal scale length of the bottom contours must be large compared to the depth and wave length.

If α is the angle of the wave crest to a contour marking a change in level, Snell's law of refraction implies that

$$\frac{C_1}{C_2} = \frac{\sin \alpha_1}{\sin \alpha_2} \tag{3.74}$$

where α_1 and α_2 represent the angle between the wave crest and contour line for celerities C_1 and C_2 corresponding to the depth of water either side of the contours. It is a fairly simple operation, except where contours assume a complex pattern, to explore the approximate refraction pattern by tracing the paths of initially equidistant orthogonals, assuming that steps in bed level occur midway between contours and that the orthogonals behave according to equation 3.74 at each point. The procedure for drawing refraction diagrams by hand can be speeded up considerably by using a refraction template.[54]

A point of interest from equation 3.74 is that where a wave approaches a steep drop in the sea bed to deeper water, total reflection occurs for α_1 greater than a maximum value

$$\alpha_1 = \sin^{-1} \left(\frac{C_1}{C_2} \right) \tag{3.75}$$

since $\alpha_2 = \pi/2$ for this limiting case, where C_1 and C_2 relate to depths to each side of the drop.

Where linear theory of waves cannot be assumed, where the pattern of sea bed contours is complex, or where several different sets of conditions are to be evaluated, the problem justifies the use of a computer program. The curvature of the wave orthogonal expressed in cartesian coordinates is

$$\frac{d\theta}{ds} = -\frac{1}{C} \left(\frac{\partial h}{\partial x} \sin \theta - \frac{\partial h}{\partial y} \cos \theta \right) \frac{dC}{dh} \tag{3.76}$$

where h is depth, x and y horizontal co-ordinates, s distance along the orthogonal, θ angle between the orthogonal and x-axis (see figure 3.22) and C the wave celerity (equations 3.12), the derivative with respective to depth being

$$\frac{dC}{dh} = \frac{g\left[1-(C/C_0)^2\right]}{C+\dfrac{gh}{C}\left[1-(C/C_0)^2\right]} \tag{3.77}$$

where C_0 is the deep water wave speed. Consequently the solution to equation 3.76 may be found from the value of wave speed which is purely a local function of depth and the first derivatives of depth.

Neglecting reflection, diffraction and external generative forces it can be assumed that the wave energy flux is everywhere directed along the orthogonals. [44] The wave height at two successive points on an orthogonal may be approximated by

$$\frac{H_1}{H_2} = K_r K_s K_f \tag{3.78}$$

where K_r is a refraction coefficient, K_s is a shoaling coefficient and K_f a friction coefficient. The energy flux per unit length of wave crest is proportional to $C_g H^2$ so that if b is the distance along a wave crest between a pair of orthogonals

$$C_g H^2 b = \text{const} \tag{3.79}$$

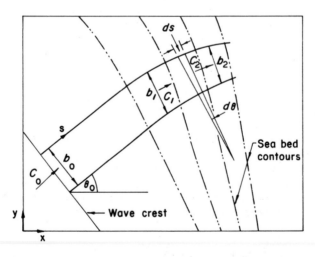

Figure 3.22 *Reference diagram for wave refraction*

if energy losses due to bottom friction are neglected (that is, $K_f = 1$). Hence

$$\frac{H_2}{H_1} = \left(\frac{C_{g1}}{C_{g2}}\right)^{1/2} \left(\frac{b_1}{b_2}\right)^{1/2} \tag{3.80}$$

The first bracketed term in equation 3.80 is the shoaling coefficient K_s which reflects the change in wave height of a wave train purely due to differences in depth. Using equation 3.28 this may be written as

$$K_s = \left[\frac{C_1 (1 + \xi_1)}{C_2 (1 + \xi_2)}\right]^{1/2} \tag{3.81}$$

where

$$\xi = \frac{4\pi h/L}{\sinh 4\pi h/L} \tag{3.82}$$

The variation of wave height in shoaling water is shown in figure 3.23. The second bracketed term in equation 3.80 is the refraction coefficient K_r which reflects the change in wave height of a wave train purely due to convergence or divergence of the wave orthogonals so that

$$K_r = \left(\frac{1}{\beta}\right)^{1/2} \tag{3.83}$$

where

$$\beta = \frac{b_2}{b_1} \tag{3.84}$$

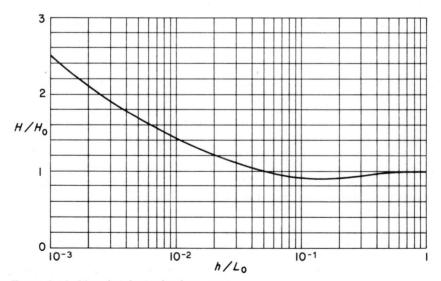

Figure 3.23 *Wave height in shoaling water*

and is known as the ray separation factor.[45] In the case of a straight shore with parallel contours

$$\frac{b_1}{\cos \alpha_1} = \frac{b_2}{\cos \alpha_2} \tag{3.85}$$

so that

$$\beta = \frac{\cos \alpha_2}{\cos \alpha_1} \tag{3.86}$$

Over complex bottom topography β can be determined from a wave refraction diagram by measuring the distance between the orthogonals. However, Munk and Arthur [45] derived the governing equations for the ray separation factor with distances along the orthogonal as the independent variable. These are

$$\frac{d^2\beta}{ds^2} + p(s) \frac{d\beta}{ds} + q(s)\beta = 0 \tag{3.87}$$

where $p(s)$ and $q(s)$ are functions of s given by

$$p(s) = -\frac{1}{C} \left(\frac{\partial C}{\partial x} \cos \theta + \frac{\partial C}{\partial y} \sin \theta \right) \tag{3.88}$$

$$q(s) = \frac{1}{C} \left(\frac{\partial^2 C}{\partial x^2} \sin^2 \theta - \frac{\partial^2 C}{\partial x \, \partial y} \sin 2\theta + \frac{\partial^2 C}{\partial y^2} \cos^2 \theta \right) \tag{3.89}$$

where θ is the angle between the ray and the x-axis.

The formulation given here uses rectangular coordinates and therefore is only valid for a small geographic area for which the curvature of the Earth can be neglected. Treatment of the sphericity of the Earth's surface requires an alternative formulation in terms of spherical polar coordinates.[46, 47]

The assumption that bottom friction can be neglected is widely used. As linear wave theory is also assumed, the result is that wave refraction patterns, shoaling and refraction coefficients are independent of wave height. However, this may be unacceptable if the wave travels more than, say, approximately 20 wave lengths.[48]

The possibility of causing refractive focusing should not be overlooked when considering measures which result in major variations to offshore topography. Focusing of long swell in such a manner has caused damage, for example, at Long Beach, California and at Botany Bay, New South Wales. An example of multiple caustics is shown in figure 3.24.

The preceding equations are not valid for large sea bed slopes or in regions where wave orthogonals converge or diverge very rapidly. Specifically, in the case of a caustic where wave rays cross, according to equation 3.84, β tends to zero and K_r tends to infinity which is clearly untenable. When there is an appreciable variation in wave height along a wave crest there must be a lateral flow of energy

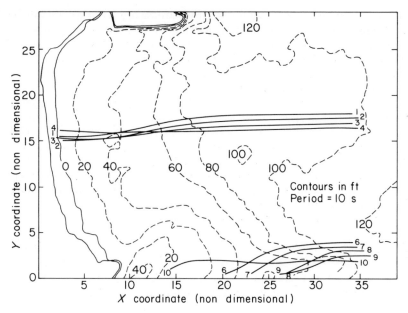

Figure 3.24 *Example of multiple wave caustics*

along the wave crest and across the wave orthogonals so that the preceding equations no longer apply. A complete derivation of the refraction equations and the treatment of caustics is given by Chao.[49] Analytical and experimental studies of refraction in the region of a caustic have been carried out by Pierson. [50]

All refraction methods require the bathymetry to be represented by a grid of depth values. Depending on the irregularity of the sea bed, and denseness of the wave rays, caustics may occur. The number of caustics found in a refraction diagram will generally be reduced if some topographical smoothing is carried out. [51, 52] A study of comparing different sea bed representations has been reported [53] from which it was concluded that while the general pattern of wave refraction diagrams shows similar characteristics for different interpolation functions, there can be considerable local differences in wave height and direction. Abernethy and Gilbert [51] have investigated the anomalies that can arise when constructing conventional refraction diagrams, that is, a selected number of rays refracted from the offshore boundary towards the shoreline. They have presented examples for which the method can result in large variations in refraction coefficients, depending on the density of the rays used in the calculation. They concluded that there is an inherent bias towards high wave heights, an excessive sensitivity to frequency, offshore direction and position which is greatest in regions where refraction coefficients are large. They overcame these difficulties by constructing a large number of rays so closely spaced that the variation in refraction coefficient across them would be expected to be negligible. This technique has been shown to be more stable than conventional techniques, but the computational costs are large.

It has been noted in section 3.2 that Airy wave theory is not strictly valid in very shallow water approaching the breaker line. Nevertheless correspondence between refraction diagrams, based on linear theory and observation, has been found to be reasonable, even in this region. Linear theory can often be used beyond its theoretical limits for many engineering problems, where error is no greater than uncertainty of the data.

Depth refraction using first-order cnoidal wave theory has been investigated for the simple case of straight parallel bottom contours.[54] It is shown that the cnoidal wave would theoretically break at a greater water depth than linear waves due to greater amplification. Also the cnoidal wave orthogonal was found theoretically to refract less than the linear wave.

Recent numerical methods for refraction problems are rapidly turning away from the wave ray methods. A better representation of the shallow water wave environment is required and wave spectra provide a more realistic model of waves than monochromatic wave trains. A number of investigators [55, 56] have studied the theoretical aspects of the transformation of wind wave spectra in shoaling water. Numerical methods have also been developed which calculate the wave parameters directly at grid points. These methods include finite difference relaxation techniques [57] and finite element methods, [58] but problems are encountered in defining general boundary conditions.

3.4.3 Effects of Currents and Waves

When short surface gravity waves are propagated in a current field they will undergo changes in length, direction, amplitude and speed. The effect on refraction is that when the current is in the direction of wave propagation the waves are lengthened, so that the refraction is stronger. The converse is true for an opposing current.

If it be assumed that the current velocity component in the direction of wave propagation can be simply added to the still water wave speed to obtain the modified wave speed, the refractive effects can easily be approximated.[59]

Where current components are v_x and v_y the curvature of the wave ray (equation 3.76) becomes

$$
\begin{aligned}
\frac{\mathrm{d}\theta}{\mathrm{d}s} = - &\left[\left(\frac{\partial v_x}{\partial x} - \frac{\partial v_y}{\partial y} \right) \frac{\sin 2\theta}{2} + \frac{\partial v_y}{\partial x} \sin^2 \theta - \frac{\partial v_x}{\partial y} \cos^2 \theta \right. \\
&\left. + \frac{\mathrm{d}C}{\mathrm{d}h} \left(\frac{\partial h}{\partial x} \sin \theta - \frac{\partial h}{\partial y} \cos \theta \right) \right] / (C + v_x \cos \theta + v_y \sin \theta)
\end{aligned}
\tag{3.90}
$$

If a current field can be predetermined, equation 3.90 can be used to estimate the combined depth and current refraction so long as wave and current interaction is disregarded. It should be noted that the wave ray is no longer in the same direction as the wave orthogonal.

Consequently the wave intensity equations can no longer be used to estimate wave heights. The problem can, however, be reformulated in terms of a wave ray separation factor.[60] When a wave obliquely crosses a boundary at which a noticeable change of current occurs, it will be refracted, as illustrated by figure 3.25. Consider a wave system of initial celerity C_1 and length L_1 in still water, approaching the boundary at angle α_1 and having a subsequent celerity C_2 and wave length L_2 in a current v. If the refracted wave system makes an angle α_2 with the boundary, equating the rate at which wave crests pass a fixed point

$$\frac{C_1}{L_1} = \frac{C_2 + V \sin \alpha_2}{L_2} \tag{3.91}$$

Furthermore, along the boundary (see figure 3.25)

$$\frac{L_1}{L_2} = \frac{\sin \alpha_1}{\sin \alpha_2} \tag{3.92}$$

For waves in deep water, $C \propto L^{1/2}$, that is

$$\frac{C_1^2}{C_2^2} = \frac{L_1 (C_2 - v \sin \alpha_2)}{L_2 C_2} \tag{3.93}$$

whence, using equations 3.91, 3.92 and 3.93

$$\sin \alpha_2 = \frac{C_1^2 \sin \alpha_1}{(C_1 - v \sin \alpha_1)(C_1 - 2v \sin \alpha_1)} \tag{3.94}$$

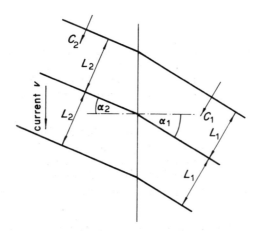

Figure 3.25 *Reference diagram for wave refracted by current*

For water of depth $0.5 > h/L > 0.04$, α_2 must be solved by iteration. For shallow water, assuming no change of depth at boundary, $C_1 = C_2$ and hence from equations 3.91 and 3.92

$$\sin \alpha_2 = \frac{C_1 \sin \alpha_1}{C_1 - v \sin \alpha_1} \tag{3.95}$$

As in the case of sudden change of depth (equation 3.75), it will be seen from equation 3.95 that complete reflection by a current will occur in shallow water if $C_1 \sin \alpha_1 \geqslant (C_1 - v \sin \alpha_1)$ or $v \geqslant C_1 (\operatorname{cosec} \alpha_1 - 1)$.

The height of the wave (H_2) in the current may also be related to the original height (H_1) by equating wave energy transfer across the boundary for the appropriate length of wave crest; thus from equation 3.31 $P_2 = P_1$ and hence

$$\frac{1}{8} \rho g H_1^2 C_{n1} C_1 \cos \alpha_1 = \frac{1}{8} \rho g H_2^2 C_{n2} C_2 \cos \alpha_2 \tag{3.96}$$

whence

$$\frac{H_1^2}{H_2^2} = \frac{C_{n2} C_2 \cos \alpha_2}{C_{n1} C_1 \cos \alpha_1} \tag{3.97}$$

For deep or shallow water that is, $h/L \geqslant 0.5$ or $h/L \leqslant 0.04$, $C_{n1} = C_{n2}$.

The assumption used above, that the wave speed relative to the current is given by the velocity of propagation in still water, is only valid if the current is constant with depth. For a small current varying as the one-seventh power of depth the error involved in the simple addition of mean current and wave speed is very small.[61]

The effect of currents on wave height is difficult to determine. According to Longuet-Higgins and Stewart [62] the assumptions that the energy of waves, in a non-uniform current with mean value $\bar{v}$, is propagated with a velocity $\bar{v} + C_g$, and that no further interaction takes place, are incorrect. They found that the interchange of energy between the wave and the current should include a radiation stress. They considered deep currents in very deep water for three cases

(1) a current in the direction of wave propagation and the horizontal variation in velocity compensated by a vertical upwelling;
(2) a current in the direction of wave propagation and the horizontal variation in velocity compensated by a horizontal inflow;
(3) waves traversing a simple horizontal current with a vertical axis of shear.

For each case quite different expressions for wave amplitude result, but in all cases it was assumed that the mean water level should be maintained.

Jonsson et al. [63] considered a vertically constant current field over a gently sloping bed. Energy was assumed to be conserved as a constant mean energy level. For conservation of discharge in a varying current field a set-up or set-down of the mean water level was assumed. This has been extended to the two-dimensional problem of current and depth refraction by Skovgaard and Jonsson.[60] The governing equations are solved iteratively by alternately determining the current field and the wave field. Similar methods, combining two level iterative scheme with relaxation techniques have also been developed, [57, 56] which can describe wave and current interaction in the presence of rip currents.

3.4.4 Wave Breaking

The condition of a wave breaking is dependent on the maximum wave steepness at which the wave can remain stable. In shoaling water, the limiting steepness decreases as a function of relative depth and beach slope perpendicular to the direction of propagation. Breaking waves are generally classified as spilling, plunging or surging depending on beach slope and wave steepness.[64] In principle a plunging breaker occurs when the crest velocity exceeds that of the body of the wave, a spilling breaker occurs when the crest velocity remains appoximately equal to that of the wave and a surging breaker occurs when the base of the wave surges up the beach before the crest can plunge forward. When studying wave refraction it is often necessary to find the height of wave and the depth of water at the point of breaking. Equation 3.80 allows the height of the wave H_1 at any point, to be related to the wave height H_0 in deep water by the use of the wave height coefficient. Figure 3.2 permits the wave length, L_1, to be related to the deep water wave length L_0. In consequence, at any point it is possible to evaluate the wave steepness H_1/L_1 and the ratio of depth of water to height of wave, h_1/H_1. The wave may be traced on figure 3.13 as it progresses. Either it will appear to cross the line of limiting wave steepness, in which case it must break at the point of the intersection, or it will pass into the region of the solitary or the cnoidal wave.

Consider a wave between orthogonals spaced at b_0 in deep water and b_1 in shallow water. If it runs inshore into the 'solitary wave zone' as indicated by figure 3.13, equation 3.60 may be used to derive the wave height again equating rate of energy transmission between orthogonals. Thus, $P_0 = P_1$ so that

$$\frac{C_0}{2} \frac{E_0 b_0}{L_0} = \frac{C_0}{2} \left(\frac{1}{8} \rho g H_0^2 \right) b_0 = \frac{C_1 E_1}{L_1} b_1 \qquad (3.98)$$

but $T = L_0/C_0 = L_1/C_1$, hence from equation 3.60 since $\gamma = H/h$, (see section 3.2.4)

$$\frac{1}{16} L_0 H_0^2 b_0 \approx \frac{8}{3} h_1^3 b_1 \left[\frac{H_1^3}{3 h_1^3} \right]^{1/2}$$

that is

$$\frac{H_1}{H_0} \approx \frac{H_0^{1/3}}{8 \cdot 5 h_1} \left[\frac{L_0 b_0}{b_1} \right]^{2/3} \tag{3.99}$$

For the breaking solitary wave where $H_b/h_b = 0.78$ (see section 3.2.4), equation 3.98 may be written as

$$\frac{H_b}{h_0} \approx \frac{1}{3 \cdot 3} \left[\frac{L_0 b_0}{H_0 b_1} \right]^{1/3} \tag{3.100}$$

and this relationship permits determination of the breaking height and depth.

It must once more be stressed that the relationship of equation 3.100 is very inexact for such a high value of (H/h). Munk [9] finds that equation 3.100 gives a reasonably good result for $H_0 b_1/L_0 b_0 \leqslant 0.02$. It has been observed that changes in wave amplitude, celerity and profile deviate substantially from solitary wave theory when a solitary wave travels up a slope.

Swart [39] classified breaking waves by defining a wave energy dissipation coefficient p. Plunging waves were classified as $p = 1$ and spilling waves by $p = 0$. He found a good correlation between p and the percentage of energy dissipated by breaking $= 1 - (H_{b2}/H_{b1})^2$ where H_{b1} and H_{b2} represent wave height immediately before and after breaking respectively. Assuming a relationship between the dissipation coefficient and the breaker index γ ($= H_b/h_b$, section 3.2.4) the best fit to data was found to be

$$\gamma = 0.33p + 0.46 \tag{3.101}$$

However, a large amount of scatter was shown, attributed to the fact that it was assumed that γ is purely a function of breaker type.

Maximum breaker height may also be approximated [13] using criteria

$$\frac{H_b}{h_b} = b - a \frac{H_0}{gT^2} \tag{3.102}$$

where

$$a = 4.46g \left(1 - e^{-19s} \right) \tag{3.103}$$

and

$$b = \frac{1.56}{\left(1 + e^{-19.5s} \right)} \tag{3.104}$$

which introduces the beach slope, s, as a parameter and is written for use with metric units.

It seems probable that one of the reasons for the fairly wide degree of scatter in measured data is that a potential instability in the wave form may exist for some time until some quite small irregularity causes a collapse. In any event the most reliable estimate can be made from field data for each particular site, but the above expressions may be used to estimate the possible range of values.

3.5 Diffraction of Waves

Diffraction of water waves is a process by which energy is transferred laterally along a wave crest. The most obvious example occurs when waves are intercepted by an impervious structure such as a breakwater. The presence of an obstruction sets up radiating disturbances and these combine to give rise to wave trains in the lee or shadow of the obstruction. Mathematical solutions for some specific problems have been taken from the theory of acoustic and light waves and applied to water waves in constant depth.

3.5.1 Semi-infinite Breakwater

Penney and Price [65] developed a solution in such a way for Airy waves incident on a semi-infinite breakwater. The wave pattern can be described as occurring in three different regions. Referring to figure 3.26, the origin of the coordinate system is taken to be at the tip of the breakwater with the x and y-axes running parallel and normal to the breakwater as shown. The regions may be idealised as follows.

(1) $0 < \theta < \theta_0$ is the shadow zone of the breakwater in which the solution consists of only the scattered waves. In this area the wave crests form circular arcs centred at the origin.

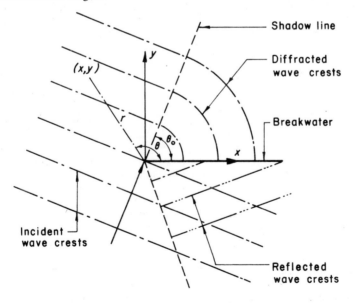

Figure 3.26 *Diffraction of waves by an impermeable breakwater*

(2) $\theta_0 < \theta < (\theta_0 + \pi)$ is the region in which the scattered waves and the incident waves are combined. It is assumed that the wave crests are undisturbed by the presence of the breakwater.

(3) $(\theta_0 + \pi) < \theta < 2\pi$ is the region in which the incident waves and the reflected waves are superimposed to form an apparent short crested wave system for oblique incidence and a partial standing wave for normal incidence.

Values of diffraction coefficient K_d which is the ratio of diffracted wave height to incident wave height are shown in table 3.5 in terms of polar coordinates non-dimensionalised with respect to wave length.

Figure 3.27 shows the pattern of diffraction coefficients for normal wave incidence. For waves that encounter the breakwater obliquely, the pattern is similar for $30° \leqslant \theta_0 \leqslant 150°$, the line along which the wave diffraction coefficient is approximately 0.5, marking the edge of the geometric shadow, and the remainder of the pattern appropriately skewed.

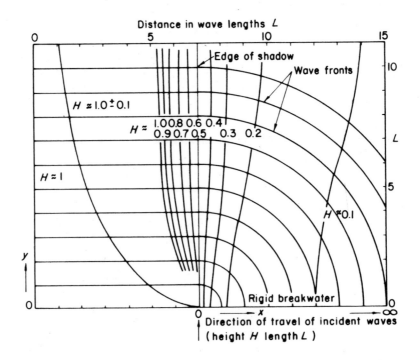

Figure 3.27 *Diffraction of waves by a long breakwater; after Penney and Price [65]*

3.5.2 Breakwater Gap

When considering a structure such as a harbour, solution for wave diffraction through a gap in a breakwater may be more appropriate, depending on the

TABLE 3.5 *Diffraction coefficients, K_d*

θ_0 (°)	r/L	θ (°)												
		0	15	30	45	60	75	90	105	120	135	150	165	180
15	1/2	0.49	0.79	0.83	0.90	0.97	1.01	1.03	1.02	1.01	0.99	0.99	1.00	1.00
	1	0.38	0.73	0.83	0.95	1.04	1.04	0.99	0.98	1.01	1.01	1.00	1.00	1.00
	2	0.21	0.68	0.86	1.05	1.03	0.97	1.02	0.99	1.00	1.00	1.00	1.00	1.00
	5	0.13	0.63	0.99	1.04	1.03	1.02	0.99	0.99	1.00	1.01	1.00	1.00	1.00
	10	0.35	0.58	1.10	1.05	0.98	0.99	1.01	1.00	1.00	1.00	1.00	1.00	1.00
30	1/2	0.61	0.63	0.68	0.76	0.87	0.97	1.03	1.05	1.03	1.01	0.99	0.95	1.00
	1	0.50	0.53	0.63	0.78	0.95	1.06	1.05	0.98	0.98	1.01	1.01	0.97	1.00
	2	0.40	0.44	0.59	0.84	1.07	1.03	0.96	1.02	0.98	1.01	0.99	0.95	1.00
	5	0.27	0.32	0.55	1.00	1.04	1.04	1.02	0.99	0.99	1.00	1.01	0.97	1.00
	10	0.20	0.24	0.54	1.12	1.06	0.97	0.99	1.01	1.00	1.00	1.00	0.98	1.00
45	1/2	0.49	0.50	0.55	0.63	0.73	0.85	0.96	1.04	1.06	1.04	1.00	0.99	1.00
	1	0.38	0.40	0.47	0.59	0.76	0.95	1.07	1.06	0.98	0.97	1.01	1.01	1.00
	2	0.29	0.31	0.39	0.56	0.83	1.08	1.04	0.96	1.03	0.98	1.01	1.00	1.00
	5	0.18	0.20	0.29	0.54	1.01	1.04	1.05	1.03	1.00	0.99	1.01	1.00	1.00
	10	0.13	0.15	0.22	0.53	1.13	1.07	0.96	0.98	1.02	0.99	1.00	1.00	1.00
60	1/2	0.40	0.41	0.45	0.52	0.60	0.72	0.85	1.13	1.04	1.06	1.03	1.01	1.00
	1	0.31	0.32	0.36	0.44	0.57	0.75	0.96	1.08	1.06	0.98	0.98	1.01	1.00
	2	0.22	0.23	0.28	0.37	0.55	0.83	1.08	1.04	0.96	1.03	0.98	1.01	1.00
	5	0.14	0.15	0.18	0.28	0.53	1.01	1.04	1.05	1.03	0.99	0.99	1.00	1.00
	10	0.10	0.11	0.13	0.21	0.52	1.14	1.07	0.96	0.98	1.01	1.00	1.00	1.00
75	1/2	0.34	0.35	0.38	0.42	0.50	0.59	0.71	0.85	0.97	1.04	1.05	1.02	1.00
	1	0.25	0.26	0.29	0.34	0.43	0.56	0.75	0.95	1.02	1.06	0.98	0.98	1.00
	2	0.18	0.19	0.22	0.26	0.36	0.54	0.83	1.09	1.04	0.96	1.03	0.99	1.00
	5	0.12	0.12	0.13	0.17	0.27	0.52	1.01	1.04	1.05	1.03	0.99	0.99	1.00
	10	0.08	0.08	0.10	0.13	0.20	0.52	1.14	1.07	0.96	0.98	1.01	1.00	1.00
90	1/2	0.31	0.31	0.33	0.36	0.41	0.49	0.59	0.71	0.85	0.96	1.03	1.03	1.00
	1	0.22	0.23	0.24	0.28	0.33	0.42	0.56	0.75	0.96	1.07	1.05	0.99	1.00
	2	0.16	0.16	0.18	0.20	0.26	0.35	0.54	0.69	1.08	1.04	0.96	1.02	1.00
	5	0.10	0.10	0.11	0.13	0.16	0.27	0.53	1.01	1.04	1.05	1.02	0.99	1.00
	10	0.07	0.07	0.08	0.09	0.13	0.20	0.52	1.14	1.07	0.96	0.99	1.01	1.00
105	1/2	0.28	0.28	0.29	0.32	0.35	0.41	0.49	0.59	0.72	0.85	0.97	1.01	1.00
	1	0.20	0.20	0.24	0.23	0.27	0.33	0.42	0.56	0.75	0.95	1.06	1.04	1.00
	2	0.14	0.14	0.13	0.17	0.20	0.25	0.35	0.54	0.83	1.08	1.03	0.97	1.00
	5	0.09	0.09	0.10	0.11	0.13	0.17	0.27	0.52	1.02	1.04	1.04	1.02	1.00
	10	0.07	0.06	0.08	0.08	0.09	0.12	0.20	0.52	1.14	1.07	0.97	0.99	1.00
120	1/2	0.25	0.26	0.27	0.28	0.31	0.35	0.41	0.50	0.60	0.73	0.87	0.97	1.00
	1	0.18	0.19	0.19	0.21	0.23	0.27	0.33	0.43	0.57	0.76	0.95	1.04	1.00
	2	0.13	0.13	0.14	0.14	0.17	0.20	0.26	0.36	0.55	0.83	1.07	1.03	1.00
	5	0.08	0.08	0.08	0.09	0.11	0.13	0.16	0.27	0.53	1.01	1.04	1.03	1.00
	10	0.06	0.06	0.06	0.07	0.07	0.09	0.13	0.20	0.52	1.13	1.06	0.98	1.00
135	1/2	0.24	0.24	0.25	0.26	0.28	0.32	0.36	0.42	0.52	0.63	0.76	0.90	1.00
	1	0.18	0.17	0.18	0.19	0.21	0.23	0.28	0.34	0.44	0.59	0.78	0.95	1.00
	2	0.12	0.12	0.13	0.14	0.14	0.17	0.20	0.26	0.37	0.56	0.84	1.05	1.00
	5	0.08	0.07	0.08	0.08	0.09	0.11	0.13	0.17	0.28	0.54	1.00	1.04	1.00
	10	0.06	0.06	0.06	0.06	0.07	0.08	0.09	0.13	0.21	0.53	1.12	1.05	1.00
150	1/2	0.23	0.23	0.24	0.25	0.27	0.29	0.33	0.38	0.45	0.55	0.68	0.83	1.00
	1	0.16	0.17	0.17	0.18	0.19	0.22	0.24	0.29	0.36	0.47	0.63	0.83	1.00
	2	0.12	0.12	0.12	0.13	0.14	0.15	0.18	0.22	0.28	0.39	0.59	0.86	1.00
	5	0.07	0.07	0.08	0.08	0.08	0.10	0.11	0.13	0.18	0.29	0.55	0.99	1.00
	10	0.05	0.05	0.05	0.06	0.06	0.07	0.08	0.10	0.13	0.22	0.54	1.10	1.00
165	1/2	0.23	0.23	0.23	0.24	0.26	0.28	0.31	0.35	0.41	0.50	0.63	0.79	1.00
	1	0.16	0.16	0.17	0.17	0.19	0.20	0.23	0.26	0.32	0.40	0.53	0.73	1.00
	2	0.11	0.11	0.12	0.12	0.13	0.14	0.16	0.19	0.23	0.31	0.44	0.68	1.00
	5	0.07	0.07	0.07	0.07	0.08	0.09	0.10	0.12	0.15	0.20	0.32	0.63	1.00
	10	0.05	0.05	0.05	0.06	0.06	0.06	0.07	0.08	0.11	0.11	0.21	0.58	1.00
180	1/2	0.20	0.25	0.23	0.24	0.25	0.28	0.31	0.34	0.40	0.49	0.61	0.78	1.00
	1	0.10	0.17	0.16	0.18	0.18	0.23	0.22	0.25	0.31	0.38	0.50	0.70	1.00
	2	0.02	0.09	0.12	0.12	0.13	0.18	0.16	0.18	0.22	0.29	0.40	0.60	1.00
	5	0.02	0.06	0.07	0.07	0.07	0.08	0.10	0.12	0.14	0.18	0.27	0.46	1.00
	10	0.01	0.05	0.05	0.04	0.06	0.07	0.07	0.08	0.10	0.13	0.20	0.36	1.00

geometry of the breakwaters. In this case the diffraction pattern due to one side of the breakwater gap will be modified by the diffraction pattern due to the other side of the gap. Solutions have been developed for a relatively large gap ($b \geqslant L$ where b is the gap width) and for a relatively small gap.

A solution for a large gap essentially results from the double application of the semi-infinite breakwater solution for the case of normal incidence. Graphs and tables have been published by Johnson [66] for a variety of gap widths ($\leqslant 5L$). An example is shown in figure 3.28. As indicated for the region in the shadow of either breakwater ($|x| \geqslant b/2$) the wave crests are approximately circular. Immediately behind the entrance the diffraction coefficient will be 1.0 at $x = 0$, decreasing to approximately 0.5 at $x = \pm b/2$ and the wave crests will be approximately parallel to the breakwater. At some distance behind the entrance the wave crests follow a circular curve and the diffraction coefficient becomes approximately uniform across this range with a value of $b/(Ly)^{1/2}$. For waves striking an entrance obliquely Johnson suggested that the normal incidence results may be used skewed to the direction of wave approach with

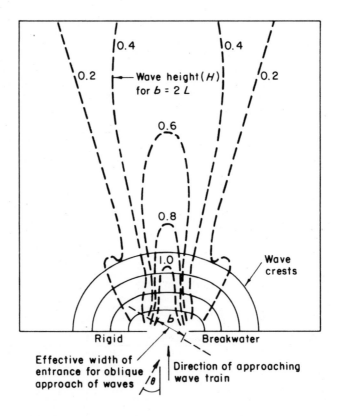

Figure 3.28 *Diffraction of wave entering harbour entrance (b $\geqslant$ L); after Johnson [66]*

an assumed gap width of the projected width normal to the direction of the incident wave ($b \cos \theta$) as indicated in broken lines on figure 3.28. For gap widths greater than 5 wave lengths, each breakwater can be assumed to be independent.

For waves passing through a narrow gap ($b < L$) it can be assumed that the waves approximately diverge in a semi-circle from the gap so that at distances greater than about $4L$ from the centre of the gap the wave diffraction coefficient will be $(b/\pi r)^{1/2}$ where r is the radius of the arc.

One or other of the cases described in sections 3.5.1 or 3.5.2 may frequently be used to provide a first approximation of a particular circumstance. Wiegel [67] provides a number of more complex examples. He also shows that the use of Airy wave theory in diffraction problems does not introduce serious error.

3.5.3 Combined Refraction and Diffraction

The previous results relate to diffraction in areas of constant depth. If the sea bed is varying in depth both refractive effects and shoaling should be considered in wave height calculations. It has been suggested that in these cases waves may be diffracted for 5 wave lengths beyond the breakwater and then refracted onwards. However, due to recent developments with the use of advanced numerical methods it is possible to treat the problem in a far more general sense so that the proper combination of wave diffraction and refraction may be considered.[58, 68]

3.6 Reflection of Waves

If the crest of a wave whose surface form is given by the equation

$$\eta_1 = \frac{H_1}{2} \cos 2\pi \left(\frac{x}{L} - \frac{t}{T} \right) \tag{3.105}$$

advances parallel to a barrier at $x = 0$, then a partial reflection will occur represented as

$$\eta_2 = \frac{H_R}{2} \cos 2\pi \left(\frac{x}{L} + \frac{t}{T} \right) \tag{3.106}$$

The sum of these two waves will be represented by

$$\eta = \eta_1 + \eta_2 \tag{3.107}$$

At points such as $x = L, 2L$, etc.

$$\eta_1 + \eta_2 = \left[\frac{(H_I + H_R)}{2} \right] \cos \frac{2\pi t}{T} \tag{3.108}$$

and thus a standing wave will be set up here with an amplitude greater than that of the incident wave. For a high enough value of H_R a violent collision occurs between the advancing and receding crests, with a resulting plume, known as 'clapotis'. The vertical water particle velocities and other characteristics may be derived by summing the appropriate equations for the two waves.

Miche [69] relates the angle to the horizontal, α (in radians), of the face of a seawall or beach to $(H_0/L_0)_{max}$, the maximum steepness of the deep water wave; for total reflection to occur

$$\left(\frac{H_0}{L_0}\right)_{max} = \frac{1}{\pi}\left[\frac{2\alpha}{\pi}\right]^{1/2}\sin^2\alpha \tag{3.109}$$

The slope must extend into water deep enough to ensure that the wave has not broken before striking the surface. Where the incident wave has been refracted, it is necessary to consider the steepness of the equivalent deep water wave $(H_0/L_0)'_{max}$ where

$$\left(\frac{H_0}{L_0}\right)'_{max} = \left(\frac{b_0}{b_1}\right)^{1/2}\left(\frac{H_0}{L_0}\right)_{max} \tag{3.110}$$

where b_0 and b_1 represent the distance between corresponding orthogonals for the deep water wave and for the wave at the wall respectively (see section 3.4.2).

For a wave whose deep water steepness $H_0/L_0 < (H_0/L_0)_{max}$ [or the equivalent steepness $(H_0/L_0)'_{max}$ for the refracted wave], the ratio of height of reflected wave to incident wave

$$\frac{H_R}{H_I} = \frac{\rho(H_0/L_0)}{(H_0/L_0)_{max}} \tag{3.111}$$

where ρ is 1.0 for a smooth faced wall, ~0.8 for an impervious beach, and ~0.3 to 0.6 for a regularly sloped rock pitching. Wiegel compares the theory with results of model experiments.[12] Reflection of the breaking wave is discussed in section 2.3.

Where a periodic or solitary wave approaches a steep barrier at an oblique angle, the amplitude of the wave against the barrier may be magnified by the phenomenon known as the Mach stem described in section 7.2.2.

3.7 Generation of Longshore Currents

When gravity waves approach a coastline at an oblique angle a mean current is generated parallel to the shoreline. The most widely used theoretical framework for studying longshore currents is that derived by Longuet-Higgins [70] from the theory of radiation stress.

The concept of radiation stress was introduced in order to explain some of the non-linear effects of surface gravity waves. This has been used to describe non-linear interactions between waves, wave and current interaction, wave set-up, surf beat and the generation of longshore currents. Radiation stress is defined as the excess flow of momentum due to the presence of waves.

It can be shown that the components of the increase in momentum in orthogonal directions result in a momentum flux tensor given by [71]

$$S_{ij} = E \begin{bmatrix} \dfrac{1}{2} + \dfrac{4\pi h/L}{\sinh 4\pi h/L} & 0 \\ 0 & \dfrac{2\pi h/L}{\sinh 4\pi h/L} \end{bmatrix} \tag{3.112}$$

in terms of coordinates perpendicular and parallel to the direction of wave propagation.

Consider waves approaching a straight plane coastline at an oblique angle as shown in figure 3.29. The x and y-axes are in the direction normal and parallel to the shoreline respectively. It can be shown that local rate of dissipation of wave energy is directly proportional to the local stress exerted by the waves neglecting any momentum flux due to the currents.

Assuming that the wave height is limited by the wave breaking criterion throughout the surf zone, that the shallow water relationships for Airy wave theory apply and that the approach angle θ is small, the net stress exerted by the waves in the surf zone is

$$\tau_y = -\frac{5}{16}\gamma^2 \, \rho g h s \sin\theta \tag{3.113}$$

where $s = -dh/dx$ the beach slope and γ is the wave breaker index (see section 3.4.4).

If a steady state exists, this driving force will be opposed by both bottom friction and turbulent friction due to mixing. The average resistive shear stress normal to wave direction can be approximated by

$$\tau_n = \frac{2}{\pi}\rho f_c \, \hat{u}_0 \, v \tag{3.114}$$

where v is the average longshore current, $\hat{u}_0$ is the maximum orbital velocity of the wave at the bed and the friction coefficient f_c is analogous to, but not necessarily equal to, the wave friction factor discussed in section 3.4.1.

If it is assumed that the turbulent friction of the fluid is negligible, equations 3.113 and 3.114 must sum to give zero. Consequently the longshore velocity is directly proportional to depth and varies linearly from zero at the shoreline to

$$v_0 = \frac{5\pi}{16 f_c} \, \gamma \, (g h_b)^{1/2} \, s \sin\theta_b \tag{3.115}$$

at the breaker line where subscript b relates to wave breaking conditions.

In order to include the effects of lateral mixing it has been proposed that a

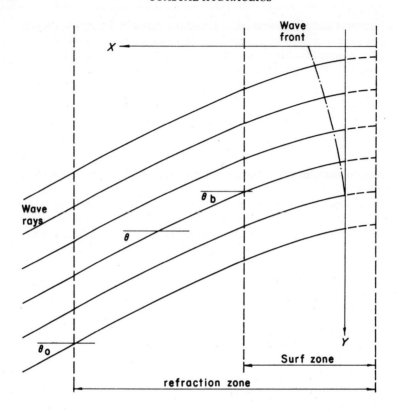

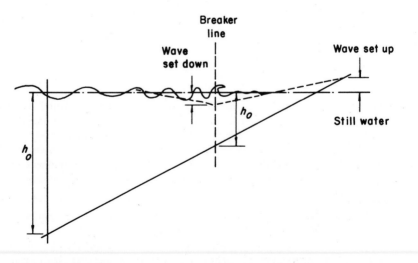

Figure 3.29 *Schematic view of waves approaching a straight coastline*

psuedo-horizontal eddy viscosity should take the form

$$\mu_e = N\rho |x|(gh)^{1/2} \tag{3.116}$$

where N is a dimensionless constant and the equation of motion becomes

$$\tau_y + \overline{\tau}_n + \frac{\partial}{\partial x}\left(\mu_e h \frac{\partial v}{\partial x}\right) = 0 \tag{3.117}$$

By non-dimensionalising the variables to $X = x/x_b$ and $V = v/v_0$ and applying appropriate boundary conditions the solution to equations 3.113, 3.114 and 3.117 is

$$V = \begin{cases} B_1 X^{P1} + AX & 0 \leqslant X \leqslant 1 \\ \\ B_2 X^{P2} & 1 < X < \infty \end{cases} \tag{3.118}$$

where

$$A = \frac{1}{1 - 2.5P} \quad (P \neq 0.4) \tag{3.119}$$

$$B_1 = \frac{P_2 - 1}{P_1 - P_2} A \tag{3.120}$$

$$B_2 = \frac{P_1 - 1}{P_1 - P_2} \tag{3.121}$$

$$P = \frac{\pi s N}{\gamma f_c} \tag{3.122}$$

$$P_1 = \frac{3}{4} + \left(\frac{9}{16} + \frac{1}{P}\right)^{1/2} \tag{3.123}$$

and

$$P_2 = -\frac{3}{4} - \left(\frac{9}{16} + \frac{1}{P}\right)^{1/2} \tag{3.124}$$

A separate solution at the singularity $P = 0.4$ is also given. The parameter P is non-dimensional and represents the relative importance of horizontal mixing. A family of solutions for the velocity profile across the surf zone is shown in figure 3.30. The case of $P = 0$ corresponds to equation 3.115.

Values of the mixing coefficient N according to equation 3.122 have been estimated by James [72] using field data.[73] There were no clear trends in the results. However, Longuet-Higgins suggests that most field data will fit to curves

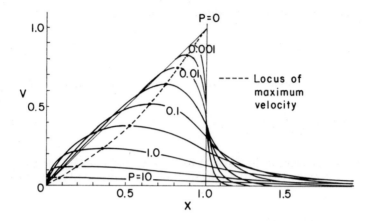

Figure 3.30 *Distribution of longshore currents as a function of the mixing para-*
meter P; after Longuet-Higgins [70]

corresponding to $0.1 < P < 0.4$ which indirectly brackets values for N if a friction
coefficient has been estimated. However, lateral mixing is insignificant when
considering irregular waves, since the component of each part of the spectrum
results in similar curves to those shown in figure 3.30 when lateral mixing is
ignored.

Longuet-Higgins [70] suggested that the friction coefficient f_c should have a
value of the order of 0.01. Measured data indicates that the friction factor
should at least be a function of beach slope and can vary between 0.002 and
0.1.[76] Since both ripple dimensions and beach slope are generally a function
of wave characteristics, this would seem to be a reasonable conclusion. Furthermore, the conditions required to use equation 3.114 are not obviously met and
more consistent results can be obtained if the shear force due to the current is
considered as a contributory factor to the resultant shear force.

Waves approaching a beach also cause a set-up or set-down in the near water
level due to the onshore component of radiation stress. Inside the surf zone
the set-up η becomes appreciably positive as shown diagrammatically in figure
3.29. Bowen *et al.* [75] have shown theoretically with supporting experimental
results that

$$\frac{d\eta}{dx} = \frac{1}{1 + 8/3\gamma^2} \frac{dh}{dx} \tag{3.125}$$

Equation 3.113 can be modified to include the effects of set-up by replacing
γ by γ_* where

$$\gamma_* = \frac{1}{1 + 3/8\gamma^2} \tag{3.126}$$

The wave set-up thus tends to decrease the theoretical magnitude of the longshore current. However, considering the scatter in measured data and the uncertainties in estimating the friction factor and mixing parameter, this refinement cannot generally be justified.

The longshore current theory described is limited to uniform slope, linear wave theory, small angles of incidence, linear wave transformation in the surf zone and the neglect of longshore variation in breaker height. Several one-dimensional theories have been developed [72, 76, 77, 78] the formulations for which differ in treatment for some of these aspects. These methods generally require more complex numerical solutions and there is little quantitative difference in the results, the differences being less than the degree of scatter in measured data. However, two-dimensional aspects such as the variation of a longshore wave height in the lee of a headland can be significant.[79] The associated phenomena of rip currents and edge waves are discussed in chapter 4.

3.8 Prediction of Waves in Shallow Water

Waves arriving at a point in shallow water may be subject to one or more of the processes described in the previous section. However, most of the phenomena can only be described mathematically for monochromatic wave trains. In reality the sea is composed of a mixture of wave forms of differing period and amplitude which combine to form a wave spectrum as described in section 3.3.6.

The refraction of a wave spectrum involves differential effects on each component of the spectrum. Longuet-Higgins [56] considered each component of a unidirectional spectrum on the grounds that each part of the spectrum can be treated independently and showed that the total energy of an offshore spectrum would be transferred to the shallow water zone.

Karlsson [55] has considered the Pierson Moskowitz directional spectrum (see section 3.3.6), but has neglected external generative or degenerative forces. For waves travelling up a plane beach, wave attenuation was found theoretically to be slightly greater in transitional depths but similar in shallow depths when compared to a monochromatic wave train. It was also shown that there should be a greater concentration of wave energy around the direction of the largest waves in the spectrum.

The directional spread of the shorter period waves tends to remains less affected by shoaling water as refraction begins at smaller depths (see section 3.4.2). Therefore in shallow water the longer period waves may be amplified to a greater extent and there will be a shift in the peak period of the spectrum to a higher value and a corresponding increase in significant wave height.

The type of behaviour will depend very much on the characteristics of the deep water wave spectrum and the relative depths of concern. At intermediate depths, for example, the reverse to the above may occur. Furthermore, steeper waves will break earlier than shallow waves, losing some if not all of their energy. In this case the spectrum will become truncated for specific wave height to length or wave height to depth ratios. An example of a refracted deep water spectrum is shown in figure 3.31.

For complex topography the offshore spectrum may be related to the inshore

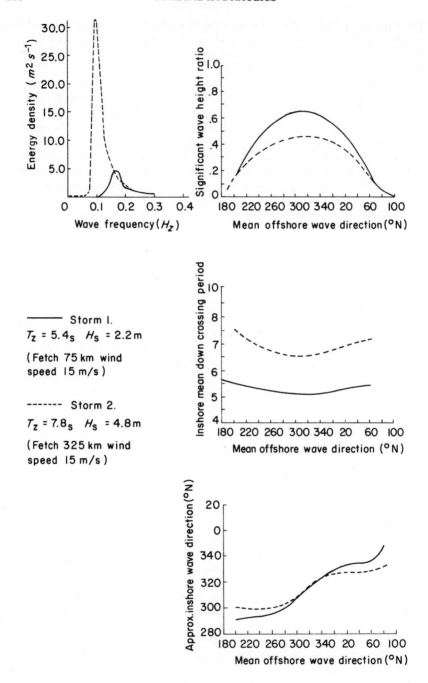

Figure 3.31 *Deep water and shallow water spectra for refracted waves*

spectrum by refracting very many wave rays from a point of interest to deep
water at small angular increments and for each period in the spectrum.[51]
It is then possible to relate the energy from each component of the offshore
spectrum to the inshore point by a series of transfer functions.

There are no general analytical methods that can allow for all the losses or
input of energy in the wave system collectively. In the case of a harbour or
submerged object, diffraction and hence transmission of wave energy along wave
crests will occur. There will be dissipation of wave energy due to bottom
friction and percolation as discussed in section 3.4.1. Over long fetches there
will be an input or dissipation of energy into or out of the system due to wind
stress. Any significant current may also modify the wave spectrum. Each of
these aspects must be treated separately and the combined effects judged
accordingly.

3.9 Oscillations in a Harbour

The water contained in a harbour will have certain natural frequencies of
oscillation, depending on the geometry of the water boundaries. Oscillations
of unacceptable magnitude are caused in certain harbours by resonance
between one or more of the natural periods and rhythmical disturbances in
the sea adjacent to the harbour entrance. Short-period waves may usually be
ignored since they become rapidly damped within a harbour; the critical
waves are those of 20 s period or upwards (referred to as infra-gravity or
long-period waves) and the causes of such oscillations have been attributed,
in different circumstances, to

    (1) tsunamis (see section 2.3.4)
    (2) surges or seiches (see section 2.3.3)
    (3) instability of wind
    (4) eddy trains caused by strong currents flowing across the harbour
entrance
    (5) surf-beat.

Surf-beat is the name given to the slow fluctuation in surface level of the
sea, caused by waves, particularly long swell, arriving in groups rather than in
continuous regular trains, and breaking on the shore. The rise in level is
associated with the rate of destruction of momentum of the waves.
Alternatively the rise in sea level may be associated with steep waves (see
section 2.2.1). Tucker [80] has measured at Perranporth, Cornwall, a ratio
of about 1:15 between the height of the long-period surf-beat and that of
the associated swell.

Long-period waves are affected by reflection and refraction. Wave focusing
attributable to these factors appears to be responsible for the notorious
oscillations experienced in Table Bay Harbour, Cape Town. Wilson [81]
describes records over a period of 15 years indicating that amplitudes of
greater than 90 mm are experienced on an average of 4 days per month
during the summer, with periods of 41 to 55 min. The most important
criterion is that of the surging of moored ships caused by the horizontal move-

ments associated with such long-period waves and an amplitude of only 25 mm
may be critical. Thus, from equation 3.36, maximum horizontal velocity

$$\hat{u} = \frac{LH}{2hT} = \frac{CH}{2h} = \frac{H(gh)^{1/2}}{2h} \qquad (3.127)$$

and displacement each side of the mean position

$$\frac{D}{2} = \int_0^{T/2} u \, dt = \frac{1}{2^{1/2}} \left(\frac{T}{2}\right) \hat{u} = \frac{HT(2gh)^{1/2}}{8h} \qquad (3.128)$$

Wilson [82] discusses the conditions of surging that may lead to damage to
ships at berth, concluding that damage is unlikely to occur provided that
$H/T < 1.2$ mm/s.

The fundamental mode of oscillation of a basin of length l with vertical
walls is

$$T = \left[\frac{4\pi l}{g} / \tanh\left(\frac{\pi h}{l}\right)\right]^{1/2}$$

that is, when the wave length of the oscillation is $2l$. Other possible wave lengths
are thus

$$L = \frac{2l}{j} \quad j = 1, 2, 3, \cdots \qquad (3.129)$$

In general

$$T_j = \left[\frac{4\pi l}{jg} / \tanh\left(\frac{\pi jh}{l}\right)\right]^{1/2} \qquad (3.130)$$

for an enclosed, approximately rectangular harbour. For small values of j, waves
entering a harbour with corresponding resonant periods may cause considerable
build-up in the absence of an appropriate energy dissipator.

For large lakes, generally shallow in comparison to long-period oscillations
(seiches), shallow water approximations may be used so that

$$T_j = 2l/[j(gh)^{1/2}] \quad j = 1, 2, 3, \cdots \qquad (3.131)$$

while for shallow basins open at one end, the fundamental modes of oscillation
occur at quarter wave length so

$$T_j = 4l/[(2j - 1)(gh)^{1/2}] \quad j = 1, 2, 3, \cdots \qquad (3.132)$$

For complex shapes numerical methods are used to obtain solutions.

3.10 Ship Waves

Lamb [2] provides an account of surface waves created by disturbance at a point and develops the basic theory to explain the form of bow and stern waves caused by a moving vessel, whereby each change in hull section, predominantly at the bows and stern, constitutes a moving area of disturbance. In addition, a series of wave crests forms astern of the vessel, progressing at the same speed as the vessel.

Most theoretical accounts of ship's waves assume deep water waves but Sorensen [83] describes tests in shallow water, compared against theory. He also provides a selected bibliography on the general subject of ship waves.

Generally the diverging wave makes a pattern curved in plan to each side of the ship, meeting at a cusp, real or imaginary. For deep water, where the Froude number

$$Fr = V_s/(gh)^{1/2} \tag{3.133}$$

is very small, V_s being the ship's speed, the half-angle of the cusp is about $20°$; this increases to $90°$ as $Fr \to 1$.

Since the following wave proceeds at the ship's speed, its wave length must be such as to satisfy equation 3.12, or its simpler form

$$C(=V_s) = \left(\frac{gL_0}{2\pi}\right)^{1/2} \tag{3.134}$$

in deep water.

In shallow water, where $Fr > 1$ the two waves are found to combine to create a single system of waves diverging at an angle (corresponding to the supersonic Mach angle) of $\sin^{-1}(gh/V_s)^{1/2}$.

The civil engineer's principal interest in ship waves lies in questions of damage caused by wash. This is not normally a coastal problem but Sorensen [83] provides data on measurements taken in the Oakland Estuary.

Example 3.1

What are the orbital velocities and radii at a depth of 10 m for a 10 s wave, 0.5 m high, in 20 m depth of water?

By equation 3.13, a 10 s wave will have a deep water length of 1.56×10^2 $= 156$ m, that is, $h/L_0 = 0.128$. From figure 3.2, $\tanh 2\pi h/L \approx 0.78$ so that $L \approx 121$ m by equation 3.15. $H/gT^2 = 0.00051$ and $h/gT^2 = 0.02$. Hence from figure 3.13 the wave may be treated as an Airy wave.

From equation 3.17 the maximum horizontal and vertical orbital velocities are

$$\frac{\pi \times 0.5 \cosh 2\pi \times 10/121}{10 \sinh 2\pi \times 20/121} \text{ and } \frac{\pi \times 0.5 \sinh 2\pi \times 10/121}{10 \sinh 2\pi \times 20/121}$$

respectively; that is

$$\frac{\pi}{20}\frac{\cosh 0.52}{\sinh 1.04} \quad \text{and} \quad \frac{\pi}{20}\frac{\sinh 0.52}{\sinh 1.04}$$

thus

$$\frac{\pi}{20}\frac{1.14}{1.24} \quad \text{and} \quad \frac{\pi}{20}\frac{0.54}{1.24}$$

giving

0.144 m/s and 0.068 m/s

Hence the horizontal and vertical orbital radii, since each may be considered separately as a sinusoidal motion, are 0.144 x $5/\pi$ and 0.068 x $5/\pi$ = 0.23 m and 0.11 m respectively.

Example 3.2

What is the particle motion along the bed for a 15 s wave, 3 m high in 10 m depth of water?

By equation 3.15

$$L_0 = 1.56 \times 15^2 = 350\,\text{m} \quad \text{and} \quad h/L_0 = 0.029$$

$h/gT^2 = 0.0045$, $H/gT^2 = 0.0014$ and hence the wave may, by figure 3.13 be treated as a Boussinesq solitary wave. The forward motion on the sea bed beneath the crest, neglecting any return flow of water, is given by section 3.2.4

$$a \left(\frac{g}{h}\right)^{1/2} = \frac{3(9.81)^{1/2}}{10^{1/2}} = 3\,\text{m/s}$$

The return flow of water between the crests is given by equations 3.57 and 3.59 as

$$4h^2 \left(\frac{a}{3h}\right)^{1/2} \Big/ hT_{\text{sol}} = \frac{40\,(1/10)^{1/2}}{15} = 0.85\,\text{m/s}$$

Example 3.3

What will the probable maximum and significant wave heights be for: (a) 15 m/s

*wind blowing for 6 h over a fetch of 35 km? (b) 20 m/s wind blowing for 2 h
over a fetch of 95 km?*

(a) On figure 3.14, a line on the 15 m/s ordinate encounters 35 km before
intersecting the 6 h line. Thus the sea is fully developed after about 2.5 h with
1.5 m (H_s) and 5.5 s (T_p). For a storm lasting 6 h the average number of incident
waves would be $(6 \times 60 \times 60)/5.5 = 3927$. Using equations 3.65 *et seq.*, $H_{max} =$
$(0.5 \ln 3927)^{1/2} H_s = 2.07 H_s = 3.1$ m.

(b) On figure 3.14, a line on the 20 m/s ordinate intersects the 2 h line before
encountering 95 km, and, for such a fetch, the sea would only be fully developed
after about 4 h. For the period of 2 h, $H_s \approx 2.5$ m and $T_p \approx 6$ s. The average
number of incident waves would be $(2 \times 60 \times 60)/6 = 1200$ so that $H_{max} =$
$(0.5 \ln 1200)^{1/2} H_s = 1.88 H_s = 4.7$ m.

Example 3.4

*A deep water wave of height 2 m and period 15 s is refracted so that the distance
between orthogonals is reduced to 50% where the depth of water is 10 m. What
will be the height of the wave here, assuming no energy losses?*

We have $L_0 = 1.56 \times 15^2 = 350$ m by equation 3.13. If we assume that the
wave is an Airy wave, then figure 3.23 indicates an increase in wave height in
10 m depth, assuming no refraction, of 15% for $h/L_0 = 0.029$. From equation
3.80 the wave height coefficient $= 1.15 \times (2)^{1/2} = 1.62$.

Thus the wave height, in 10 m of water, is 1.62 times its height in deep water
if the wave can be considered as an Airy wave. But, $h/gT^2 = 0.0045$ and
$H/gT^2 = 0.0014$, so that from figure 3.13 Boussinesq solitary wave theory
should be used. If $H_0 = 2$ m, equation 3.99 gives the height of the solitary wave
in 10 m as approximately

$$\frac{2^{4/3} \times (350 \times 2)^{2/3}}{8.5 \times 10} = \frac{2.5}{85} \times 78 = 2.3 \text{ m}$$

Example 3.5

*A train of 8 s 4 m high waves strikes a long breakwater at 45°. What will be the
approximate height of wave at a point 100 m behind a gap in the breakwater
40 m wide in 15 m depth of water?*

From figure 3.2, since $L_0 = 1.56 \times 8^2 = 100$ m and $h/L_0 = 0.15$ $h/L \approx 0.17$
and $L \approx 88$ m hence $b < L$ (see section 3.5) and, because of the angle of
incidence of the wave, the effective width of opening $= 40 \times \cos 45 = 28$ m.
Thus the wave height 100 m behind the opening $\approx 4(28/\pi 100)^{1/2} = 1.2$ m.

Example 3.6

An 8 s period wave in 8 m of water approaches a dredged channel 15 m deep at an angle of 40° between the wave front and the channel edge. What will be the refractive effect of the channel? At what angle of approach would the wave be reflected off the side of the channel?

L_0 = 100 m from equation 3.20

From equation 3.11 and figure 3.2

Wave speed in 8 m depths is 8.11 m/s

Wave speed in 15 m depths is 10.22 m/s

From equation 3.43 the refracted angle is

$$\sin^{-1}\left(\frac{\sin 40 \times 10.22}{8.11}\right) = 54.1°$$

Hence the wave front is turned by 14.1°. The critical angle of approach is

$$\sin^{-1}\left(\frac{8.11}{10.22}\right) = 52.5°$$

that is any wave approaching at an angle between the wave front and the line of the channel greater than this will be reflected.

Example 3.7

A 3 m breaking wave, with period 11 s approaches a beach, slope 1:75, at an angle of 5° to the beach. Calculate the longshore current velocity profile assuming that the friction factor may be taken as 0.003 and the mixing parameter N as 0.012.

Firstly find the breaking point. Using equations 3.101 to 3.104, a = 9.79, b = 0.881 so that $\gamma = H_b/h_b$ = 0.86 and h_b = 3.48 at a distance of 261 m from the shoreline.

From equation 3.115 the velocity at the breaker line with no mixing would be

$$v_0 = \frac{5 \times \pi \times 0.86}{16 \times 0.003}(9.81 \times 3.48)^{1/2} \times \frac{1}{75} \times \sin 5 = 1.9\,\text{m/s}$$

Equations 3.119 to 3.124 give

$$P = \frac{\pi \times 0.012}{0.86 \times 75 \times 0.003} = 0.195$$

$$P_1 = -\frac{3}{4} + \left(\frac{9}{16} + \frac{1}{0.195}\right)^{1/2} = 1.636$$

$$P_2 = -\frac{3}{4} - \left(\frac{9}{16} + \frac{1}{0.195}\right)^{1/2} = -3.136$$

$$A = 1/(1 - 2.5 \times 0.195) = 1.95$$

$$B_1 = \left(\frac{-3.136 - 1}{1.636 + 3.136}\right) \times 1.95 = -1.69$$

$$B_2 = \left(\frac{1.636 - 1}{1.636 + 3.136}\right) \times 1.95 = 0.26$$

From equation 3.118 the velocity profile may be tabulated as follows:

X	Distance from shoreline (m)	v/v_0	Longshore current, v (m/s)
0.1	26.1	0.156	0.30
0.2	52.2	0.268	0.51
0.3	78.3	0.349	0.66
0.4	104.4	0.402	0.76
0.5	130.5	0.431	0.82
0.6	156.6	0.437	0.83
0.7	182.7	0.422	0.80
0.8	208.8	0.387	0.74
0.9	234.9	0.332	0.63
1.0	261.0	0.260	0.49
1.1	287.1	0.193	0.37
1.2	313.2	0.147	0.28
1.3	339.3	0.114	0.22
1.4	365.4	0.091	0.17
1.5	391.5	0.073	0.14

Reference

1. G.B. Airy, Tides and waves, *Encyc. Metrop.*, Article 192 (1845)
2. H. Lamb, *Hydrodynamics,* 6th edn, (Cambridge University Press, 1945)
3. Lord Rayleigh, On progressive waves, *Proc. Lond. math. Soc.*, 9 (1877)
4. G.G. Stokes, On the theory of oscillatory waves, *Camb. Trans.*, 8 (1847)
5. R.G. Dean, Stream function representation of nonlinear ocean waves, *J. geophys. Res.*, **70**, No. 18 (1965)
6. J. Boussinesq, Théorie des ondes et de remous qui se propagent le long d'un canal rectangulaire horizontal, en communiquant au liquide contenu dans ce canal des vitesses sensiblement pareilles de la surface au fond, *J. Math. pures Appl.*, ser 2, **17** (1872) 55-108
7. J. McCowan, On the solitary wave, *Phil. Mag.*, **32** (1892) 45-58
8. R.L. Weigel and K.E. Beebe, The design wave in shallow water, *J. Waterways Div. Am. Soc. civ. Engrs*, **82**, WW1 (1956)

9. W.H. Munk, The solitary wave theory and its application to surf problems, ocean surface waves, *Ann. N. Y. Acad. Sci.,* **51** (1949) 376–423

10. R.A. Bagnold, Sand movement by waves: some small-scale experiments with sand at very low density, *J. Instn civ. Engrs,* **27** (1947) 447–69

11. D.J. Korteweg and G. de Vries, On the change of form of long waves advancing in a rectangular canal, and on a new type of long stationary waves, Phil. Mag. **39** (1895) 422–43

12. R.L. Wiegel, *Oceanographical Engineering* (Prentice-Hall, Englewood Cliffs, N.J., 1964)

13. *Shore Protection Manual* (U.S. Army C.E.R.C., 1975)

14. B. Le Méhauté, An introduction to hydrodynamics and water waves, *Water Wave Theories,* vol. II, TR ERL 118-POL-3-2 (U.S. Dept. of Commerce, ESSA, Washington, D.C., 1969)

15. D.H. Swart and C.C. Loubser, Vocoidal theory for all non-breaking waves, *Proceeding of the 16th Coastal Engineering Conference, Hamburg, 1978,* vol. I, pp. 467–86

16. B. Kinsman, *Wind Waves,* (Prentice-Hall, Englewood Cliffs, N.J., 1965)

17. C.L. Bretschneider, Field investigation of wave energy loss of shallow water ocean waves (U.S. Army Corps of Engineers, Beach Erosion Board) Tech. Memo No. 46 (1954)

18. F.E. Snodgrass, Propagation of ocean swell across the Pacific, *Phil. Trans. R. Soc., A* **1103** (1966) 431–97

19. C.L. Bretschneider, Wave generation by wind, deep and shallow water, in *Estuary and Coastline Hydrodynamics,* ed. A.T. Ippen (McGraw-Hill, New York, 1966) pp. 133–96

20. C.L. Bretschneider and R.O. Reid, Changes in wave height due to bottom friction, percolation and refraction (U.S. Army Corps of Engineers, Beach Erosion Board) Tech. Memo No. 45 (1954)

21. C.L. Bretschneider, The generation and decay of wind waves in deep water, *Trans. Am. geophys. Un.,* **33** (1952) 381–9

22. G. Neumann, On ocean wave spectra and a new method of forecasting wind-generated sea (U.S. Army Corps of Engineers, Beach Erosion Board) Tech. Memo No. 43 (1953)

23. M. Darbyshire and L. Draper, Forecasting wind-generated sea waves, *Engineering,* (1963) 482–4

24. R. Frost, The relationship between Beaufort force wind speed and wave height, *Met. Off. Sci. Paper No. 25* (H.M.S.O., 1966)

25. C.L. Bretschneider, Hurricane design wave practice, *J. Waterways Harbours Div. Am. Soc. civ. Engrs.* **83**, WW2 (1957)

26. T. Saville, Jr., The effect of fetch width on wave generation (U.S. Army Corps of Engineers, Beach Erosion Board) Tech. Memo No. 70 (1954)

27. A. Savina and C. Fons, Analyse et prevision de l'état de la mer, *Houille blanche* (1966) 331–6

28. L. Draper, Derivation of a 'design wave' from instrumental records of sea waves, *Proc. Instn civ. Engrs,* **26** (1963) 291–304

29. M.J. Tucker, Analysis of records of sea waves, *Proc. Instn civ. Engrs.,* **26** (1963) 305–16

30. L. Draper, The analysis and presentation of wave data – a plea for uniformity, *Proceeding of the 10th Coastal Engineering Conference, Tokyo, 1966*

31. L. Draper, Revisions in wave data presentation, *Proceedings of the 15th Coastal Engineering Conference, Hawaii, 1976,* vol. I, pp. 3–9

32. D.J. Cronin, P.S. Godfrey, P.M. Hook and T.A. Wyatt, Spectral fatigue analysis for offshore structures, in *Numerical Methods in Offshore Engineering* (Wiley, Chichester, 1978) ch.9

33. L. Draper and J.S. Driver, Winter waves in the northern North Sea at 57° 30'N, 3° 00'E, recorded by M.V. Famita, National Institute of Oceanography Report A48 (1971)

34. M. de St. Q. Isaacson, Second approximation to gravity wave attenuation, *Proc. Am. Soc. civ. Engrs.*, **103**, WW1 (1977)

35. M. de St. Q. Isaacson, The viscous damping of cnoidal waves, *J. Fluid Mech.*, **75** (1976) 449-57

36. I.G. Jonsson and N.A. Carlsen, Experimental and theoretical investigations in an oscillatory turbulent boundary layer, *J. Hydraul. Res.*, **14** (1976) 45-60

37. R.P. Savage, Laboratory study of wave energy losses by bottom friction and percolation (U.S. Army Corps of Engineers, Beach Erosion Board) Tech. Memo No. 31 (1953)

38. R.A. Bagnold, Motion of waves in shallow water. Interaction between waves and sand bottoms, *Proc. R. Soc. A* **187** (1946) 1-15

39. D.H. Swart, Offshore sediment transport and equilibrium beach profiles, Delft Hydraulics Laboratory Publication No. 131 (1974)

40. I.G. Jonsson, The wave friction factor revisited, Technical University of Denmark, Institute of Hydrographics and Hydraulic Engineering Progress Report 37 (1975)

41. K. Kajiura, A model of the bottom boundary layer in water waves, *Bull. Earth Res. Inst. Tokyo Univ.* **46** (1938)

42. J.W. Kamphuis, Friction factor under oscillatory waves, *Proc. Am. Soc. civ. Engrs,* **101**, WW2 (1975)

43. B. Johns, The form of the velocity profile in a turbulent shear wave boundary layer, *J. Geophys. Res.*, **80** (1975)

44. J.A. Battjes, Refraction of water waves, *Proc. Am. Soc. civ. Engrs,* **94**, WW4 (1968)

45. W.H. Munk and R.S. Arthur, Wave intensity along a refracted ray, U.S. National Bureau of Standards Circular 521: Gravity Waves (1952)

46. Y.Y. Chao, The theory of wave refraction in shoaling water including the effects of caustics and the spherical earth, New York University Department of Meteorology and Oceanology, School of Engineering and Science, GSL Report TR-70-7 (1970)

47. J.R. Hardy, Some grid and projection problems in the numerical calculation of wave refraction, *J. geophys. Res.*, **73** (1968) 7083-7

48. O. Skovgaard, I.G. Jonsson and J.A. Bertelsen, Computations of wave heights due to refraction and friction, *Proc. Am. Soc. civ. Engrs,* **101**, WW1 (1975) 15-32; closure **102**, WW1 (1976) 100-5

49. Y.Y. Chao, An asymptotic evaluation of the gravity wave field near a smooth caustic, *J. geophys. Res.*, **79** (1971)

50. W.J. Pierson Wave behaviour near caustics in models and in nature in *Waves on Beaches*, ed. R.E. Meyer (Academic Press, New York, 1972) ch.4

51. C.L. Abernethy and G. Gilbert, Refraction of wave spectra, Hydrology Research Station Report No. INT 117 (1975)

52. O. Skovgaard and J.A. Bertelsen, Refraction computations for practical applications, *Proceedings of the ASCE International Symposium on Ocean Wave Measurement and Analysis, New Orleans, 1974,* pp. 761-73

53. L.R. Poole, Comparison of techniques for approximating ocean bottom

topography in a wave refraction computer model, NASA Report No. NASA TN D-8050 (1975)

54. O. Skovgaard and M.H. Petersen, Refraction of cnoidal waves, *Coastal Engng,* **1** (1977) 43-61

55. T. Karlsson, Refraction of continuous ocean wave spectra, *Proc. Am. Soc. civ. Engrs,* **95**, WW4 (1969) 437-48

56. M.S. Longuet-Higgins, On the transformation of a continuous spectrum by refraction, *Proc. Camb. phil. Soc.,* **53** (1957) 226-9

57. W.A. Birkemeier and R.A. Dalrymple, Nearshore wave circulation induced by wind and waves, *2nd Annual Symposium of ASCE Waterways, Harbors and Coastal Engineering Division, San Francisco, 1975,* vol. II, pp. 1062-81

58. O.C. Zienkiewicz and P. Bettess, Diffraction and refraction of surface waves using finite and infinite elements, University College of Wales, Swansea, Report C/R/274/76 (1976)

59. R.S. Arthur, Refraction of shallow water waves: The combined effect of currents and underwater topography, *Trans. Am. geophys. Un.,* **31** (1950)

60. O. Skovgaard, and I.G. Jonsson, Current depth refraction using finite elements, *Proceedings of the 15th Coastal Engineering Conference, Hawaii, 1976,* vol. I, pp. 721-37

61. J.N. Hunt, Gravity waves in flowing water, *Proc. R. Soc. A,* **231** (1955) 496-504

62. M.S. Longuet-Higgins and R.W. Stewart, The changes in amplitude of short gravity waves on steady non-uniform currents, *J. Fluid Mech.,* **10** (1961) 565-83

63. I.G. Jonsson, O. Skovgaard and J.D. Wang, Interaction between waves and currents, *Proceedings of the 12th Coastal Engineering Conference, Washington, 1970,* pp. 489-508

64. C.J. Galvin, Jr., Breaker type classification on three laboratory beaches, *J. geophys. Res.,* **73** (1968) 3651-9

65. W.G. Penney and A.T. Price, Diffraction of sea waves by breakwaters and the shelter afforded by breakwaters, *Phil. Trans. R. Soc. A,* **244** (1952) 236-53

66. J.W. Johnson, Generalised wave diffraction diagrams, *Proceedings of the 2nd Coastal Engineering Conference, 1952,* Council for Wave Research 6-23

67. R.L. Weigel, Diffraction of waves by semi-infinite breakwater, *Proc. Am. Soc. civ. Engrs,* **88**, HY1 (1962) 27-44

68. J.C.W. Berkhoff, Computation of combined refraction and diffraction, *Proceedings of the 13th Coastal Engineering Conference, Vancouver, 1972,* ch. 24

69. R. Miche, Mouvements ondulataires des mers en profondeur constante ou décroissant, *Annl Ponts Chauss. (1944)* 25-78, 131-64, 270-92, 367-406

70. M.S. Longuet-Higgins, Longshore currents generated by obliquely incident sea waves, *J. Geophys. Res.,* **75** (1970) 6778-89, 6790-801

71. M.S. Longuet-Higgins and R.W. Stewart, Radiation stress in water waves; a physical discussion with applications, *Deep Sea Res.,* **11** (1964) 529-62

72. I.D. James, A non-linear theory of longshore currents, *Estuar. Coastal Mar, Sci.,* **2** (1974) 235-49

73. D.L. Inman, R.J. Tait and C.E. Nordstrom, Mixing in the surf zone, *J. Geophys. Res.,* **76** (1971) 3493-514

74. D.H. Swart and C.A. Fleming, Longshore water and sediment movement, *Proceedings of the 17th Coastal Engineering Conference, Sydney, 1980*

75. A.J. Bowen, D.L. Inman and V.P. Simmons, Wave set-down and wave set-up, *J. geophys. Res.*, **73** (1968) 2569–77

76. A.J. Bowen, The generation of longshore currents on a plane beach, *J. mar. Res.*, 27,2 (1969) 206–15

77. I.G. Jonsson, O. Skovgaard and T.S. Jacobsen, Computation of longshore currents, *Proceedings of the 14th Coastal Engineering Conference, Copenhagen, 1974*, pp. 699–714

78. E.B. Thornton, Variation of longshore current across the surf zone, *Proceedings of the 12th Coastal Engineering Conference, Washington, 1970*, ch. 18

79. M.R. Gourlay, Non-uniform alongshore currents, *Proceedings of the 15th Coastal Engineering Conference, Hawaii, 1976*, pp. 701–20

80. M.J. Tucker, Surf beat: sea waves of 1 to 5 minutes period, *Proc. R. Soc. A*, **202** (1950) 565–73

81. B.W. Wilson, Origin and effects of long period waves in ports, Permanent International Association of Navigation Congresses, 19th Congress (London) Sect. 2, Comm. 1 (1957) pp. 13–61

82. B.W. Wilson, The threshold of surge damage for moored ships, *Proc. Instn civ. Engrs*, **38** (1967) 107–34

83. R.M. Sorensen, Investigation of ship-generated waves, *Proc. Am. Soc. civ. Engrs*, **93**, WW1 (1967) 85–99

4

Coastal Sediment Transport

4.1 Limits for Littoral Drift

The fundamentals of sediment transport have been covered in chapter 1. This chapter considers the movement of sediment in the marine environment and methods of attempting to describe and hence predict its movement.

The movement of material around inshore coastal areas is of fundamental interest to engineers wishing to build any type of structure on or close to the shoreline as well as for the planning of dredging and spoil disposal. Sediment movement is responsible for a large number of morphological features which occur during the process of coastal accretion and erosion. It is a particularly difficult process to measure.

It is often possible to predict qualitatively the morphological changes that can be expected to occur under different physical conditions. It is considerably more difficult to make quantitative predictions of sediment deposition and erosion. The rate and direction of sediment movement in the coastal environment represent the resultant of a multitude of powerful factors.

The net movement of sediment in a coastal zone is generally classified as (a) longshore movement, being movement under the action of waves and currents parallel to the shoreline, and (b) onshore – offshore movement, being sediment transport normal to the coastline.

For waves approaching the shore, the following zones may be considered, excluding special cases resulting from wave growth and decay

(1) deep water zone
(2) intermediate zone, where depth of water begins to influence the characteristics of the wave
(3) shallow water zone
(4) breaker zone
(5) surf zone – the region inside the breaker line
(6) swash zone – the region in which there is an uprush and backwash as a result of the breaking wave.

The location of each zone is related to the wave characteristics, principally their length and height; each zone merges into the next without a distinct boundary until the wave reaches the breaker zone.

In attempting to demarcate the seaward limit of littoral drift, the problem is much the same as for wave limits. The complications of variation in particle size and tidal current also intervene as these affect the depth of water in which littoral processes occur. Littoral drift is liable to be experienced where the energy of the sea, predominantly wave energy, is spent at the sea bed at a rate sufficient to cause large-scale movement of loose bed material; frequently this is confined to the breaker, surf and swash zones.

With the exception of bulk sediment transport models (section 4.7.1) predictive models for oscillatory flow generally fall into two categories: instantaneous models, for which the time scale for the calculation is very much less than a wave period ($t \ll T$) and quasi-steady models for which the calculation time scale is of the same order or greater than the wave period. Although attempts have been made at models based on the former approach, [1] detailed experimental results on sediment suspension under waves are so limited that they cannot easily be verified. Furthermore the present status of the theory of sediment and fluid interaction is probably inadequate to tackle the problem in such detail. The second approach is far more acceptable from the engineering point of view, both with respect to field measurements and to theoretical development. As for unidirectional flow the sediment may be considered to be transported as bed load and suspended load as shown in figure 4.1

4.2 Suspended Load

As described in section 1.3.6 one-dimensional suspended load distribution may

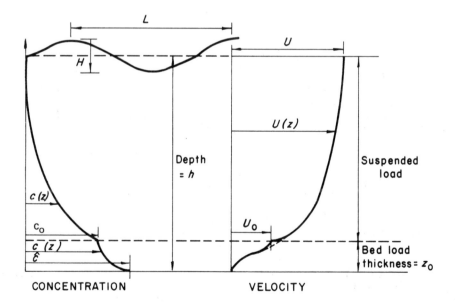

Figure 4.1 *Definition of terms for velocity and concentration distributions*

be reduced to

$$\epsilon_s \frac{dc}{dz'} + cw_s = 0 \tag{4.1}$$

which is identical to the dispersion equation for unidirectional flow, when the volume of the fluid displaced by the sediment is neglected. It is also assumed that the fall velocity of the particles is uniform and unaffected by fluid acceleration. To solve equation 4.1 it is necessary to specify the vertical distribution of eddy viscosity or dispersion coefficient ϵ_s. Note that in other sections of this work except chapter 1 z is measured upwards from the sea surface (that is, $z' = z + h$).

As sediment suspension occurs at levels for which the shear stresses due to the oscillating motion are extremely difficult to measure, it is more convenient to find a sediment exchange coefficient which is not based on shear stress distribution. Due to the relatively low intensity of turbulence outside the breaker zone, velocity fluctuations are comparable to the settling velocity of the sediment.[2] Under these conditions it has been shown by Einstein and Chien [3] that the momentum exchange coefficient no longer gives a good estimate of the sediment exchange coefficient.

Various forms of eddy viscosity distribution have been investigated including the case of zero viscosity for which the sediment is assumed to be supported entirely by wave orbital motion. Either laboratory measurements for distribution of turbulent velocity fluctuations or concentration distributions measured in the field must be used to determine the sediment diffusion coefficient.

It may be assumed [4, 5] that

$$\frac{\epsilon_s}{\epsilon_0} = \left(\frac{z'}{z_0}\right)^\lambda \tag{4.2}$$

where the sediment diffusion coefficient is a function of depth related to a value ϵ_0 at reference level z_0 and ξ is a positive non-dimensional constant. Equation 4.2 cannot satisfy the boundary conditions at the free surface, but as sediment concentration under waves attenuates rapidly away from the bed this inconsistency may be considered admissible.

The solution to equations 4.1 and 4.2 is

$$\ln\left(\frac{c}{c_0}\right) = \frac{w_s z_0}{\epsilon_0(1-\lambda)}\left[1 - \left(\frac{z'}{z_0}\right)^{1-\lambda}\right] \tag{4.3}$$

when $\lambda \neq 1$ and

$$\frac{c}{c_0} = \left(\frac{z'}{z_0}\right)\exp\left(-\frac{wz_0}{\epsilon_0}\right) \tag{4.4}$$

when $\lambda = 1$ and c_0 is a reference concentration at the same reference level z_0.

The simplest distribution results from constant diffusivity over depth ($\lambda = 0$) when

$$c = c_0 \frac{-w_s}{\epsilon_0}(z' - z_0) \tag{4.5}$$

One of the expressions for the diffusion coefficient based on equation 4.5 is

$$\epsilon_0 = K\frac{HL}{T} \tag{4.6}$$

where K, a dimensionless coefficient, can be shown to be of the order 2.8×10^{-5}.

Alternatively Bhattacharya [7] found that his data conformed well with equation 4.4 and expressed the reference diffusion coefficient as

$$\epsilon_0 = \epsilon'\frac{hz_0}{T} \tag{4.7}$$

where ϵ' is a normalised diffusion coefficient assumed to be a function of h/H.

It can be seen from equations 4.6 and 4.7 that the expressions relate purely to wave action, assuming the current to make negligible contribution to holding material in suspension. This is frequently the case in coastal waters and many sediment models are based on the concept that the wave action purely stirs up the sediment into suspension, whilst any transport must be due to a super-imposed current.

A slightly different approach has been proposed by Bijker [8] who based a sediment transport model on unidirectional flow methods for which only the shear stress was modified to allow for the combination of waves and currents. Using the Einstein–Rouse formulation for uniform flow

$$\epsilon_s = \kappa v_{*wc}\frac{z'}{h}(h - z') \tag{4.8}$$

and from equation 4.1

$$\frac{c}{c_0} = \left(\frac{h - z'}{z'}\frac{z_0}{h - z_0}\right)^{\frac{w}{\kappa v_{*wc}}} \tag{4.9}$$

where v_{*wc} is the shear velocity due to waves and currents defined as

$$\frac{v_{*wc}}{v_{*c}} = \left[1 + \tfrac{1}{2}\left(\xi\frac{\hat{u}_0}{v}\right)^2\right]^{1/2} \tag{4.10}$$

Bijker found that

$$\xi = \frac{P\kappa Ch}{g^{1/2}} \tag{4.11}$$

where

$$Ch = 18 \log\left(\frac{12h}{k_N}\right) \qquad (4.12)$$

is the Chezy roughness coefficient and P is a constant with an experimental value of 0.45.

Based on similar ideas and a concentration distribution of the form given by equation 4.4, an empirical expression for the exponent has been proposed [5] as

$$\frac{w_s z_0}{\epsilon_0} = 1.05\left(\frac{w_s}{\kappa v_{*\,wc}}\right)^{0.96}\left(\frac{k_N}{h}\right)^{0.013\left(\frac{w_s}{\kappa v_{*\,wc}}\right)} \qquad (4.13)$$

Equations 4.12 and 4.13 require the definition of a roughness length. Bijker chose a value for k_N as one-half of the ripple height and assumed that the reference level is the same. However, much greater roughness lengths have been found elsewhere. In the predictive sense this shifts the problem to one of determining ripple dimensions which is discussed in chapter 5.

The preceding discussion concerns the determination of suspended sediment concentration profiles. In order to arrive at a sediment transport rate a velocity field must be applied. Excluding phenomena such as mass transport under (non-linear) waves, this can usually be confined to the superimposed current system. Bijker and others have retained the uniform flow analogy and used the classical logarithmic velocity profile described by

$$v = \hat{v} - \frac{v_*}{\kappa}\ln\frac{z'}{h} \qquad (4.14)$$

where $\hat{v}$ is the maximum velocity at the free surface.

Alternatively a seventh-power distribution has been used [10] for which

$$v = \hat{v}\left(\frac{z'}{h}\right)^{1/7} = \frac{8}{7}\,\bar{v}\left(\frac{z'}{h}\right)^{1/7} \qquad (4.15)$$

In either case the velocity field must be known and the suspended sediment transport rate is

$$q_s = \int_{z_0}^{h} cv\, dz' \qquad (4.16)$$

In order quantitatively to determine a suspended sediment concentration profile it is also necessary to define a reference concentration. This is usually done by considering a bed load model which is applicable to sediment motion next to the stationary boundary.

4.3 Bed Load

Following the principles of tractive force methods introduced in section 1.3.7, and assuming that the applied shear stress in excess of the threshold shear stress $\bar{\tau}_c$ must be dispersed within the bed load layer then

$$\bar{\tau}_d = \bar{\tau}_{wc} - \bar{\tau}_c \qquad (4.17)$$

where the overbars refer to time-averaged quantities over a wave period. $\bar{\tau}_{wc}$, the mean shear stress due to the combined effect of waves and currents, needs care in evaluation. An expression for the bottom shear stress normal to the direction of wave propagation is given by

$$\bar{\tau}_n = \frac{2}{\pi} \rho f_c \hat{u}_0 \nu_n \qquad (4.18)$$

where ν_n is component of current velocity normal to the wave direction, f_c is a friction factor analogous to but not necessarily equal to the wave friction factor f_w. For the condition $u_0 \gg \nu$ the mean shear stress parallel to the direction of wave propagation is [11]

$$\bar{\tau}_p = \frac{4}{\pi} \rho f_c \hat{u}_0 \nu_p \qquad (4.19)$$

where ν_p is the component of current velocity parallel to the wave direction. Clearly in equations 4.18 and 4.19 when the current velocity is zero the net shear is zero. These expressions are therefore inappropriate, because sediment will still be stirred into motion when there is no current. This apparent inconsistency arises because the time mean of the vector sum of the wave orbital velocity and the current velocity does not reflect the scalar effect of shear stress acting on the bed.

If it be assumed that the orbital motion of waves and the motion of a current may be superimposed in the bottom boundary layer a solution can be determined [12] by (see equation 4.10)

$$\frac{\bar{\tau}_{wc}}{\tau_c} = 1 + 0.5 \left(\xi \frac{\hat{u}_0}{\nu} \right)^2 \qquad (4.20)$$

where τ_c is the shear stress due to the current above and ξ is defined by equations 4.11 and 4.12. The shear stress due to the current alone is given by

$$\tau_c = \rho g \frac{\nu^2}{Ch^2} \qquad (4.21)$$

The value of P in equation 4.11 may be considered as a variable dependent on the flow regime at the bed.[13] Then an alternative coefficient may be derived

$$P_j = \left(\frac{f_w}{2\kappa^2}\right)^{1/2} \tag{4.22}$$

and correspondingly

$$\xi_j = Ch \left(\frac{f_w}{2g}\right)^{1/2} \tag{4.23}$$

Then, substituting equations 4.21 and 4.23 into 4.20 results in

$$\overline{\tau}_{wc} = \rho \frac{gv^2}{Ch^2} + 0.25 \, \rho f_w \hat{u}_0^{\;2} \tag{4.24}$$

in which the limiting case of zero current velocity gives

$$\overline{\tau}_w = 0.25 \rho f_w \hat{u}_0^{\;2} \tag{4.25}$$

While equation 4.24 has been derived by accounting for the difference in direction between the wave and current, no information is given about the mean direction of the resultant shear. It is often assumed that the mean sediment transport is in the same direction as the prevailing current. If the expressions given in equations 4.18 and 4.19 are considered, the mean resultant shear can only be in the same direction as the current when the current is normal or parallel to the direction of wave motion. Furthermore the direction and magnitude of the bed gradient will also influence the resultant direction of the bed load.

Bed load models used in conjunction with suspended load models rely on some definition of a reference concentration which is derived from field or experimental data.

An exponential concentration distribution in the bed load layer given by

$$c = \hat{c} \left(\frac{c_0}{\hat{c}}\right) z/z_0 \tag{4.26}$$

may be used so that, using equation 1.40, the bed load thickness assumed to be the transition level is given by [10]

$$z_0 = \frac{\overline{\tau}_d \, ln(c_0/\hat{c})}{g(\rho_s - \rho)(c_0 - c)(\tan \alpha - \beta)\cos \beta} \tag{4.27}$$

where α is friction angle (see section 1.3.6) and where β is the bed slope in the direction of the prevailing current. Values of c_0 when correlated to a dimensionless parameter $\tau_w/[g(\rho_s-\rho) Tw_s]$ are shown in figure 4.2, for one particle size.

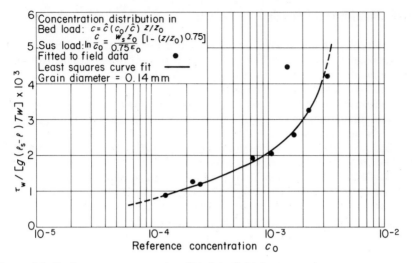

Figure 4.2 *Reference concentration fitted to field data*

As a complementary bed load model to equations 4.8 and 4.9, Bijker modified the Frijlink formula to include a stirring parameter so that the ratio of the bed load to the fluid flux per unit width of flow may be written as

$$\bar{c}_b = b(1 - p) \frac{(g D_{50}^2)^{1/2}}{hCh} \exp\left(-0.27 \frac{\Delta_s D_{50} g}{\mu v_{*wc}^2}\right) \tag{4.28}$$

where p is the porosity of sediment, b is a constant, $\Delta_s = (\rho_s - \rho)/\rho$ and μ is a ripple factor which represents that part of the bed shear that is not used to overcome bed resistance and

$$\mu = \left(\frac{Ch}{C_{D_{90}}}\right)^{3/2} \tag{4.29}$$

where

$$C_{D_{90}} = 18 \log\left(\frac{12h}{D_{90}}\right) \tag{4.30}$$

The value of b in equation 4.28 may be taken as $5\mu^{1/2}$. Assuming that the thickness of the bed load, z_0, is equal to the roughness length and that concentration of sediment in the bed load is sensibly constant in the vertical, the reference concentration may be implied as

$$c_0 = \frac{\bar{c}_b \bar{v} h}{\bar{v}_b k_N} \tag{4.31}$$

where $\bar{v}_b$ is a mean velocity of material in the bed load determined from the assumed velocity distribution.

4.4   Roughness Length

The problem of determining how much applied shear stress is available to transport sediment and how much is used to overcome bed form resistance is linked to the roughness length of the bed, a parameter that frequently appears in both bed load and suspended load calculations.

Roughness length is essentially an empirical parameter associated with the physical dimensions of a boundary expressed either as the grain size or as ripple size. It is basically used to overcome the lack of detailed knowledge of events in the boundary layer and may be used as an empirical parameter to be determined by best fit of formulae to experimental data.[14]

The Delft Hydraulics Laboratory [5] suggest an empirical framework for estimating both ripple dimensions and roughness length when data on ripple geometry and corresponding roughness lengths are plotted as the ratio of the roughness length to ripple height against bed form steepness. Based on very limited data the best correlation is given by

$$\frac{k_N}{\Delta_r} = 25 \left(\frac{\Delta_r}{\lambda_r} \right) \tag{4.32}$$

where Δ_r is the ripple height and λ_r the ripple wavelength so that the bed geometry must be known in order to estimate k_N.

The evaluation of ripple dimensions remains largely empirical (see chapter 5). Where waves are associated with currents, the waves dominate ripple formation where bottom orbital velocity is more than 10 times average current shear velocity; currents dominate when this ratio is less than 3. Many formulae have been proposed for bed form geometry [5, 15] but present knowledge is insufficiently advanced to apply any of these predictions generally, particularly in view of the fact that ripples vary in relation to depth of water and wave climate. A valid alternative approach is to treat the roughness length, or its counterpart of friction factor, as an empirical factor in optimisation of experimental or field data. It can thus be used as a further means of tuning a particular predictive model. As a general rule of thumb roughness lengths in the marine environment should be in the range $10 \, \text{mm} < k_N < 200 \, \text{mm}$.

4.5   Bed Forms and Effective Shear Stress

As discussed in section 1.3.8 it is normal practice in unidirectional flow calculations to consider the applied shear on the bed to be dispersed primarily by form drag on bed features and by the surface drag on the particles.

It has already been shown that the bed load model proposed by Bijker included a parameter μ to account for bed form resistance. Similar considerations will be described in section 4.6.

Under waves, ripple dimensions tend to be more orderly than in unidirectional flow; bed form resistance in a study area may not vary greatly for a limited range of wave conditions, even though ripple size varies with particle size and water depth which in turn vary across a beach profile.

While it is known that transport rates over rippled beds are substantially different to those over flat beds, the assumption that all of the applied shear is dispersed by the moving grains in the bed load layer gives a sensible variation in estimated conditions although it will clearly tend to overestimate shear stresses.

4.6 Prediction of Total Sediment Load

Total sediment transport load may be calculated by combining the bed load and suspended load models described in sections 4.1 and 4.2. Generally bed load and suspended load models from different origins should not be mixed unless the assumptions made are strictly similar. In particular the distinction between bed load and suspended load is not well defined observationally and the hypotheses made are quite subjective.

An alternative approach is to consider the total sediment load as a whole, disregarding any distinction between bed load and suspended load. The formulae for one total load sediment transport model may be summarised [16] as follows

$$F_{wc} = \frac{\bar{v} I_{wc}{}^{n}}{C_D{}^{1-n} Ch^n (\Delta_s D_{35})^{1/2}}$$ (4.33)

$$I_{wc} = \left[1 + \frac{1}{2} \left(\frac{\xi_j \hat{u}_0}{\bar{v}} \right)^2 \right]^{1/2}$$ (4.34)

where ξ_j is defined by equation 4.23 and

$$C_D = 18 \log \left(\frac{10h}{D_{35}} \right)$$ (4.35)

$$n = 1 - 0.2432 \ln (D_{gr})$$ (4.36)

with $0 \leqslant n \leqslant 1$ and D_{gr} is a dimensionless grain size parameter defined as

$$D_{gr} = \left(\frac{g \Delta_s}{v^2} \right)^{1/3} D_{35}$$ (4.37)

The total sediment transport is then given by

$$Q = \left(\frac{1}{1-p} \right) D_{35} \bar{v} \left(\frac{Ch}{g^{1/2}} \right)^n I_{wc}{}^{1-n} \frac{C}{A^m} (F_{wc} - A)^m$$ (4.38)

$$m = \frac{9.66}{D_{gr}} + 1.34$$ (4.39)

A is a beginning of movement criterion where

$$A = \frac{0.23}{D_{gr}^{1/2}} + 0.14 \tag{4.40}$$

$$C = \exp\left[\, 2.86 \ln (D_{gr}) - 0.4343 \,\left[\ln (D_{gr})\right]^2 - 8.128 \,\right] \tag{4.41}$$

All of the constants shown above are similar to those for uniform flow, but they may be modified to allow for the dependence of beginning of movement on wave orbital velocity.[17] Equation 4.40 applies when current velocities predominate $(u_0/v*_c \leqslant 3)$. If wave particle velocities predominate $(u_0/v*_c \geqslant 10)\, A$ becomes

$$A = 2.29 \left(\frac{f_w}{\Delta_s g}\right)^{1/2} \frac{T^{0.043}}{D_{50}^{0.12}} \tag{4.42}$$

A linear transition between the limiting values may be assumed.

A variable representative wave height can be considered. When used for a particular model sediment transport rates should then be representative of the complete wave spectrum. Assuming Rayleigh distributed wave heights (see section 3.3.6) and a principle of superposition, the representative wave height can vary between the median wave height and significant wave height with a tendency towards the latter at lower transport rates.[16]

Finally, an extremely straightforward expression to apply for approximate calculations of total sediment load may be derived from the oscillatory flow equivalent of Engelund and Hansen's uniform flow total sediment load predictor

$$Q = 0.05\bar{v} \,\frac{Ch v*_{wc}^4}{g^{5/2}\Delta_s^2 D_{50}} \tag{4.43}$$

This expression tends to overestimate sediment transport rates especially at low transport rates because of the lack of a threshold of movement criterion.

4.7   Longshore Drift

Longshore drift is a particular form of sediment movement in the coastal zone and is essentially confined to the surf zone region. Models of various degrees of complexity can be used for predictive purposes.

4.7.1   Total Energy Bulk Sediment Transport Models

The earliest predictive models of longshore drift were made using energy methods which assume that all of the available energy of waves approaching the shoreline can be related empirically to the bulk rate of longshore sediment movement. These methods are still being developed [18] and serve a useful purpose for preliminary calculations.

For waves approaching a shoreline at an angle α the wave energy flux per unit length of coastline per wave may be represented as $(EC_g) \cos \alpha$. Relating this quantity to the sand transport along the beach the immersed sand transport rate (I_1) may be written [19]

$$I_1 = K(EC_g)_b \sin \alpha_b \cos \alpha_b \tag{4.44}$$

where subscript b refers to wave breaking conditions. This is related to the volume transport rate Q_0 by

$$I_1 = (\rho_s - \rho)ga'Q_0 \tag{4.45}$$

where $a' = 1/(1+e)$ where e is the void ratio of the material (approximately 0.6 for most beach sands).

Many of the bulk longshore transport rate formulae are of the form of equation 4.44. Making a few shallow water and other approximations

$$I_1 = K \frac{\rho g}{16} H_{b_{rms}}{}^2 C \sin 2\alpha_b \tag{4.46}$$

Alternatively it is often necessary to use the offshore wave conditions due to lack of any other information. In this case $C_g \approx \frac{1}{2} C_0 = gT/4\pi$ and the wave refraction coefficient K_r is used to allow for inshore conditions so that

$$I_1 = K \frac{\rho g^2}{64\pi} T(H_0 K_r)^2_{rms} \sin 2\alpha_b \tag{4.47}$$

While equation 4.47 might be more convenient to use it is by no means correct. The wave refraction coefficient is applied to the offshore wave height but the shoaling and friction coefficients are not. Neglect of the latter will result in an overestimation of longshore drift, but neglect of the former could result in a large underestimation.

The above expressions are written for the root mean square wave height as the representative parameter. Significant wave height may be used to evaluate the energy flux factor, but it results in a level of energy that is twice that when the r.m.s. value is used. Whichever representative wave height is used is not important so long as the value of the coefficient is calibrated accordingly.

Using H_{rms} the dimensionless coefficient has been estimated to be 0.77.[20] However, equations 4.46 and 4.47 are more conveniently expressed as a volume transport rate via equation 4.45 when

$$Q_0 = K' \frac{\rho g}{16} (H_b)^2_{rms} C \sin 2\alpha_b \tag{4.48}$$

In this form K' is no longer dimensionless and its value is dependent on the units used and the units required for Q_0. For example given $K = 0.77$ and appropriate values for ρ_s, ρ and a', the value of K' would be 2.55×10^3 when the energy flux is evaluated in N/s and Q_0 is in m³/annum. The value would become 1.27×10^3 if the significant wave height were used in the calculation. Analysis of the available field data shows that K could range from 0.048 to 1.605. Part of this variability can be attributed to errors in wave measurement and sediment transport measurement, but the variation of K within individual data sets is relatively small.[21]

Using the coefficient in its dimensionless form allows the density and porosity to be varied via equation 4.45. A unified value for K' cannot do so and can only be applied to beach of quartz density sand. Lighter material will be more readily transported than dense material. The coefficients should also be a function of grain size of the bed material and available data indicate that if equation 4.48 is written as

$$Q_0 = K'' (H_0 K_r)^2_{rms} T \sin \alpha_b \cos \alpha_b \tag{4.49}$$

K'' should vary as [16]

$$K'' = 365 \times 10^4 \log \left(\frac{0.00146}{D_{50}} \right) \tag{4.50}$$

for 0.1×10^{-3} m $< D_{50} < 1.0 \times 10^{-3}$ m where Q_0 is given in m³/annum.

Relationships described in this section are not necessarily confined to sand transport -- they may be applied equally to shingle transport provided that due consideration is given to density properties and particle size characteristics. This will involve a re-evaluation of the coefficient of proportionality for the different threshold of movement criteria. It is important that the size of particle transported should be related to the size of material forming beach and bed within the surf zone: large particles will be transported more rapidly over a bed of finer particles.

Although these models give no information with respect to the distribution across the surf zone, their advantage is that it is not necessary to define the wave form or flow conditions inside the surf zone.

4.7.2 Local Sediment Transport Models

An alternative means of estimating longshore transport rates is to use models of the type described in section 4.6 coupled with a longshore current model. However, it is particularly difficult to fully describe both waves and currents in a confused state of the sea after waves have broken and some assumptions are commonly made when idealising surf zone conditions. These may be summarised as follows.

(1) *Wave Height*. It is often assumed that height to depth ratio of a wave at the breaker point remains a constant through the surf zone. This is a convenient assumption that may hold for purely spilling breakers, but there is no field or experimental data to support the supposition. A more plausible theory [22] for wave transformation in the surf zone uses more complicated expressions, which introduce further unknown parameters such as a friction coefficient, but give reasonable agreement to some experimental data.[23]

(2) *Wave Form*. It is often assumed that even after breaking a wave can be described by simple first-order theory, however inappropriate, in the absence of a satisfactory general theory. However, a promising line of advance treats the wave form inside the breaker line as a bore.

(3) *Beach Profile*. The application of most one-dimensional longshore current theories requires the assumption that the beach is straight and plane. Consequently it is necessary to idealise a natural beach to the closest equivalent plane. This is also true of course for bulk longshore drift models which use the beach slope in their formulation.

(4) *Water Flow*. Describing the flow of fluid in the surf zone region generally involves one of the longshore current theories using estimated coefficients for friction and for mixing. Refinements, such as wave set-up are not generally justified, considering the uncertainty that surrounds some of the other parameters.

Using one or more of the assumptions described above a general sediment transport model may be combined with a longshore current model to give estimates of longshore sediment transport rates. This requires considerably more 'tuning' than a bulk sediment transport model but is more realistic in terms of sediment transport distribution across the surf zone and response to general parameters. This type of model may also be modified and extended as the need to make such simplifying hypotheses as (1) to (4) above is overcome in models of the surf zone.

4.8 Beach Evolution Models

The next progression from calculating sediment transport rates at discrete points on a coastline is to investigate the effects when rates are dissimilar at adjacent points or in particular where some structure interferes with the natural process of longshore drift. For example, an impervious breakwater built on a coast which experiences longshore movement of sediment will probably destroy the local equilibrium conditions. In the simplest case where there is a predominant sediment movement in one direction accretion will take place on the updrift side and erosion at some point on the downdrift side, beyond the shelter of the obstruction.

By assuming that the coastline erodes or accretes in parallel slices Pelnard-Considère [24] wrote the continuity equation as

$$\frac{\partial Q_x}{\partial x} + h \frac{\partial y}{\partial t} = 0 \tag{4.51}$$

the derivation of which can be easily realised by referring to figure 4.3. The accompanying equation of motion will depend on the sediment transport model used. Analytical solutions can only be obtained for very simple models.

For example equation 4.48 may be reduced to give an equation of motion

$$Q_x = K'\left(\theta - \frac{\partial y}{\partial x}\right) \tag{4.52}$$

for an invariant wave height and small angles of approach ($\sin 2\,\alpha_b \approx 2\,\alpha_b$). θ is the angle of wave approach relative to the x-axis and dy/dx is the inclination of the shoreline (that is $\alpha_b = \theta_b - dy/dx$).

In the special case of a breakwater ($x = 0$) implanted on a previously straight coastline ($y = 0$) the boundary conditions are as follows

(1) At $t = 0, y = 0$

   $Q_x = Q_0$ for all x

(2) At $t > 0$ and $x = 0, Q_x = 0$

   $\dfrac{dy}{dx} = \theta$

(3) At $t > 0$ and $x = -\infty, Q_x = Q_0$

   $\dfrac{dy}{dx} = 0$

   $y = 0$

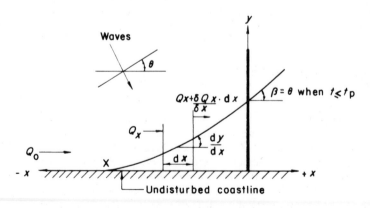

Figure 4.3 *Reference diagram for beach evolution models*

where Q_0 is the transport rate in the absence of the breakwater. Note that condition (2) results in the wave direction and shoreline being equal at the breakwater.

Equation 4.52 becomes

$$Q_x = Q_0 - K' \frac{\partial y}{\partial x} \qquad (4.53)$$

Combining equations 4.51 and 4.53 gives

$$\frac{Q_0}{\theta} \frac{\partial^2 y}{\partial x^2} - h \frac{\partial y}{\partial t} = 0 \qquad (4.54)$$

the solution to which is

$$y = 2\theta \left(\frac{Q_0 t}{\pi \theta h}\right)^{1/2} [\, e^{-u^2} - u(\pi \xi)^{1/2} \,] \qquad (4.55)$$

where

$$u = -2x \left(\frac{\theta h}{Q_0 t}\right)^{1/2} \qquad (4.56)$$

and

$$\xi = 1 - 2 \left[\frac{1}{\sqrt{\pi}} \int_0^u e^{-u^2} du \right] \qquad (4.57)$$

The expression in square brackets is the probability integral. Equation 4.55 may be evaluated with the aid of figure 4.4. Along the line of the breakwater

$$(y)_{x=0} = 2 \left(\frac{Q_0 t \theta}{\pi h}\right)^{1/2} \qquad (4.58)$$

Using this expression the point at which sand transport can be expected to occur around the end of the breakwater can be calculated. It can also be shown that the point on the updrift side (X) at which the shoreline is modified by the accreting material is approximately

$$X = \frac{3}{\theta} (y)_{x=0} \qquad (4.59)$$

When the beach material starts to move around the end of the breakwater the

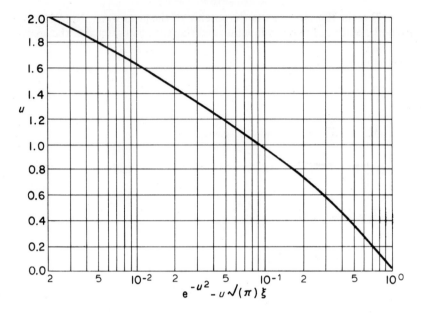

Figure 4.4 *Relationship between u and* $e^{-u^2} - u(\pi\xi)^{1/2}$

boundary conditions change so that for $x = 0$

$$Q_x = Q_p$$

$$\frac{dy}{dx} = \beta$$

and

$$Q_p = Q_0 \left(1 - \frac{\beta}{\theta}\right)$$

where Q_p is the volume transport rate passing the breakwater and β is the angle of the shoreline at the breakwater ($x = 0$) which is no longer equal to the direction of wave attack. It can be shown that

$$Q_p = Q_0 \left[1 - \frac{2}{\pi \left(\dfrac{t}{t_p} - 0.38\right)^{1/2}} \right] \qquad (4.60)$$

where t_p is the time at which bypassing commences. However, the values calculated from this relationship are only valid for $t/t_p > 2$. Corrected values for lower time ratios are given by the curve in figure 4.5.

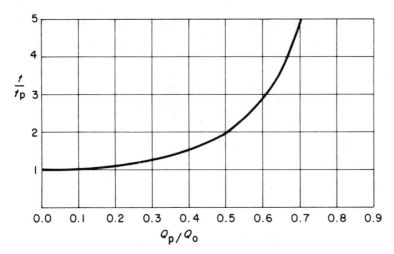

Figure 4.5 *Sand transport ratios for bypassing a breakwater*

'One-line' theories become generally inadequate when the alongshore sand transport is only partially interrupted by a structure, since inshore–offshore sediment movement is ignored. A 'two-line' theory [25] deals with partial sand transport past an obstruction by dividing the inshore sea bed into two regions: an inshore beach profile containing the obstruction and the offshore beach profile. Each zone is represented by a line and inshore–offshore sand transport is included in the idealisation. The depth beyond the offshore region is assumed to be so great that no sand transport occurs. The theory is based on the assumptions that (1) the littoral drift along the beach and inshore zone is linearly dependent on the angle of wave attack and consequently the direction of the beach and inshore zone respectively and (2) the onshore–offshore sediment transport depends on the steepness of the profile, that is, if the distance between the line of the beach and the line representing the inshore zone is less than a certain equilibrium distance, the profile is considered to be too steep and offshore transport takes place. Alternatively the profile may be too shallow and onshore transport is assumed to take place. In both cases the process is assumed to be linear and does not include the effects of diffraction around a structure and the effects of currents.

Changes in beach plan and slope as described above result in less emphasis being placed on the sediment transport formula itself, and rather more on the simplest solution, which recognises that in real problems some degree of calibration is required using integrated wave conditions over a period of weeks or months. However, with the ever increasing use and availability of high-speed computers finite difference schemes may be derived to represent the governing equations in a simple form. Referring to figure 4.6 the continuity equation (equation 4.51) may be written in finite difference form as

$$y_{n+1,\,t+1} = \frac{1}{h}\left(\frac{Q_{n,t} - Q_{n+1,t}}{\Delta x}\right)\Delta t + y_{n+1,\,t} \tag{4.61}$$

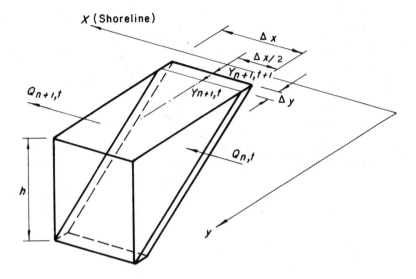

Figure 4.6 *Reference diagram for beach plan shape models*

which gives the advance or recession of the shoreline. The angle between the breaking wave front and the shoreline is given by

$$\alpha_n = \theta_n - \tan^{-1}\left(\frac{y_{n,t} - y_{n-1,t}}{\Delta x}\right) \tag{4.62}$$

so that using a suitable time step successive beach changes may be calculated. Note that a staggered scheme should be used rather than a central difference scheme [26] because although the latter leads to a tidier formulation, the transport rate at the central point is dependent on the beach angle calculated from the outer points irrespective of the position of the shoreline at the central point itself. This can result in a highly irregular predicted shoreline.

Generally the finite difference beach evolution models allow a fairly large amount of flexibility in the way they are applied. For example such models are frequently combined interactively with wave refraction models so that the latter is continually adjusted to the changing sea bed. Similarly the type of sediment transport model may be varied. In its simplest form the bulk sediment transport models discussed in this chapter can be used to calculate transport rates at each discrete section along the beach. This concept has been extended to attempting to introduce the distribution of sediment transport rate across the surf zone by relating the sediment model to a longshore current theory. Such schemes usually ignore the discontinuity of fluid flow within the surf zone but attempts have been made to account for continuity of flow by introducing an onshore–offshore flow of fluid together with a related onshore–offshore movement of sediment. [26]

4.9 General Sediment Transport Models

Beach evolution models can be useful for prediction when calibrated against historical beach changes. However, problems arise when structures which protrude into or through the surf zone are introduced because such phenomena as wave diffraction, wave reflection and diversion of longshore currents will occur in the presence of the structure and complicate the problem.

Solutions can be attempted by modelling as far as possible all factors in the physical situation for which a mathematical solution (usually numerical) can be obtained. Clearly such models are limited to the extent of theoretical development of the phenomena involved, and particularly their interaction.

One such model [27] attempted to describe wave refraction, wave diffraction, longshore currents, circulation currents and resultant sediment transport in the vicinity of a cooling water basin for a power station. Although the mathematical model was not capable of reproducing complex eddy patterns that were observed in a physical model of the structure, the predicted sediment deposition patterns as shown in figure 4.7 were markedly similar to those measured in a physical model. Such models can be used in the more general sense for many different types of problem.[28]

In recent years advances have been made in the numerical modelling of waves and currents over complex topography and these can now deal with wave-induced currents, wave and current interaction and the development of rip currents. The majority of these models use finite difference solutions.[29] For the case of an intervening structure a finite element model has been developed for calculating wave-produced currents. The combined wave refraction, reflection and diffraction problem is initially solved from which the radiation stresses can be established. These are used as forcing terms in the shallow water equations. Pre-

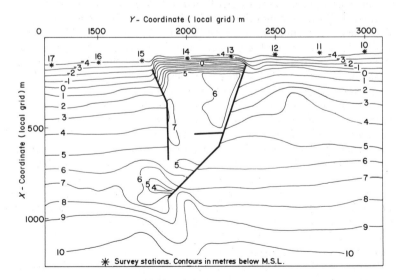

Figure 4.7 *Example of predicted sea bed changes*

liminary investigations have shown that this technique can produce realistic current patterns including eddy formations, in the vicinity of a structure.[30]

4.10   Onshore-Offshore Sediment Transport

Onshore–offshore sediment transport is a mechanism that is distinctly different from alongshore movement of sediment. At present there are no theoretical models that are capable of combining the two into a single model.

The physical aspects of onshore–offshore sediment transport are often quite obvious. For example, winter wave climates generally produce a steep beach face from which material is dragged offshore to form a breaker bar. This is nature's way of protecting a beach. In the summer period when the wave climate is generally much reduced the material finds its way onshore again to form a more gentle profile. On a gentle shoaling bed the distance that sediment is transported offshore may be measured in hundreds of metres.

Some of the possible mechanisms of onshore and offshore sediment transport have already been covered in previous section. These may be summarised as follows.

(1) *Gravity*. This alone creates a component of force for offshore sediment transport. Once sediment has been set in motion there will always exist a gravity component of force acting in the direction of maximum slope, that is, generally offshore. In some cases this motion can be self-sustaining depending on the properties of the sediment and slope of the bed. This type of motion is a particular form of density current. Other types of density current most pertinent to coastal engineering are those due to salinity often found in estuaries.

Turbidity currents are periodically found to flow from the edge of the continental shelf near the mouth of rivers with high bed load and, on a still smaller scale closer inshore, near the estuaries of silt-laden rivers. They are thought to occur near outfalls discharging a high proportion of sediment over a sloping seabed. Equation 1.45 will help to assess the likelihood of such a phenomenon in any specified set of conditions.

(2) *Mass Transport*. As described in section 3.2.1 net forward movement of fluid, and hence of sediment, at the bed occurs under a wave on a flat, smooth bed. Field measurements of this are practically non-existent, but physical model studies, although scarce, indicate that mass transport on a slope can be substantially less than the theoretical equivalent for a flat bed. Furthermore, if the bed is rough the net fluid flow at the bed can even be in the reverse direction.

(3) *Rip Currents*. A rip current is a mechanism by which substantial quantities of sediment can be transported offshore and deposited at the rip head. At the same time the return flow to the surf zone is capable of transporting sediment towards the shore, but in relatively smaller quantities.

(4) *Onshore-Offshore Winds*. When the wind blows on the sea surface the resultant stress drives the surface fluid in the direction of the wind. The wind-induced current will generally be a maximum at the sea surface and diminish with depth. In order to maintain an equilibrium there must be a return flow. Consequently in the case of onshore winds there is not only a certain amount of

set-up, but a return flow at the sea bed which is capable of transporting substantial quantities of sediment offshore. The reverse may also be true when an offshore surface current is induced. There are no theoretical models to describe this phenomenon in the nearshore zone.

(5) *Wave Asymmetry*. It is well known that linear wave theory is not strictly applicable in the region approaching the breaker line. Its use in a sediment model results in a purely stirring motion with no net sediment movement. However, under finite amplitude waves the near bottom orbital velocity has a larger forward velocity for a shorter duration under the wave crest and a smaller backward velocity for longer duration under the wave trough. This motion is distinct from mass transport which is essentially a boundary layer phenomenon. The effects of wave particle velocity asymmetry are difficult to estimate and a proper application of a sediment transport model by considering the motion in two separate phases [31] has the undesirable result of expressing sediment transport rates as a small difference between two large quantities.

No theoretical models for the above five mechanisms have been sufficiently developed beyond idealised situations to incorporate into a comprehensive model. Most onshore–offshore sediment transport models consider the problem as that of equilibrium on the hypothesis that (a) a general equilibrium beach profile exists for any given set of sediment properties and wave conditions and (b) any deviation from the equilibrium profile will result in onshore or offshore sediment transport, that is, the long-term rather than the short-term problem. If the profile is steep compared to the equilibrium profile, onshore transport should take place and vice versa if the profile is comparatively shallow. The two-line theory already described in section 4.8 incorporating this type of mechanism into the beach evolution model has been extensively developed [13, 16] on a largely empirical basis. Simplifications are necessary to obtain meaningful prediction when dealing with combinations of onshore–offshore sediment transport and alongshore transport. It is normal practice, at present, to consider them as entirely independent processes and to apply each model alternately in each time step.

4.11 Beach Nourishment

Beach nourishment is often a most satisfactory means of protecting a shoreline. Interference with natural processes is reduced to a minimum and, where material is imported, the land area gained may have a value. However, selection of suitable borrow material is most important if a nourishment scheme is to be successful. Fine material tends to be unstable on a beach and moves offshore rapidly spreading itself over large areas. Coarse material will tend to be more stable, but is not always economically available. It is necessary to estimate the proportion of a proposed borrow material that will be lost when placed as fill for a beach-restoration project.

The losses that can be expected to occur from an area that has been re-nourished can be roughly estimated using methods based on the composite grain size distribution of both the borrow material and the native beach material.

These methods [32, 33, 34] are based on comparisons between the respective grain size distributions defined on the phi scale. This is

$$\phi = -\log_2(D) = -3.322 \log_{10}(D) \tag{4.63}$$

where D is the grain diameter in mm. Grain size distributions on natural beaches generally exhibit a lognormal form and the borrow material is assumed to be similar. Grain size distributions are defined by two principal parameters

(1) the phi mean, μ, is a measure of the location of the central tendency of the grain size distribution; this can be defined in a number of ways, but for nearly lognormal distributions

$$\mu = (\phi_{84} + \phi_{16})/2 \tag{4.64}$$

where ϕ_{84} and ϕ_{16} are the eighty-fourth and sixteenth percentiles;
(2) the phi sorting or phi standard deviation, σ, which is a measure of the spread of grain sizes about the phi mean and for lognormal distributions can be approximated by

$$\sigma = (\phi_{84} - \phi_{16})/2 \tag{4.65}$$

Comparison between native material, subscripted n, and the borrow material, subscripted b, are made by considering the phi mean difference

$$\delta = \frac{\mu_b - \mu_n}{\sigma_n} \tag{4.66}$$

and the phi sorting ratio $\sigma_r = \sigma_b/\sigma_n$.
An overfill ratio, R, defined as the ratio of the volume of material that must be placed and the required design volume, can be determined to predict the required volume of fill by [33]

$$\frac{1}{R} = 1 - F\left(\frac{\theta_2 - \delta}{\sigma_r}\right) + F\left(\frac{\theta_1 - \delta}{\sigma_r}\right)$$

$$+ \frac{F(\theta_2) - F(\theta_1)}{\sigma_r} \exp\left\{\frac{1}{2}\left[\theta_1^2 - \left(\frac{\theta_1 - \delta}{\sigma_r}\right)^2\right]\right\} \tag{4.67}$$

where

$$\left.\begin{aligned} \theta_2 &= \infty \\ \theta_1 &= \max\left[-1, \frac{-\delta}{\sigma_r^2 - 1}\right] \end{aligned}\right\} \text{ for } \sigma_r \geqslant 1.0$$

and

$$\left.\begin{array}{l} \theta_1 = -1 \\[2mm] \theta_2 = \max\left[-1,\ \dfrac{1+2\delta}{1-\sigma_r^2}\right] \end{array}\right\} \text{ for } \sigma_r < 1.0$$

$F(\theta)$ is the integral of the standard normal curve. The relationship is shown graphically in figure 4.8. The diagram is split into four quadrants. Quadrants 1 and 2 represent regions where the borrow material is more poorly sorted than the native material. Quadrants 1 and 4 represent regions where the borrow material has a finer phi mean than the native material. Points which lie in quadrants 2 or 3 will generally result in a stable fill. Points lying in quadrant 1 will result in a stable fill for some combinations but losses could be large. Points lying in quadrant 4 generally indicate an unstable fill.

When estimating the volume of fill required for a particular situation, the following factors should also be considered.

(1) Handling losses. If the borrow material contains moderate or large fractions of fine sand and silt, significant losses can be expected to occur during dredging operations.

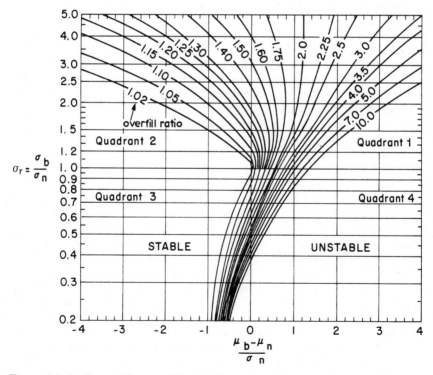

Figure 4.8 *Isolines of the overfill ratio, R, versus phi mean difference and phi sorting ratio; after James [34]*

(2) Initial profile losses. If the formed profile is at variance with the natural equilibrium profile for the borrow material, initial losses may be very large. It is normal practice to use the naturally existing foreshore slope as the design slope for the fill. However, a borrow material significantly finer than the native material will result in a beach with a flatter offshore slope and a narrower backshore than required by the design. Alternatively a coarser well-sorted material will create a steeper foreshore. Such changes can create a different environment with respect to such features as breaker type and longshore currents. For a recreational beach, for example, a steep slope may not be acceptable.

(3) The overfill ratio should not necessarily be applied to the entire fill volume when areas of reclamation are involved. The relative proportions will depend on the relative rate of filling.

Once a beach has been reclaimed by filling and the initial losses due to sorting have taken place, a maintenance programme involving periodic renourishment may be necessary. The above method does not allow for long-term losses due to the natural movement of material along a coastline. Furthermore, the predictive methods produce results which are independent either of beach profile geometry, original or created, or of wave climate and since beach losses obviously depend on both of these factors the predictions are only useful in relative terms. Neither is the time scale given over which losses from a nourished beach may occur.

These shortcomings may be overcome to a certain extent by applying a combined alongshore and onshore–offshore sediment transport model as described earlier in this chapter. This will, however, result in a considerably more complicated model and some confidence is required in the sediment transport model applied. It can be shown that by using all the consecutive wave conditions in a period rather than only the higher waves, estimated losses could be reduced due to the onshore movement of material associated with the lower waves. When the fill material is identical to the native material, model predictions are that both the relative retreat rate and the overfill ratio should be greater than unity when the fill profile is steeper than the natural equilibrium profile, because this encourages offshore movement of material.

4.12   Summary and Conclusions

This chapter has attempted to deal briefly with the theoretical aspects of sediment transport in the marine environment. At present models available are relatively elementary and there is ample room for development. The problem of theoretical representation is not a singular one. Proper application of sediment transport models themselves depend on adequate models for fluid flow and these need to be developed. Longshore drift is a major component of sediment transport and is driven by longshore currents. Consequently near-shore fluid flow models are necessary if a detailed sediment transport model is to be applied. In the simplest case of a plane beach, one-dimensional longshore current models may be used, recognising that for complex topography or in the lee of structures variations in alongshore wave height can have significant effects.

The nearshore zone is divided by the breaker line into two regions between which there can be an exchange. The most visually apparent exchange mechanism is a rip current which carries water and sediment out of the surf zone. Rip currents, in a general sense, may be generated when the set-up in the surf zone is sufficient to break through the breaker line, for example, where opposing long-shore currents meet. Rip currents can also be associated with standing edge waves [35] which may be of the same frequency as the incident waves producing a pattern of rip currents with the same longshore spacing as the longshore wave length of the edge wave. Numerical models which can potentially reproduce rip currents and other nearshore current patterns are quite complex and extensive computational effort is required to solve even one wave condition imposing practical limits on the use of such a model. This is always a merit in simplicity and for projects of small scale, economy must dominate other considerations.

It is worth remembering that where the water is clear, a remarkable degree of qualitative detail of sand movement may be obtained from the air, preferably as coloured aerial photographs.

Calibration of a sediment model to the site under consideration involves extended collection of field data, the organisation of which is discussed in chapter 8. For a detailed sediment transport model alone it is necessary to measure sediment concentration, grain characteristics, wave height, wave period, wave direction, current speed and direction and ripple dimensions. Due to the complexity of the interactive processes it is very important for these parameters to be measured simultaneously, bearing in mind that, no matter how advanced the adopted modelling technique may be, the quality of predictions will depend directly on the quality of the input data.

In conclusion, it will often be found that when applying different sediment transport models quite large discrepancies appear in the results. Care should be taken not to attempt to apply a model outside the range of physical conditions for which it was derived. Also, if possible, more than one model should be applied to each problem so that an estimate of the range of results can be sensibly achieved. While sand is the material mainly discussed above, the same rules apply to shingle with the simplification that little transport occurs seaward of the surf zone.

Example 4.1

A cooling water intake head is to be placed in 7 m of water. Its elevation above the sea bed is to be such that under the design wave condition of $H_s = 1.5$ m, $T_z = 8$ s, the relative concentration of sediment is less than 10 per cent of that at the bed. The sediment size is 0.15 mm diameter with a density of 2650 kg/m³, the density of sea water is 1030 kg/m³ and typical ripple dimensions are 7.5 mm height and 70 mm length. What should be the height of the intake above the bed if the design current is 0.5 m/s?

The maximum water particle displacement at the sea bed is

$$a_0 = \frac{H}{2 \sinh 2\pi h/L}$$

from equation 3.16

$$L_0 = \frac{gT^2}{2\pi} = 100 \text{ m}$$

For $h = 7$ m, $\sinh 2\pi h/L = 0.716$ so that $\hat{a}_0 = 1.047$. Maximum water particle velocity at the bed $= 2\pi\hat{a}_0/T$ (see equation 3.17) $= 0.82$ m/s. Using equation 4.32

$$\text{roughness length} = \frac{25 \times 7.5^2}{70} = 20 \text{ mm}$$

From equation 4.12

$$Ch = 18 \log\left(\frac{12 \times 7 \times 1000}{20}\right) = 65.2 \text{ m}^{1/2}/\text{s}$$

The shear velocity due to the current alone is

$$v_{*c} = \frac{\bar{v}g^{1/2}}{Ch} = \frac{0.5 \times (9.81)^{1/2}}{65.2} = 0.024 \text{ m/s}$$

Using equation 4.11

$$\xi = \frac{0.45 \times 0.4 \times 65.2}{(9.81)^{1/2}} = 3.75$$

so that the shear velocity due to waves and currents (equation 4.10) is

$$v_{*wc} = 0.024 \left[1 + \frac{1}{2}\left(\frac{3.75 \times 0.82}{0.5}\right)^2\right]^{1/2} = 0.107 \text{ m/s}$$

The fall velocity for an 0.15 mm diameter particle is 0.0167 m/s so that equation 4.13 may be evaluated.

$$\frac{w_s z_0}{\epsilon_0} = 1.05 \left(\frac{0.0167}{0.4 \times 0.107}\right)^{0.96} \left(\frac{20}{1000 \times 7}\right)^{0.013 \left(\frac{0.0167}{0.4 \times 0.107}\right)} = 0.413$$

Assume that the reference level is half the roughness length, that is $z_0 = 10$ mm. Using equation 4.14 c/c_0 required to be 0.1

$$z/z_0 = (0.1)^{-1/0.413} = 264$$

So that the intake head would have to be 2.64 m above the sea bed.

Example 4.2

Estimate the relative sediment concentration for the same conditions as example 4.1, but using equations 4.20 and 4.23.

In this case the wave friction factor must be evaluated from the ratio of the maximum particle displacement at the bed and the roughness length as given in figure 3.22. Thus

$$f_W = 0.028$$

$$\xi_j = 65.2 \left(\frac{0.028}{2 \times 9.81} \right)^{1/2} = 2.46$$

from equation 4.23

$$v_{*wc} = 0.024 \left[1 + \frac{1}{2} \left(\frac{2.46 \times 0.82}{0.5} \right)^2 \right]^{1/2} = 0.073$$

$$\frac{wz_0}{\epsilon_0} = 0.59$$

At 2.64 m above the bed

$$\frac{c}{c_0} = \left(\frac{2.64}{10} \times 1000 \right)^{-0.59} = 0.037$$

that is, for the same level the alternative method predicts a relative concentration that is nearly a factor of three smaller.

Example 4.3

Given the same conditions as in example 4.1, what would be the total sediment transport rate (a) according to equation 4.38, (b) according to equation 4.43 when $D_{35} = 0.12$ mm, $D_{50} = 0.15$ mm, porosity is 0.35 and $v = 10^{-6}$ m^2/s?

$$D_{gr} = \left[\frac{9.81 \times (2650 - 1030)}{(10^{-6})^2 \times 1030} \right]^{1/3} \times \frac{0.12}{1000} = 2.99$$

$$n = 1 - 0.2432 \ln 2.99 = 0.734$$

$$m = \frac{9.66}{2.99} + 1.34 = 4.57$$

$$C_D = 18 \log \left(\frac{10 \times 7 \times 1000}{0.12} \right) = 103.79$$

$$C = \exp\{2.86 \ln (2.99) - 0.4343 (\ln 2.99)^2 - 8.128\} = 0.004$$

From example 4.1 $U_0/v_{*c} = 0.82/0.024 = 34$ so that equation 4.42 applies and

$$A = 2.29 \left[\frac{0.028 \times 1030}{(2650 - 1030) \times 9.81} \right]^{1/2} \frac{8^{0.043}}{(0.00015)^{0.12}} = 0.307$$

$$I_{wc} = 3.023$$

from example 2

$$F_{wc} = \frac{0.5 \times 3.023^{0.734}}{103.79^{0.266} \; 65.2^{0.734} \left[\left(\frac{2650 - 1030}{1030} \right) \frac{0.12}{1000} \right]^{1/2}} = 1.11$$

$$Q = \frac{1}{(1 - 0.35)} \frac{0.12}{1000} \times 0.5 \times \left(\frac{65.2}{9.81^{1/2}} \right)^{0.734} \times 3.023^{0.266} \times 0.004$$

$$\times \left(\frac{1.11 - 0.307}{0.307} \right)^{4.57}$$

$$= 0.0003725 \; \text{m}^3/\text{m/s}$$

that is 32.3 m³/m/day.

Using equation 4.43

$$Q = \frac{0.05 \times 0.5 \times 65.2 \times 0.073^4}{(9.81)^{5/2} \left(\frac{2650 - 1030}{1030} \right)^2 \left(\frac{0.15}{1000} \right)}$$

$$= 0.000414 \; \text{m}^3/\text{m/sec}$$

that is 35.8 m³/m/day which is in fairly close agreement with the above.

Example 4.4

Given a characteristic significant wave height of 2 m, period 7s attacking a 1:50 gradient beach at 5°, calculate the rate of longshore drift.

Using equation 3.102

$$a = 4.46 \times 9.81 \times (1 - e^{-19/50}) = 13.83$$

$$b = \frac{1.56}{(1 + e^{-19.5/50})} = 0.9302$$

$$\frac{H_b}{h_b} = 0.9302 - 13.83 \times \frac{2}{9.81 \times 7^2} = 0.87$$

$$h_b = 2.3 \; \text{m}$$

For shallow water

$$C \approx (9.81 \times 2.3)^{1/2} = 4.75 \text{ m/s}$$

$$H_{rms} \approx \frac{H_s}{2^{1/2}} = \frac{2}{2^{1/2}} = 1.41 \text{ m}$$

Using equation 4.48

$$Q_0 = \frac{0.77 \times 60 \times 60 \times 24}{(2650 - 1030) \times 9.81 \times 0.6} \times \frac{1030 \times 9.81}{16} \times (1.41)^2 \times 4.75 \sin 10$$

$$= 7225 \text{ m}^3/\text{day}$$

If the sediment particle size were 0.5 mm, what would be the transport rate according to equation 4.49?

$$K'' = 365 \times 10^4 \log\left(\frac{0.00146}{0.5} \times 1000\right) = 169.9 \times 10^4$$

Since $H_b \approx H_0 K_r$

$$Q_0 = \frac{169.9 \times 10^4}{365} \times 1.41^2 \times 7 \times \sin 5 \times \cos 5 = 5624 \text{ m}^3/\text{day}$$

Example 4.5

A breakwater is situated on a beach with gradient 1:50 and is 700 m long from the 0.0 m contour. Sediment movement may be assumed to occur between the +2 m and -6 m contours and the annual rate of drift is, in the absence of the breakwater, 10^6 m³/annum and the average angle of wave attack is 5°. (a) How long will it take before the sand starts bypassing the breakwater?

The shoreline must advance $(700 + 2 \times 50) - 8 \times 50 = 400$ m before bypassing starts. Using equation 4.58

$$t = \frac{\pi \times 8 \times 400 \times 400}{4 \times 10^6 \times 5 \times \pi/180} = 11.5 \text{ years}$$

(b) What will be the rate of sand bypassing at 18 years after construction?

$$\frac{t}{t_p} = \frac{18}{11.5} = 1.56$$

corrected values from figure 4.5 give

$$\frac{Q_p}{Q_0} = 0.41$$

$$Q_p = 0.41 \times 10^6 \, \text{m}^3/\text{annum}.$$

(c) At what distance on the updrift side of the breakwater will accretion be noticed at t = 10 years?

Using equation 4.59

$$x = \frac{3}{5\pi/180} \times 2 \left(\frac{10^6 \times 10 \times 5\pi/180}{\pi \times 8} \right)^{1/2}$$

$$= 12\,800 \, \text{m}$$

(d) What will be the shoreline advance 2000 m on updrift side of the break-water at (i) 5 years and (ii) 10 years?

(i) Using equation 4.45 and figure 4.4

$$u = -2 \times (-2000) \left(\frac{5\,(\pi/180) \times 8}{10^6 \times 5} \right)^{1/2} = 1.49$$

$$y = 2 \times 5 \left(\frac{\pi}{180} \right) \frac{10^6 \times 5}{\pi \times 5 \times (\pi/180) \times 8} \times 0.015 = 4.0 \, \text{m}$$

(ii)

$$u = -2 \times (-2000) \left(\frac{5\,(\pi/180) \times 8}{10^6 \times 10} \right)^{1/2} = -1.06$$

$$y = 2 \times 5 \left(\frac{\pi}{180} \right) \left(\frac{10^6 \times 10}{\pi \times 5\,(\pi/180) \times 8} \right)^{1/2} \times 0.08 = 30.0 \, \text{m}$$

Example 4.6

Given a native beach material with

$$_nD_{84} = 0.16 \, \text{mm}$$

$$_nD_{16} = 0.38 \, \text{mm}$$

and a potential borrow material with characteristic sizes of

$$_bD_{84} = 0.08 \, \text{mm}$$

$$_bD_{16} = 0.30 \, \text{mm}$$

determine whether the fill will be stable and determine the overfill ratio required.

Using equations 4.63 through to 4.66

$$_n\phi_{84} = -3.322 \log_{10} 0.16 = 2.64$$

$$_n\phi_{16} = 1.40$$

$$_b\phi_{84} = 3.64$$

$$_b\phi_{16} = 1.74$$

$$\mu_n = \frac{2.64 + 1.40}{2} = 2.02$$

$$\mu_b = \frac{3.64 + 1.74}{2} = 2.69$$

$$\sigma_n = \frac{2.64 - 1.40}{2} = 0.62$$

$$\sigma_b = \frac{3.64 - 1.74}{2} = 0.95$$

$$\delta = \frac{2.69 - 2.02}{0.62} = 1.081$$

$$\sigma_r = \frac{0.95}{0.62} = 1.53$$

Referring to figure 4.8 the point lies in quadrant 1 for which the borrow material should be stable and the overfill ratio would be approximately 2.25.

References

1. W.T. Bakker, Sand concentration in an oscillatory flow, *Proceedings of the 14th Coastal Engineering Conference, Copenhagen, 1974*
2. T.C. MacDonald, Sediment transport due to oscillatory waves, University of California, Berkeley, Hyd. Eng. Lab., Rep HEL-2-39,(1973)
3. H.A. Einstein and N. Chien, Effect of heavy sediment concentration near the bed on velocity and sediment distribution, University of California, Berkeley, Institute of Engineering Research, M.R.D. Series No. 8 (1955)
4. J.F. Kennedy and F.A. Locher, Sediment suspension by water waves, in *Waves on Beaches*, ed. R.E. Meyer, (Academic Press, 1972)
5. Delft Hydraulics Laboratory, Computation of Longshore transport, Report R968, pt. I (1976)
6. K.F. Bowden, Turbulence, *A. Rev. Oceanogr. mar. Biol.*, 2 (1962)

7. P.K. Bhattacharya, Sediment suspension in shoaling waves, Ph. D. thesis, University of Iowa
8. E.W. Bijker, Longshore transport calculations, *Proc. Am. Soc. civ. Engrs*, **97**, WW4 (1971) 687–701
9. H.A. Einstein, The bed-load function for sediment transportation in open channel flows, *Tech. Bull. Soil Conserv. Serv. U.S. Dep. Agric.*, **1026** (1950)
10. C.A. Fleming, The development and application of a mathematical sediment transport model, Ph.D. Thesis, University of Reading (1977)
11. J.R. Hunter, A Note on Quadratic Friction in the Presence of Tides, *Estuar. Coastal Mar. Sci.*, **3** (1975) 473–5
12. E.W. Bijker, The increase of bed shear in a current due to wave action, *Proceedings of the 10th Coastal Engineering Conference, Tokyo, 1966*
13. D.H. Swart, Offshore sediment transport and equilibrium beach profiles, Delft Hydraulics Laboratory Publication No. 131 (1974)
14. I.G. Jonsson, Measurements in the Turbulent Wave Boundary Layer, *10th Congress of the International Association for Hydraulic Research, London, 1963*
15. G.R. Mogridge and J.W. Kamphuis, Experiments on bed form generation by wave action, *Proceedings of the 13th Coastal Engineering Conference, Vancouver, 1972*, ch.60
16. D.H. Swart, Predictive equations regarding coastal transports, *Proceedings of the 15th Coastal Engineering Conference, Hawaii, 1972*, pp. 1113–32
17. D.H. Swart, Weighted value of depth of initiation of movement, NR10, Stellenbosch, South Africa, 1977
18. P.D. Komar, Beach sand transport: distribution and total drift, *Proc. Am. Soc. civ. Engrs*, **103** WW2 (1977)
19. D.L. Inman and R.A. Bagnold, Littoral processes 2, in *The Sea*, vol. III, ed. M.N. Hill (Interscience, New York, 1963) 529–33
20. P.D. Komar and D.L. Inman, Longshore sand transport on beaches, *J. geophys. Res.*, **75** (1970) 5914–27
21 R.G. Dean, Review of sediment transport relationships and the data base, Proceedings of a Workshop on Coastal Sediment Transport, University of Delaware, DEL-SG-15-78 (1978)
22. K. Horikawa and C-T. Kuo, A study of wave transformation in the surf zone, *Proceedings of the 10th Coastal Engineering Conference, Tokyo, 1966*, pp. 217–33
23. Delft Hydraulics Laboratory, Waterbeweging in een kustmodel met vaste boden, Report No. M918, pt IV (1977)
24. R. Pelnard-Considère, Essai de théorie de l'evolution des formes de rivages en plages de sables et de galets, *IVième journées de l'Hydraulique*, Question III (1956)
25. W.T. Bakker, Littoral drift in the surf zone, Rijkswaterstaat Department for Coastal Research, Report No. WWK-70-161 (1971)
26. D.H. Willis, An alongshore current beach evolution model, National Research Council of Canada, Report No. HY-92 (1978)
27. C.A. Fleming and R.J. Maddrell, Mathematical predictions of dredging quantities, *Proceedings of ASCE Specialty Conference 'Sediments 77', Charleston, 1977*
28. B.A. O'Connor and C. Tuxford, Modelling siltation at dock entrances, *Proceedings of the 3rd International Symposium on Dredging Technology, Bordeaux, 1980*, pp. 359–72
29. W.A. Birkemeier and R.A. Dalrymple, Nearshore wave circulation induced

by wind and waves, *2nd Annual Symposium of ASCE Waterways, Harbors and Coastal Engineering Division, San Francisco, 1975*, pp. 1062-81

30. P. Bettess, C.A. Fleming, J.C. Heinrich, O.C. Zienkiewicz and D.I. Austin, Longshore currents due to a surf zone barrier, *Proceedings of the 16th Coastal Engineering Conference, Hamburg, 1978*

31. O.S. Madsen and W.D. Grant, Quantitative description of sediment transport by waves, *Proceedings of the 15th Coastal Engineering Conference, Hawaii, 1976*, pp. 1093-112

32. R.G. Dean, Compatibility of borrow material for beach fills, *Proceedings of the 14th Coastal Engineering Conference, Copenhagen, 1974*

33. W.R. James, Borrow material texture and beach fill stability, *Proceedings of the 14th Coastal Engineering Conference, Copenhagen, 1974*

34. W.R. James, Techniques in evaluating suitability of borrow material for beach nourishment (U.S. Army Corps of Engineers, C.E.R.C., 1975) T.M.60

35. R.A. Dalrymple, Rip currents and their causes, *Proceedings of the 16th Coastal Engineering Conference, Hamburg, 1978*, vol. II, pp. 1414-27

5

Coast and Bed Morphology

5.1   Regime of the Coast and Sea Bed

The morphology of the coast and sea bed results from the interplay of natural and man-made forces on the exposed geological formations. The natural forces are those of waves, currents, gravity and, possibly, tectonics. The factors which determine the climate of waves and the strength and direction of currents vary in many time scales, ranging from seconds to millennia. Thus at any instant of time, the shape and composition of the coast and sea bed represent a complex pattern of innumerable trends tending towards a dynamic equilibrium, over the relevant period of geological history.

The existence of granular material on the sea bed does not necessarily imply that the sediment is mobile under the prevailing action of the sea. The material may have been deposited under the powerful agency of a turbidity current or it may have survived from a period in which currents near the sea bed or wave action on the sea bed were swifter than at present. As an example of this latter circumstance, certain extensive gravel deposits on the continental shelf around Great Britain are not at present disturbed by the sea. The gravel was deposited during a period when the sea level was relatively lower and when, in consequence, the deposit was within the zone of influence of storm waves.

Section 4.2 has discussed the factors affecting bed load movement. The regime of a mobile sea bed depends on exposure to storms, depth of water, gradient of bed, tidal currents and the material on the bed, that is, its size, grading and adequacy of supplies.

Interference with the natural regime may be caused by placing an obstruction on the sea bed or as a result of dredging. Generally, a solid object set on the bed, in the presence of tidal currents or waves, will cause local increases in velocities and erosion may result, its magnitude depending on the geometry and particle size of the material. Equilibrium will be restored when the slope of scour hole compensates for the corresponding increase in shearing forces at the sea bed (see equations 1.45 and 4.27).

A highly permeable object, on the other hand, may lead to reduction in local water velocities and cause accretion, operating on the principle of a snow-fence. The magnitude of the effect may be estimated by examining the hydrodynamic conditions of flow around the object.

Dredging a hole or deepening a channel in the sea bed may cause local or more widespread movement of the adjacent bed, depending on the water motion, the nature of the material and the component of side slope of the excavation in the direction of the current. Where dredging occurs in coarse material, the consequence may be one of the following.

(1) Powerful currents will tend to obliterate the depression by causing adjacent material to slump.

(2) Less powerful currents may be inadequate to move the coarse material but yet be sufficient to scour finer material away; thus the depression may remain as a permanent feature.

(3) Weak currents will tend to refill the hole with finer material.

A dredged hole will also change the wave patterns, possibly concentrating wave energy inshore [1] thus causing a partial or even total reflection of wave energy.

This example is indicative of the possible consequences of simple modification of the natural regime.

5.2 Sand Features

The understanding of the manner of the bed transport of sediment by the sea owes a great deal to the studies that Bagnold [2] has made of the comparable phenomena relating to sand movement by the wind. Each of the features found in the sea: sand ribbons, sand streams, sand ripples and sand waves (or dunes), has its aeolian counterpart, described by Bagnold. Modes of movement cover stages from incipient motion on a flat bed through the formation of ripples and dunes to the limit where the bed reverts to a smooth form. For waves Bagnold describes grains aligning themselves parallel to wave crests, soon after incipient motion, forming wavy ridges a few grains high. As the velocity of flow increases so does the strength of the vortices, at which point the majority of grains are in motion and ripples are formed. If the current is further increased, the ripple heights and wave lengths change.

Sand ribbons in the sea were first indentified from oblique asdic records [3] and a number of areas have subsequently been located by this means and by divers. The ribbons are thin carpets of sand, relatively narrow and elongated in the direction of the (tidal) current. The more rapid the current, the sharper the definition of the ribbon, the ribbon being associated with velocities in excess of 0.5 m/s (1 knot). Bagnold [2] shows that particles of sand will be carried as bed load far more rapidly along a smooth bed than along a carpet of sand. Hence, sand ribbons are found in areas in which some feature, such as initial surface roughness, has caused the sand grains to accumulate and thence to spread as a ribbon downstream. Similarly, elongated ribbons have been observed on tidal mud banks where local velocities are high. Sand streams on the other hand are found to occupy depressions in the sea bed, the accumulation being caused by gravity in conjunction with the currents which give rise to transport.

Bagnold [2] established, in a classic experimental study of the dynamics of sand movement in ripples, that the pitch of the ripple is related to the average orbit of particles of sand whose initial motion is caused by impact with other particles returning to the bed and which, off the bed, are affected by drag and inertial forces.

The presence and dimensions of sand ripples are strongly associated with bed roughness or friction factors and hence with predictions of sediment transport and currents close to the bed, steady or fluctuating (see sections 4.4 and 4.5).

From tests in an oscillating water tunnel, Mogridge and Kamphuis [4] determined relationships between bed form height Δ_r, length λ_r (see figure 5.1) and orbital excursion d_0 at the bed so that

$$\log \left(\frac{\lambda_r}{D_{50}} \right) = a_1 \log \left(\frac{d_0}{D_{50}} \right) + b_1 \tag{5.1}$$

$$\log \left(\frac{\Delta_r}{D_{50}} \right) = a_2 \log \left(\frac{d_0}{D_{50}} \right) + b_2 \tag{5.2}$$

where a_1, a_2, b_1 and b_2 are constants and $d_0 = 2a_0 + \bar{U}T$, a_0 being the orbital amplitude (first-order wave theory) and $\bar{U}T$ is the net particle movement at the edge of the boundary layer during one wave cycle. The curves illustrating the relationships are shown in figure 5.2.

Much experimental data of sand ripples is provided by Inman.[5] Dingler and Inman [6] show that for a level bed

(1) If ripple steepness Δ_r/λ_r is plotted against the wave form of Shields' relative stress criterion [4]

$$\theta = \frac{\rho \hat{u}_0^2}{\rho_s D} \tag{5.3}$$

where $\hat{u}_0$ is maximum near bottom velocity and D is grain size, vortex ripples $(\Delta_r/\lambda_r \sim 0.15)$ occur for $\theta < 40$ (but greater than threshold of bed movement). For $40 < \theta < \sim 240$, ripples are transitional from vortex ripples to sheet flow, beyond which the ripples become flattened.

(2) Transitional ripples migrate in the direction of the wave at 0 to 40 mm/min, the rate increasing with increasing theoretical bottom wave drift current.

(3) Grain size has negligible effect on steepness of ripples but maximum values of Δ_r and λ_r depend on grain size. Ripple steepness is constant for $40 > \theta$, $\theta > $ (threshold of motion), decreasing towards zero as $\theta \to 240$.

(4) Ripple symmetry, ratio of (crest-to-trough distance)/λ_r ranged from 0.36 to 0.61, about 75 per cent of values between 0.45 and 0.55.

For ripples in shallow water, Yalin [7] and Yalin and Karahan [8] have found an approximate relationship between a/a_0 and λ/λ_0 where a is the orbital length of particle motion at the boundary layer level, a_0 and λ_0 being the upper limits for the relationship; $a_0 \sim \lambda_0$ and values are given for λ_0/D and $\xi(= \nu T/D_{50}^2)$, ν being kinematic viscosity, T wave period and D grain size.

Heights of sand waves may be less than 1 m or as great as 15 m or more, with ratios of wavelength to height commonly lying between about 10 and 50.

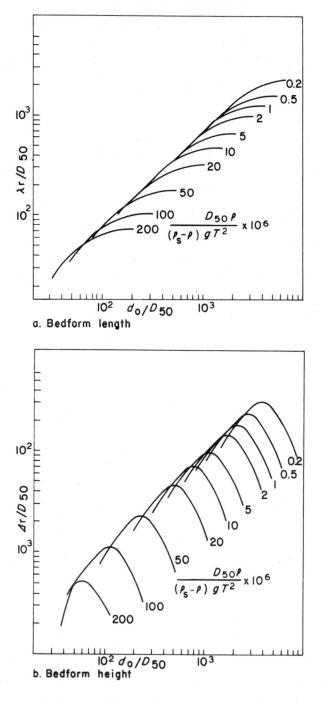

a. Bedform length

b. Bedform height

Figure 5.1 *Mogridge–Kamphuis design curves for bed forms*

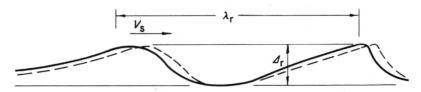

Figure 5.2 *Diagram of sand wave*

Yalin [9] derived interesting relationships between pitch, maximum height, maximum current velocity and water depths for unidirectional flow by an elementary use of dimensional analysis. He suggests that sand wave height cannot exceed one-sixth of the depth of water. Available marine data especially in bank areas, where the largest waves are on the flanks and the smallest near the top, suggests that this limit is about right. The wave crests form approximately transverse to the direction of the principal currents and, as indicated in figure 5.2, present an asymmetrical profile with the steep face indicating the direction of advance. Sand grains are carried up the rear flank and deposited along the leading edge of the crest. Thus, referring to figure 5.2, if the profile of the sand wave, advancing at a rate V_s, remains unaltered and the wave is approximately symmetrical, a volumetric rate of bed transport of sand will be

$$q_b = \tfrac{1}{2} V_s \Delta_r \tag{5.4}$$

per unit width of sand wave, where Δ_r is wave height, ignoring variations in porosity. In fact, particularly in areas of limited quantities of sand, considerable variation is observed in the position, orientation and dimensions of sand waves, even during a single cycle of neap/spring tides. It is consequently difficult in practice to measure the rate of bed transport in sand waves.

If the time integral of the ebb and flow of a tidal current in a channel is separately computed over a tidal cycle, the residual flow is the name given to the mean rate of flow corresponding to the difference between the ebb and flood tide integrals. Stride [3] states that the residual flow caused by a difference of only 0.05 m/s between maximum ebb and flood streams suffices to cause assymmetry of the sand wave and a measurable rate of advance. Where channels of residual ebb and flood flows exist alongside each other, the sand waves may adopt a sinuous form in plan (figure 5.3) and the relationship between the waves may be expected to undergo continual change. The crests may also be expected to depart considerably from straight lines with dominant flood and ebb sand waves coexisting where the ebb and flood currents are not directly opposed, as in many estuarial channels, or where a rotatory current system prevails (see section 2.4.1).

Around the southern part of Great Britain, Stride [3] records the principal areas of sand waves as indicating a movement out of the western part of the English Channel towards the west, in conjunction with a predominantly northern movement in the southern part of the North Sea. Van Veen [10] in 1936 indicated that the average annual sand load of the Rivers Maas and Rhine amounts to well over a million cubic metres as a source of supply of sand per year.

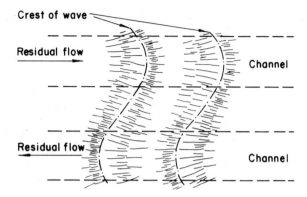

Figure 5.3 *Sand waves in adjacent ebb and flood channels*

In the absence of special topographical features, sand banks are generally cigar-shaped and aligned with their long axis parallel to the direction of the tidal currents. While the Dogger Bank and, possibly, the Varne Bank owe their presence to natural shoals of underlying coarser or more durable material, the features are usually more mobile and their positions and forms represent no more than a short-term equilibrium between opposing forces. Off the Kent coast, for instance, periodic records of the variation of the Goodwin Sands are available over 100 years. Robinson and Cloet [11] describe the considerable inshore movement of the Brake Bank in Sandwich Bay over a similar period.

5.3   Features of Estuaries (Seaward End)

Factors affecting differential scour and siltation are delicately balanced in certain wide and shallow river estuaries. Surveys carried out at intervals over long periods frequently reveal the gradual evolution of new features, explicable by a variation in the balance between ebb and flood tide streams.

Ebb-dominant channels on the landward side become flood-dominant channels at the seaward end of the estuary. In the areas where neither is dominant coarse sediment tends to collect. Although there may be a clearly defined flow residual in the channel the flood or ebb flow may be concentrated on opposite sides of the channel and thus sediment circulates within the channel, some escaping and coarser material being deposited on the bar between the channels.

Rhythmic series of ridges orientated parallel to the tidal currents have been recognised in many areas of the world. Most are composed of sand but some may be mud or silt and their spacing has been found to be proportional to the depth of water. In the Thames Estuary the arrangement of elongate banks fits a definite pattern and Maddrell, [12] using charts of the area since 1862, has examined the changes and predicted future changes in the outer estuary. Apart from changes in the flood and ebb-dominant channels the general spacing of the outer portions of the banks is developing towards the relationship found by Off. [13] The above is qualitative, as must be exploration by means of hydraulic models with mobile beds. A particular feature of present studies is the determination of suitable sites for the disposal of dredging spoil at sea, to prevent its immediate return to the circulation system of the estuary.

5.4 Coastal Features

The geographical features described below are primarily caused by the action of the sea as a medium of littoral transport; features caused by differential erosion by the sea on account of geological variation are beyond the scope of this book.

5.4.1 Offshore Banks

Here we are concerned not so much with the forces affecting the variations in size and position of offshore banks (see section 5.3) as the effects that such variations have on the coastline. To take an example, Cloet [14] describes the variations of the Goodwin Sands since 1844, by the comparison of hydrographic records. Over a longer period, records are available of the variation in alignment of the shingle coast, separated from the Goodwin Sands by the Downs, in earlier times an important anchorage because of the shelter allowed by the Goodwins. It is known that between the mid-sixteenth and mid-eighteenth centuries the coast was accreting to the north (Deal) and eroding to the south (Walmer) (figure 5.4), while during the last two hundred years the situation has been reversed

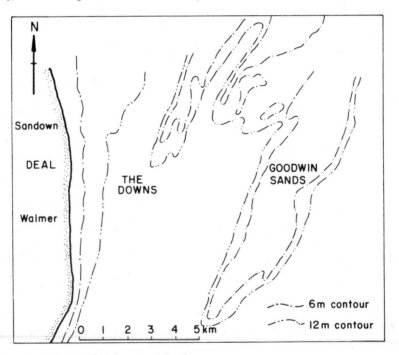

Figure 5.4 *Coast of Walmer and Deal*

(and, more recently, affected by restrictions to shingle supplies from the south). These variations in trends appear to be directly related to the variation in shelter and in refraction of waves approaching from the North Sea. While a variation in conditions may only require a small change in the angle of wave incidence to restore equilibrium, the consequent corresponding variation in alignment of a stretch of coastline may well entail appreciable shifts of material. Thus, the variations referred to above at Walmer and Deal accounted for a swing of the coastline of about 200 m in a length of about 4000 m, that is, a change in orientation of about 3°.

5.4.2 Offshore Bars

The formation of a bar on a sloping foreshore is discussed in section 5.6 and those in estuaries in section 5.3. The other common form of bar submerged for all or part of the tide is that formed at an entrance to a river or coastal inlet. This type of bar is caused by the decreasing capacity of the seaward ebb current, with or without a river discharge, to maintain its bed load or suspended load, which will generally be much greater than that of the sea. A river bar is most likely to be formed where there is an adequate supply of sand, a fairly flat area offshore and a confined area of discharge to the sea. The latter feature will tend to create a seaward jet current on the ebb, gradually expanding and diffusing as indicated in Figure 5.5. The theory and case studies of such phenomena are discussed by Wiegel.[15] On the other hand, the flood tide, if any, will have no tendency to be concentrated across the line of the bar, which may thus exist as a permanent feature, for example, the Tay Estuary, subject only to the degree of variation caused by violent changes in river discharge or as the result of storms. Littoral drift of sand across the mouth of a river is frequently found to occur along the river bar and this will help to preserve its linear form.

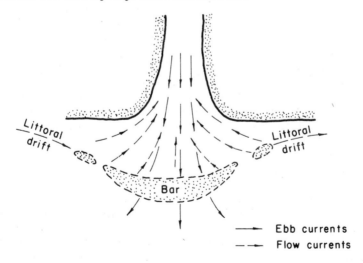

Figure 5.5 *River bar*

5.4.3 Coastal Banks and Spits

Geographers recognise a wide variety of types of spit; a spit will tend to form at any point where a projecting headland is associated with a strong littoral drift and an offshore shoal. Under these circumstances there will be a sudden change in the longshore component of expenditure of wave energy (section 4.7.1), with resulting deposition of sand or shingle at the point. This accretion will either develop until the updrift line of foreshore is so altered as to arrive at a new balance of rates of drift or the material may continue to accumulate and build out as a spit, with or without secondary ridges developed to leeward of the main spit. While shingle (or sand) supplies remain adequate, the line of the spit may simply continue that of the line of the adjacent coast; where supplies are restricted, the updrift end of the spit may be driven back by the sea until, ultimately, the spit may be approximately parallel to the crest line of the principal storm waves, to suit the reduced longshore drift. Chesil Bank off the Dorset Coast is a good example of a spit, attached to the land at each end, in a state of equilibrium, and facing directly into the prevailing south-westerly seas. It is interesting to note that the east end of this spit is more exposed to the sea than its west end, partly because of sea bed contours immediately offshore from the bank. The result is that the bank stands higher and steeper at its east end and that a longitudinal sorting process is in evidence with the large material, as large cobbles, tending to be carried eastwards and the finer material, as medium to fine shingle, tending to be carried westwards.

5.4.4 Tombolos

The tombolo represents a sufficiently specific type of spit to warrant its separation from the remainder. Tombolo is the name given to an isthmus of mobile material that may develop from a coastline to form an attachment to an offshore island. Tombolos may owe their origin primarily to geological factors, and Chesil Bank (see above) joining Portland to the Dorset Coast represents such a type, although the details of early history remain debatable. The type of tombolo to be considered further here, however, may be entirely explained by considerations of littoral drift and wave refraction.

The partial shelter of an offshore island leads to a cusp-shaped accretion on the adjacent coast of the mainland and the stages in development of this cusp, until a causeway is formed between mainland and island, are illustrated diagrammatically in figure 5.6. The mechanism is similar to that described in greater detail under the offshore breakwater in section 6.5. Ultimately the tombolo may form a causeway to the island. It is not a coincidence that the name is Italian since the absence of tidal currents in the Mediterranean assists the development of the feature and several examples are found off the coast of Italy.

Another interesting locality is the Makran Coast of Pakistan, where there are two large tombolos, Gwadar and Ras Ormara, each with a headland about 12 km long and about the same distance off the general shoreline. The depth of water between the coast and the extremity of each headland is about 7 m. The maximum range of tide is about 2 m. The beach material is a fine shelly sand and

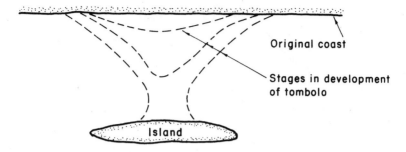

Figure 5.6 *Formation of tombolos*

the features appear to have attained approximate equilibrium under prevailing conditions. A gently shoaling sea bed offshore ensures that the crests of the long monsoon waves, of period 11 to 13 s, approach the coast approximately parallel to the bed contours.

5.4.5 Bays

A bay usually owes its existence to the presence of relatively durable rock constituting the containing headlands. The form and composition of the foreshore and the offshore zone will depend to a greater or lesser extent (subject to geological complications) on the degree and relative direction of exposure to wave attack. Useful deductions on the degree of exposure and its variation with compass bearing, especially in areas where the coast is rocky, may frequently be made by studying the variation in beach composition and profile around a bay. A good example of this is Port Erin bay in the Isle of Man where the beach deposits vary from coarse gravel to fine sand, depending on their degree of exposure.

The crenellated shape of the coasts of Great Britain provides a fund of evidence on the way in which stable bays form in mobile beach material between relatively stable headlands. In such bays a number of characteristics can be noted.

(1) The plan shape varies depending on the orientation of the coastline to the predominant storm direction as described in section 4.8. The down-drift end of the bay tends to have a straight coastline parallel to the predominant inshore waves. The up-drift end is sharply curved, shaped by wave diffraction round a relatively wide headland.

(2) A coastline facing the predominant waves tends to be symmetrically curved between the headlands (Figure 5.7).

(3) The erosion of an established bay shoreline is limited by the rate of attrition of the headlands.

(4) When a surplus of beach material arrives from rivers discharging into a bay, this tends to form a spit across the bay between the headlands.

(5) The distance shorewards to which a bay erodes is related to the distance between headlands.

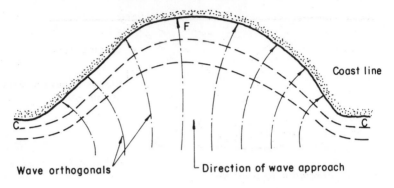

(a) Bay facing directly into prevailing waves

--- Offshore contours
F   Area of finest beach
C   Area of coarsest beach

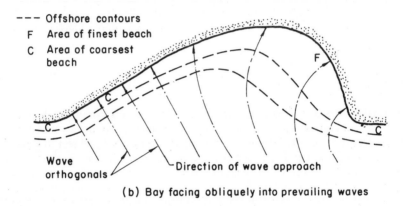

(b) Bay facing obliquely into prevailing waves

Figure 5.7 *Bay form in relation to prevailing waves*

5.5 Beach Features

Variations in beach morphology are dependent on wave and tidal currents to which the beach is subjected. The degree of exposure is reflected by the material making up the beach and offshore zone and thus the morphology is dependent on these materials.

5.5.1 The Effect of Grain Size

The gradient of an apparently stable beach and the adjacent nearshore sea bed represents a balance between constructive (inshore) and destructive (offshore) forces. Moreover, different kinds of stability may be represented at a particular situation, which may be classified as follows.

(1) Long-term stability, where the littoral bed material is of such a size as to be moved by only the largest infrequent storm wave. An example of such a

beach is the east end of Chesil Bank west of Portland. This condition represents the design criterion for artificial spending beaches, which must be capable of absorbing wave energy under the most adverse conditions, without need for periodic restitution.

(2) Seasonal stability, where the beach profile may vary cyclically through the year due to marked seasonal trends of wind or swell. Examples of such beaches are to be found in particular on the Pacific Coast of the United States; up to 60 m of seasonal variation in the position of high-water mark is recorded, for instance, at Carmel, California.

(3) Stability to suit variation of wind and waves, a variant of (2) familiar to the coastal engineer of Great Britain. The beach profile may be considered to be in a perpetual state of adjustment, changing rapidly in storms and recovering slowly in calm weather.

(4) Stability over a tidal cycle. Appreciable variation in profile over the tidal cycle may be detected at any shingle or sandy coast in heavy seas. The extent of variation is masked to the casual observer since the foreshore is only seen when it is exposed and the difference at other states of the tide is not perceived.

From the basic statements of equilibrium of bed load transport derived by Bagnold, [16] if ΔE_1 and ΔE_2 represent energy losses from bed friction for an advancing and returning wave current respectively, and if m_1 and x_1 relate to mass and mean distance of material moved forward, m_2 and x_2 relate to material moved back, then, where a is a constant, Bagnold postulates that

$$\Delta E_1 = a \; \frac{\rho_s - \rho}{\rho_s} \; gm_1x_1 \cos \beta(\tan \alpha + \tan \beta) \tag{5.5}$$

$$\Delta E_2 = a \; \frac{\rho_s - \rho}{\rho_s} \; gm_2x_2 \cos \beta(\tan \alpha - \tan \beta) \tag{5.6}$$

where m_1, m_2, x_1 and x_2 are unknown, β is bed slope in the direction of the wave and α is the angle of repose of the bed material. It will be seen that these relationships assume the same value for a for inshore or offshore movement and, as the orbital motion becomes more asymmetrical, this assumption becomes less tenable. For stability in the relatively short-term sense, statistically $m_1x_1 \approx m_2x_2$ and hence from equations 5.5 and 5.6

$$\frac{\Delta E_1 - \Delta E_2}{\Delta E_1} = \frac{2 \tan \beta}{\tan \alpha + \tan \beta} \tag{5.7}$$

If $E_2 = cE_1$, from equation 5.7, for $\Delta E_1/\Delta E_2 = E_1/E_2$

$$\tan \beta = \left(\frac{1-c}{1+c}\right) \tan \alpha \tag{5.8}$$

Thus, since α does not vary greatly for natural beach material, β depends directly on c, with limits of

$\beta = 0$ when $c = 1$, that is, no energy loss
$\beta = \alpha$ when $c = 0$, that is, full loss of energy

This concept provides a qualitative explanation for the principal features of the profile of a beach under wave action. For a position under given conditions of wave and depth of water, c will be reduced with increasing grain size of the bed material, not only due to surface roughness but also due to the energy losses of water percolating through the bed. Thus, where the water velocity is large enough to cause movement of the size of particle present (see section 4.2), material will tend to accumulate where the slope is compatible with equation 5.8: larger material at the steepest part of the beach where the greatest loss of energy occurs, smaller material where the slope is flatter and the destruction of wave energy less. This accounts for the familiar sorting action by the sea, with the coarsest material being carried the furthest distance up the beach (Figure 5.8). The degree of sorting may be expressed as $(D_{75}/D_{25})^{1/2}$ where D represents particle size, and the subscript the fraction of the sample smaller than D, that is, D_{25} and D_{75} represent the finer and coarser quartiles. Values of $(D_{75}/D_{25})^{1/2}$ of 1.25 and 1.45 indicate well-sorted, that is, relatively uniform material, on a beach or on the sea bed respectively. The minimum size of material found on an exposed coast is about 0.1 mm.

Several analyses to assess the relative importance of grain size and wave characteristics on beach slope have been carried out on beaches in widely varying sea conditions (see for example reference 17). Simple, partial and multiple correlation have shown that the material size is the most important variable. Figure 5.9 shows the approximate range of beach slope against grain size. Apart from the influence of wave period and steepness, one of the reasons for the scatter in observations is probably due to the fact that grain size itself varies with position on the beach profile as does the beach slope itself.

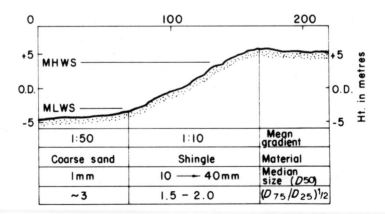

Figure 5.8 *Profile of typical shingle beach*

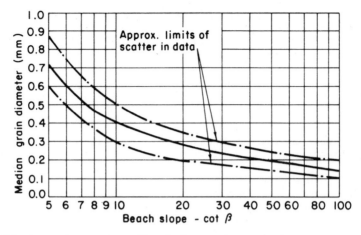

Figure 5.9 *Approximate range of beach slope against grain size*

As the wave moves inshore, the orbital motion immediately above the sea bed becomes increasingly asymmetrical, with high inshore velocity under the crest and slow offshore movement under the trough (see section 3.2) and this property accentuates the sorting action between the coarse and fine material. The finer the material, the greater the likelihood that it will be raised into suspension by the inshore movement, to be carried seaward, subsequently, by the slow offshore movement.

Another factor tending to cause inshore movement in the shallow water zone is the shoreward drift $\bar{U}$ (see equation 3.40) near the sea bed. To summarise, therefore, there are three principal factors tending towards inshore transport of material by waves, the motion being opposed by the slope of the sea bed

    (1) loss of energy of the approaching wave principally due to bed friction and percolation through the sea bed,

    (2) asymmetry of the orbital motion of the water particles of a steep wave in shallow water,

    (3) inshore drift beneath the wave, modified by wind.

Factor (1) predominates inshore of the breaker zone while factors (2) and (3) are usually the most important considerations further offshore, with factor (2) becoming relatively more important as the water shoals and the waves steepen. The resulting beach profile is discussed in section 5.5.2.

The size of material (for given immersed density, location on the sea bed and size of wave) which is just disturbed by the maximum hydrodynamic forces beneath the wave crest, is referred to as the 'incipient motion particle diameter' D_i. The size of material which oscillates along the sea bed, or in saltation, about a constant position, without a tendency to move offshore or onshore is called the 'equilibrium motion particle diameter' D_e. Generally, $D_e < D_i$ at the same point and the trends of movement will be as set out in table 5.1.

Experiments in littoral processes have usually failed to reproduce in a model the appropriate balance between forces in nature. Yalin [18] has discussed the

TABLE 5.1   *Onshore–offshore movement of material*

Particle size* D	$D < D_e$	$D = D_e$	$D_e < D < D_i$	$D > D_i$
Direction of movement	offshore	null	onshore	null

*If $D < \sim 0.05$ mm, cohesive forces will intervene and, as the size of material decreases, increasing water velocities are necessary to dislodge the particle.

several dimensionless factors which have to be satisfied if the correct ratios are to be maintained between

(1) inertial and gravity forces for waves (X or Froude number)
(2) mass and drag for particle movement (Y number)
(3) inertial and viscous forces for percolation (Z number).

It is thus invalid simply to scale down the particle size, in the ratio of the dimensional scale of a hydraulic model of a beach, to obtain similarity. The significance which can be placed on the results of tests carried out on model beaches requires careful analysis, since full dimensional similarity is extremely difficult to achieve. Model tests which make no attempt towards dimensional similarity provide little information on the balance of forces in nature.

5.5.2 The Beach Profile

As indicated in section 5.5.1 the sea generally tends to drive the coarser material in the shallow water zone towards the shore. In fact, while there is constant readjustment of a shore to suit changing conditions, long-term stability of sorting of material is indicated by the relative positions of materials of widely differing sizes. As an example, we have the familiar feature of a shingle foreshore with sand to seaward, a pronounced change in gradient marking the foot of the shingle.[19]

The form of the breaking wave, in the absence of wind, is directly related to the beach profile and the wave steepness (see figures 5.10 and 5.11). The

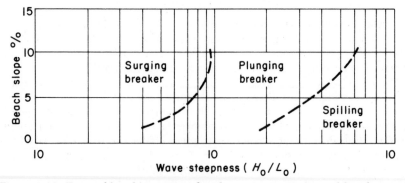

Figure 5.10 *Type of breaking wave related to wave steepness and beach gradient; after Wiegel [15]*

theoretical limiting ratio of wave height to depth of water below trough, of about 0.78 (see section 3.4.4) appears to be realised in practice except, possibly, on a very steep beach. Four forms of breaking wave are recognised

    (1) the spilling breaker
    (2) the plunging breaker
    (3) the surging breaker
    (4) the collapsing breaker

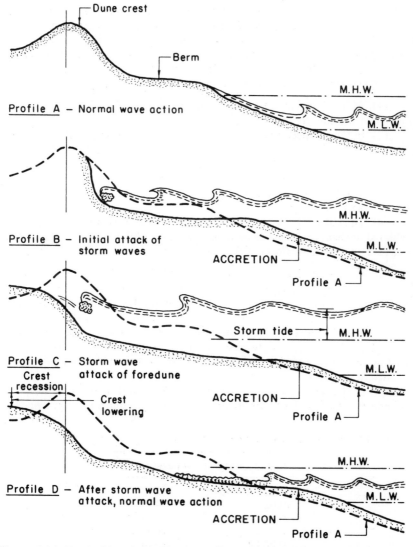

Figure 5.11 *Typical beach profiles; after* Shore Protection Manual *[21]*

Generally, a spilling breaker, gently spilling forwards at the crest without a well-defined break-point, occurs with the steepest wave and the flattest bed slope. The plunging breaker pitches forward with a roar and an ill-defined fore-foot of foam; this is the commonest type of breaker associated with a medium beach slope. On a beach whose slope is steeper than about 1:10 (extending to the depth of water at which breaking occurs) the surging breaker appears simply to lunge at the beach without any defined plunge. With a collapsing breaker the crest does simply collapse and consequently run-up is limited. A partial clapotis (see section 3.6) may be caused by reflection of a proportion of the wave energy, particularly of the latter type of breaker.

In the breaking zone of a plunging breaker, a considerable proportion of the wave energy is released in turbulence and thus heat. There is, therefore, a re-duction towards the shore in the motion along the sea bed, with a tendency for (predominantly coarse) material to accumulate at the plunge-point with an as-sociated increase in bed slope. In this way the familiar offshore bar is formed.

Surveys of exposed sand beaches disclose the following situations.

(1) At least one bar is associated with an offshore slope $< 1:75$ in con-junction with a sand shore.

(2) In the absence of large tidal variation, a bar will form at the plunge line.

(3) In the presence of diurnal and semi-diurnal tides, bars will tend to form at the plunge line associated approximately with low water. (For longer-period tides the bar is likely to be undergoing periodic adjustments and movements with the tide.)

(4) The flatter the bed slope and the steeper the wave, the greater the likelihood of there being one or more bars. Bascom [20] records a maximum of three bars on the Pacific Coast of the United States.

A bar may have height of 2 m or more above the general line of the bed slope on the most exposed shores, and it varies seasonally, in size and position to some degree, according to the variation in prevailing waves. Inshore of the bar the wave will reform to some extent and the bed profile will be appropriate to a lower wave, with reduced H/L and increased h/H ratios, and thus, generally, to a gentler slope. This tendency towards a change in profile will be somewhat re-duced by the drift caused by the wave inshore of the bar and by longshore drift discussed in section 4.5

Wiegel [15] collates the critical values of H_0/L_0 (the deep sea wave steep-ness) and H_0/D_{50} for which bars are likely to develop, from laboratory evidence

TABLE 5.2   *Limiting conditions for formation of offshore bar*

H_0/L_0 (min.)	H_0/D_{50} (max)
0.025–0.040	300
0.02	430
0.01	850
0.008	1000
0.004	1300

and beach surveys, where D_{50} is the median diameter of the sand. This information is summarised in table 5.2.

At the swash zone, the beach profile may again be associated with the principle of equation 5.8. On a smooth impervious beach $c \to 1$; on a rough permeable beach, c will tend towards zero towards the top of the wave run-up. For reasons similar to those already described under the sorting processes of section 5.5.1, coarser material will tend to be flung towards the top of the beach. This has been confirmed in studies of sand and shingle beaches and is bound to augment the tendency for the equilibrium beach profile to be concave upwards. On an eroding sand or shingle foreshore, a steep scarp will be formed towards the top of the beach and erosion will be most marked with steep storm waves (Figure 5.11). The actual angle of slope of the beach is related to the degree of saturation and thus to the internal water table. Where a shingle beach exists to no great depth above an impermeable substratum it is particularly susceptible to erosion and consequent draw-down by storm waves, since the effective over-all permeability for the returning swash will be significantly reduced for large waves.

After attack by storm waves, a beach in the course of recovery may be recognised by the presence of one or more scarps or crests below the uppermost crest, representing the swash limit at high water of the subsequent restoring seas. The recovery is essentially a relatively slow process by comparison with the rate of the original erosion, which may occur during a single tidal cycle. A point of interest is that if a storm persists during a falling tide, it is likely to take beach material further offshore than would occur if the wave height declined near the time of high water. In the presence of a seawall, or similar obstacle, causing marked erosion during a storm near high water, this effect may be reversed since continuation of the storm during the falling tide will lead to partial recovery of the beach (see figure 5.12).

Run-up is the name given to the height reached by the swash, measured above sea level. When considering the maximum height of run-up on a beach, the several features to be taken into account are

(1) the height and steepness of the deep water wave (section 3.8)

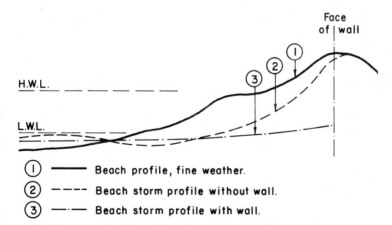

Figure 5.12 *Beach profile with and without sea wall*

(2) the effect of refraction and shoaling on the wave height coefficient (section 3.4.2).

(3) the rise in mean sea level, known as set-up, associated in particular with short steep waves (section 3.7)

(4) the changes in sea level caused by wind and weather sections 2.2.2 and 2.2.3)

(5) the effect of shore permeability.

The *Shore Protection Manual* [21] provides a number of results of empirical tests on the height of run-up, R, related to mean sea level at the time of test, on a smooth slope. These results may be directly applied to a sand beach and indicate that the ratios R/H_0 attain a maximum with the steepest slope of beach and the longest deep water wave (cf. sections 3.4 and 7.3.1). For example, a 10 s wave with a deep water steepness of about 0.02 provides the factors indicated in table 5.3. For long-period waves or tsunamis the factor would be increased several fold (section 2.3.4).

TABLE 5.3   *Run-up of a 10 s wave on a smooth impervious slope*

Beach slope	1/30	1/20	1/10
R/H_0	0.24	0.35	0.75

5.5.3 Beach Cusps

A relatively straight beach line is often seen, on closer inspection, to be scalloped to produce fairly evenly spaced cusps along the foreshore. The cusps appear to require certain conditions of beach slope, wave height and steepness and that the wave crests must approach approximately parallel to the coast. The pitch of the cusps appears generally to disappear when conditions become destructive. Observations on Long Island Sound have shown that beach cusps can indicate the existing direction of littoral transport, with the seaward portion of the cusp being moved in that direction. There is strong evidence to associate beach cusps with edge waves [22] which in turn may be the generative force behind rip currents.[23]

References

1. W.A. Price, J.M. Motyka and L.J. Jaffrey, The effect of offshore dredging on coastlines, *Proceedings of the 16th Coastal Engineering Conference, Hamburg, 1978*, vol. II, pp. 1347–58
2. R.A. Bagnold, The movement of desert sand, *Proc. R. Soc. A*, **157** (1936) 594–620
3. A.H. Stride, Current-swept sea floors near the southern half of Great Britain, *Q. Jl. Geol. Soc.*, **119** (1963) 175–99
4. G.R. Mogridge and J.W. Kamphuis, Experiments on bed form generation by wave action, *Proceedings of the 13th Coastal Engineering Conference, Vancouver, 1972*, vol. II, pp. 1123–42

5. D.L. Inman, Wave generated ripples in nearshore sands (U.S. Army Corps of Engineers, Beach Erosion Board) Tech. Memo No. 100 (1957)

6. J.R. Dingler and D.L. Inman, Wave formed ripples in nearshore sands, *Proceedings of the 15th Coastal Engineering Conference, Hawaii, 1976*, vol. II, pp. 2109–26

7. M.S. Yalin, Origin of submarine dunes, *Proceedings of the 15th Coastal Engineering Conference, Hawaii, 1976*, vol. II, pp. 2127–35

8. M.S. Yalin and E. Karahan, On the Geometry of Ripples Due to Waves, *Proceedings of the 16th Coastal Engineering Conference, Hamburg, 1978*, vol. II, pp. 1776–86

9. M.S. Yalin Geometrical properties of sand waves, *J. Hydraul. Div. Am. Soc. civ. Engrs.*, **90**, HY5 (1964) 105–19

10. J. Van Veen, Onderzoekingen in de Hoofden. Measurements in the Straits of Dover and their relation to the Netherlands coasts (1936)

11. A.H.W. Robinson and R.L. Cloet, Coastal evolution of Sandwich Bay, *Proc. Geol. Ass.*, **64** (1953) 69–82

12. R.J. Maddrell, Evolution of the outer Thames Estuary, *Dock Harb. Auth.*, **II** (1970) 52–6

13. T. Off, Rhythmic linear sand bodies caused by tidal currents, *Bull. Am. Ass. Petrol. Geol.*, **47** (1963) 324–41

14. R.L. Cloet, Hydrographic analysis of the Goodwin Sands and the Brake Bank, *Geogr. J.*, **120** (1954) 203–15

15. R.L. Wiegel, *Oceanographical Engineering* (Prentice-Hall, Englewood Cliffs, N.J., 1964)

16. R.A. Bagnold, Mechanics of marine sedimentation, in *The Sea*, vol. III, ed. M.N. Hill (Interscience, New York, 1963) pp. 507–28

17. C.A.M. King, *Beaches and Coasts*, 2nd ed. (Edward Arnold, London, 1973)

18. M.S. Yalin, A model shingle beach with permeability and drag forces reproduced, *10th Congress of the International Association for Hydrographic Research, London, 1963*

19. A.M. Muir Wood, Characteristics of shingle beaches: the solution to some practical problems, *Proceedings of the 12th Coastal Engineering Conference, Washington, 1970*, pp. 1059–76

20. W.J. Bascom, The relationship between sand size and beach face slope, *Trans. Am. Geophys. Un.*, **32**, (1951) 866–74

21. *Shore Protection Manual* (U.S. Army C.E.R.C., 1975)

22. D.A. Huntley and A.J. Bowen, Beach Cusps and Edge Waves, *Proceedings of the 16th Coastal Engineering Conference, Hamburg, 1978*, vol. II, pp. 1378–93

23. R.A. Dalrymple, Rip Currents and Their Causes, *Proceedings of the 16th Coastal Engineering Conference, Hamburg, 1978*, vol. II, pp. 1414–27

6

Planning of Coast Protection

6.1 Identification of the Problem

6.1.1 *The Natural Beach*

A natural beach of sand or shingle is an economic means of absorbing the energy of breaking waves, and thus protecting an erodible coastline. Chapter 5 indicates how a coastal regime may vary with changes in offshore topography. It is also necessary to consider how the regime may be affected by maritime works interfering with the natural processes of littoral drift. After allowing for such factors, the engineer has to consider the sufficiency of the natural beach material for continuous protection, making provision for possible short-term and long-term variations. At this stage, it may be possible to assess whether or not artificial means are necessary to augment or sustain the beach; alternatively it may be decided that some other expedient will be necessary to replace the function of the beach in full or in part. These stages in the evolution of an economic scheme of coast protection are described in outline below.

6.1.2 *Assessment of the Situation*

It is necessary at the outset to attempt to answer the following questions.

(1) What is the prevailing direction of littoral drift? Is there a seasonal variation? If so, what is the ratio of net to gross movement?

(2) Does the magnitude of littoral drift vary appreciably along the length of coastline adjacent to the site under study?

(3) What is the present rate of change of the line of the foreshore along the section under review? What does this represent as an annual volumetric loss (or gain) of material?

(4) What is the trend with time of this annual rate of change? Does it undergo cyclic variation?

(5) Must the shoreline be established at a particular position or may it be allowed to retreat? If so, at what rate and for how long?

(6) Are there additional factors that will affect the future trend?

Question (1) must be answered by direct observation, augmented if necessary by tracer studies (section 8.5.2). Question (2) (partially), (3) (partially) and (4) will be answered by the study of maps of the district (the earlier 6 in. = 1 mile series of Ordnance Sheets, now replaced by 1:10 000, are usually found in Great Britain to be available from the 1870s onwards) with further information from local records of encroachment on property. Ordnance Sheets will frequently indicate the cause for a change in the littoral regime by showing the approximate date of construction of breakwaters, or other obstructions, or of protective works, updrift of the site, affecting a length of coast whose erosion has previously provided a source of beach material.

It is also necessary to study Admiralty Charts to obtain information on the variations of offshore topography. Generally, on a shingle beach, it will be found that the gently sloping bed in the littoral zone follows the changes of the foreshore, so that the quantitative assessment of the littoral drift need only be taken between the top of the beach and the point of marked change in slope, and hence of size of beach material (see figure 5.8). For a sand beach a careful study of the 'circulation system' of the sand on the foreshore is necessary before making any such assumption. The material may be transferred between the shore and deeper water or it may be partially removed or restored as sand-blown dunes.

Question (4) requires an examination of the beach material which accumulates against obstructions and consideration of the extent of the littoral cell, that is, the length within which significant movement of drift of the littoral material is confined. Where a cell is defined downdrift by the presence of a foreland or a breakwater, it is possible to estimate directly the rate of build-up of material and thus the rate of drift. A similar estimate may be made where the downdrift limit is caused by a sudden change in exposure and hence in the direction of drift.

A classic example occurs at Dungeness Point where a predominantly eastwards shingle drift ceases at the Ness proper. Here the change of direction of the shoreline provides shelter from the south-west winds and there is very little shingle drift northwards along the east-facing shore of the feature. Figure 6.1 illustrates the situation at Dungeness. The shingle ridges may plainly be seen, whereby the history of accretion and erosion over many hundreds of years can be reconstructed. Recent ridges, followed north of the Ness near the east coast, are seen to converge, indicating the reduction in the rate of accretion in this direction, with no appreciable gain beyond the sandy offshore shoals.

In the United States, the limit of a cell on a sand shore is provided in several instances by a deep offshore canyon. Loss of sand into such a feature is less easy to estimate, especially if it is carried any considerable distance from the shore, but the feature defines the updrift limit of the adjacent cell.

Question (3) has to be answered by considering first the variations in the transverse position of the coastline, (Y_x), at selected points, (x), for a particular period as determined from available maps and other records. Estimation of the profile at each such point, taken transverse to the line of the coast, may permit determination of the volume of beach material per unit length of coastline, (V_x), represented by a unit positional change of the coast-

Figure 6.1 *Dungeness Foreland, looking north (J.K. St. Joseph, Cambridge
University Collection, Copyright reserved)*

line at x. In arriving at this estimate, it is necessary to take account of the
contribution to beach material from erosion of cliffs and other features; it is
also necessary for a sand beach to take account of the variation in profile offshore as discussed above.

The product $V_x Y_x$ is then assessed for each point x and the results
indicated in figures (or graphically) on a plan of the overall length of foreshore under consideration. This study should either cover a period of a
sufficient number of years to render local variations insignificant by comparison with long-term trends, or alternatively a large number of points
should be selected initially for the determination of $V_x Y_x$ and average values
obtained for representative lengths of the foreshore. The latter approach
should always be used where recent changes in circumstances would otherwise impair the value of information obtained over a longer period. Chapter
4 describes methods for beach 'budgeting'.

If information about the constitution of the beach material over a long
period is not available, this aspect of question (4) may usually be answered
with sufficient accuracy by examining beach material size along the length
of the littoral cell, in combination with the conditions of exposure along its
length. Thus, if an eroding foreshore on the updrift side is providing material
finer than that currently forming the foreshore at the site, the changing
regime may result in a flattened foreshore angle and a consequent acceleration
of local erosion. Allied questions relating to the geological composition of

the coast may have to be answered but these are beyond the scope of the present account (see section 4.11).

The answer to question (5) will depend on the use of the land in question. There may be specific features such as roads, buildings, seawalls, farmlands to be protected; or the permissible rate of loss of land may be assessed in direct economic terms. It is important to consider local and amenity interests with regard to cost/benefit, since these may involve factors not evident in a normal technical appraisal.

6.2 Restoration of the Beach

There are basically two methods of improving a declining beach; the methods may be used separately or in combination. Either the rate of littoral drift may be reduced along the affected length by artificial reorientation of the beach or the beach may be artificially recharged.

As indicated in section 4.8, the equilibrium rate of drift along a particular shore is related to the angle of incidence of the waves. Groynes act as arresters to drift by causing the orientation of the beach line between successive groynes to be altered so that the prevailing waves arrive more nearly parallel to the beach. Figure 6.2a shows the effect soon after construction; the beach line can be encouraged to progress seaward once beach material begins to pass the groynes. If all drift ceases, the beach will tend to align with the crests of breaking waves so that $\alpha_g = 0$. Otherwise α_g may be related to the effectiveness of the groynes in reducing drift. [1]

It is interesting to reflect that if the angle of wave incidence were greater

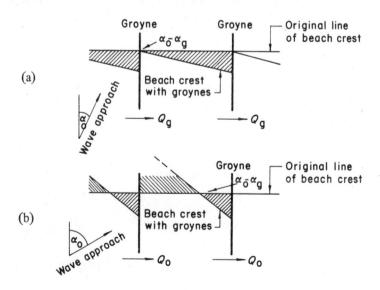

Figure 6.2 *Diagram of groyned shore*

than that for maximum rate of drift, then groynes would serve no useful
purpose, since accumulation of beach against a groyne would orientate the
beach immediately updrift of the groyne in such a way as to lead initially to
increased littoral drift. The beach crest would rapidly swing around until
the original rate of drift was restored, resulting in loss of beach (figure 6.2b).
In nature, the line of a beach at such a high angle to the waves would be so
unstable, however, that in practice the situation only arises locally, to form
a cuspate promontory, or the recurves at the downdrift ends of spits, such
as those illustrated in figure 6.3. This shows Hurst Beach from the south-east,
a spit running from Milford on the Hampshire coast to Hurst Castle, seen
nearest to the camera. A fairly weak littoral drift of shingle occurs along the

Figure 6.3 *Hurst Castle and Spit, Hants, looking north-west (J.K. St. Joseph,
Cambridge University Collection, Copyright reserved)*

spit from the north-west to south-east and at Hurst Castle the material is affected by the strong tidal currents through the narrows (about 1 km wide) separating the mainland from the Isle of Wight. The recurves are sheltered from the prevailing south-west winds and tend to become aligned parallel to the principal waves, from the east-north-east, in the West Solent.

Since littoral drift is related to the rate of expenditure of energy on a foreshore, if drift is to be reduced it is desirable to consider possible methods of sapping the power of the breaking waves. A traditional method of providing partial protection to the upper beach is by the erection of an open pallisade of piles, usually close to mean water level. It is doubtful whether such a barrier provides any appreciable protection: see section 7.3.3, for instance, for a description of the wave energy transmission past open piles in shallow water. A more substantial benefit may be obtained from the shelter afforded by a parallel breakwater offshore, as described in more detail in section 6.5.

A thin depth of beach provides an ineffectual dissipator of wave energy. The deeper the beach, up to a certain critical depth related to the mobility of the beach and percolation from the breaking wave, the less will be the rate of drift. This is because littoral drift is related to longshore energy and, the greater the destruction of total wave energy, the greater will be the destruction of the longshore component. Differences in drift related to depth of beach may be considerable on a shingle foreshore, and in such circumstances restoration of the shingle where the beach is deficient may restore the desired uniformity of the rate of drift, temporarily or even permanently.

A seawall can have a destructive effect on a beach due to the magnitude of reflected wave energy and, in addition, on a shingle beach, by preventing percolation of the upper part of the swash into the beach (figure 6.4). Model tests in which a vertical plate is thrust into the top of a stable beach illustrate the collapse of the profile in a dramatic manner. An increase in the volume of the beach material in front of the wall is equivalent to placing the wall further up the foreshore. Evidently, a wall positioned near the top of the swash will have a negligible effect on the beach profile and hence on the magnitude of littoral drift. Such a wall is only called on to provide protection on occasions of extreme tide and storm.

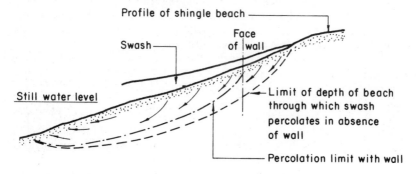

Figure 6.4 *Percolation of swash into beach*

Another palliative to the deleterious effects of a seawall is to create some form of wave energy dampening in front of the wall by means, for instance, of a permeable revetment or armouring of rock or precast concrete units. The rock may be heavy (immobile) or small (mobile beach).

There is considerable experience of low-cost means of providing protection, to fairly sheltered shores, by means of vegetation, building rubble, worn tyres, sandbags and other means. [2,3,4]

The most direct way of maintaining a stable shoreline, making good all deficiencies in littoral drift, is by the expedient of placing imported material on the foreshore. This material may be obtained from a borrow pit away from the coastline, or from offshore deposits, or may be obtained from points of accretion on the foreshore. A common method of beach recharge is to take the material from the downdrift end of a beach and return it at the updrift end (but see section 4.11).

A variant on the beach nourishment system is simply to bypass obstructions that cause unwanted accretion and scour respectively on their updrift and downdrift sides. There are a number of breakwaters on the coasts of North America which are bypassed in this manner by pumping sand across a harbour or river mouth. [5,6,7] An effective method of controlling the area of accretion for such schemes is to provide an offshore breakwater approximately parallel to the shore, behind which a tombolo (see sections 5.4.4 and 6.5) tends to form, and to pump from this accretion in the shelter of the breakwater. Fixed pumping installations can also be used to remove accumulations of sediment from navigation channels, discharging the spoil in scour areas in the lee of a downdrift breakwater.

6.3 Continuous Protection by Groynes and Revetments

6.3.1 Layout of Groynes

There are few universal rules on the layout of a system of groynes; nevertheless a set of specific empirical practices may be devised, applicable to the special conditions of one limited locality. Questions concerning the types of construction of groynes are beyond the scope of this book except to mention that, in general, resort to groyning indicates confidence that the groynes will be capable of maintaining a fairly stable coastline. Only groynes of a flexible type, for example, the type described by Duvivier, [8] could be considered for a situation where continuing recession is going to be allowed to continue. Lack of foresight in this respect has frequently caused the undermining and collapse of systems of groynes.

It should be appreciated that the design criteria of a series of groynes have to be related to the proportionate reduction of littoral drift that is required.

The fundamental basis for relating littoral drift to wave energy and angle of incidence is described in sections 4.7 and 4.8. If it be assumed that the rate of littoral drift (that is, that part of total longshore drift which directly concerns the beach), $Q = K \sin 2\alpha$ (cf. equation 4.48), then figure 6.2 illustrates how the ratio of drift with and without groynes (Q_o and Q_g respectively) are associated in the ratio

$$\frac{Q_g}{Q_0} = \frac{\sin 2(\alpha_0 - \alpha_g)}{\sin 2\alpha_0} \tag{6.1}$$

where α_0 represents ungroyned angle of incidence of waves to beach and α_g represents the change of α due to groyning. For relatively small values of α, equation 6.1 may be written

$$\frac{Q_g}{Q_0} \approx \frac{\alpha_0 - \alpha_g}{\alpha_0} \tag{6.2}$$

and the line of beach may be determined approximately (neglecting all questions of reflection and diffraction by the groynes) by estimating the proportion of original drift that occurs after groyning (and vice versa). Section 6.3.4 discusses some of the problems of such assessment.

The height of a groyne will determine the maximum beach profile updrift of it. The groyne should be designed to suit any combination of beach profiles at each side of it between the natural limiting fine and foul weather profiles (see section 5.5.2). The stability must take account of the extreme conditions of the beach, entailing the simultaneous effects of

(1) the beach having a storm profile
(2) the beach crest being inclined at the maximum angle to the general line of foreshore
(3) local scour.

Point (3) requires a little further explanation. Provision should be made against variation in concentration of wave energy and hence in rate of littoral drift along a coastline which may, even with a system of groynes, cause local variation in Q_g and hence produce local scour. This is particularly likely to occur during a period in which the direction of drift is suffering a reversal due to a change in wind direction. A certain interval of time elapses as the beach material within a groyne bay adjusts itself to take up a new form; different degrees of exposure and other variation between groynes and groyne bays will cause this adjustment to occur at different rates and erosion may be caused locally before a new regime of littoral drift is established.

Any improvement of a beach by the use of groynes will entail a corresponding deficiency downdrift unless accompanied by appropriate beach replenishment.

6.3.2 Orientation and Length of Groyne

From the practical viewpoint of maintenance, a groyne should be built transverse to the mean direction of the breaking crest of storm waves, which usually means that it should be approximately transverse to the general direction of the coastline. A small theoretical advantage in effectiveness is said to result from inclining it with the seaward end slightly downdrift; and it is considered definitely inadvisable to set the seaward end updrift. The practical consideration should prevail and a new system of groynes should be aligned directly into the maximum storm waves. Replacements of individual groynes, in a system inclined downdrift, should compromise to some extent.

The cost of building conventional groynes is greatly influenced by the period of accessibility of the foreshore. Thus, without special provision in construction, an economic limit is reached, some way inland of mean low water mark of spring tides (MLWS) and hence the length is often determined by tidal range and beach slope. The requisite length is, however, also related to the desired effectiveness of the groyne system; as the ratio of Q_g/Q_0 (see figure 6.5) becomes smaller, the necessary length of groyne becomes greater until, when $Q_g/Q_0 \rightarrow 0$, the groyne must extend to the limit of littoral drift. At Seaford, Sussex, for example, it has been found expedient, in view of the virtual absence of natural shingle supply, to construct several intermediate groynes to a length of 100 m and more into depths of water more than 3 m below MLWS, and terminal groynes to a greater length and depth. The objective has been to form a littoral cell capable of retaining virtually all the existing shingle on the foreshore. In view of the disposition of the local coastal features, the prevailing drift is reversed within the length of the cell and in consequence long groynes are required at each (downdrift) end. The intermediate long groynes form partial sub-cells with the principal object of reducing the movement of shingle with changes of wind and waves. Not only do these groynes help to maintain a more uniform beach to protect the seawall but their presence reduces the frequency with which shingle needs to be redistributed within the length of the cell, to avoid loss past the terminal groynes. Model tests [9] confirmed that, with 2.5 to 4 m high waves, shingle on the Seaford beach might be expected to travel seawards up to 120 m from the seawall (that is, to about 4 m below MLWS). It should be mentioned that the extent of seaward movement is enhanced at Seaford by the fact that the chalk substratum has only a relatively thin covering of shingle (see section 6.2). For a sand shore a groyne would have to extend very much further to attain a similar object on account of the greater seaward extent of drift (see section 4.9).

It is known, though there is a lack of quantitative data, that, where long groynes deflect the drift to seaward, the material returns obliquely to the shore. In consequence, if long groynes are built at too close a spacing, a proportion of the beach material will not be captured by each intermediate groyne bay. The effect will be more marked for sand than shingle, because of beach gradient and the mode of transport.

The landward end of a groyne should either abut the longitudinal defence offered by a cliff, seawall or revetment with low rate of erosion, or it should be taken landward of the swash line allowing for the most unfavourable combination of circumstances. Failure to recognise this requirement has caused out-flanking of groynes by the sea, with consequent failure of the system.

6.3.3 Groyne Spacing

The maximum groyne spacing will frequently be determined by the resulting variation in beach level on each side of it, based on the principle described in section 6.3.1 and illustrated in figure 6.5. Hence, for example, in a bay where the direction of wave attack is confined, groynes may be more widely spaced than on an exposed promontory.

The *Shore Protection Manual* [10] recommends a groyne spacing of 2 to 3 times the groyne length, measured from berm crest to seaward end as a general but not universal rule. There is evidence that if a groyne is very long, such as a breakwater at a harbour entrance, sand passing the outer end, being in deeper water, has less chance of being moved shorewards and tends to be lost to offshore shoals.

The stages leading to a rational determination of groyne spacing may be stated as

(1) the estimation of the desired value of Q_g/Q_0;

(2) the selection of groyne length in relation to beach profile to attain Q_g/Q_0, assuming, for a shingle foreshore, that littoral drift is evenly distributed over the width of foreshore, or for a sand beach, utilising the results of model or tracer studies on the distribution of drift;

(3) the selection of spacing so that, at periods of maximum drift, the angle of the beach crest between groynes permits the requisite groyne length to be constructed economically (section 6.3.2) avoiding excessive loading on the groyne due to variations in beach height, on the updrift and downdrift sides. A further criterion affecting spacing may be the need to ensure that a wall or revetment is provided at all times with adequate protection by the beach.

Figure 6.5 indicates diagrammatically how groyne spacing, b, affects the extreme conditions of the beach. At a groyne, for the assumed lines of beach

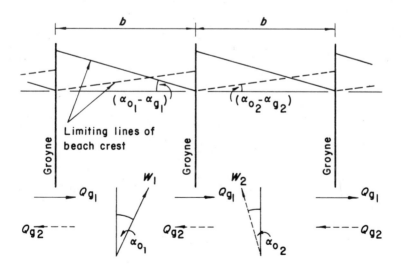

Figure 6.5 *Variation of beach on a groyned shore*

crest, the horizontal distance between points of corresponding height on the up-drift and downdrift sides will be $b \tan (\alpha_0 - \alpha_g)$. For a beach of slope β, the difference in level across the groyne will be $b \tan (\alpha_0 - \alpha_g) \tan \beta$. In fact, local shelter in the lee of each groyne will somewhat reduce this amount.

The use of gapped or permeable groynes for a sand foreshore may help to reduce local scour, but may only be considered where Q_g/Q_0 is to remain fairly high, since they cause no more than a slight reduction in the rate of littoral drift. On a shingle foreshore, groyne-induced scour need not be a serious problem and the permeable groyne is not an economic expedient.

On a sandy foreshore the height of groyne should not exceed 0.5 to 1.0 m above the beach if it is to minimise scour from wave and tidal currents, particularly at the seaward end. It is therefore advisable to provide low groynes at relatively close spacing to achieve the desired value of Q_g/Q_0. Closely spaced, relatively short, groynes on a sand beach have the additional advantage that they tend to control the rip currents [11] so that these occur at correspondingly frequent intervals (see section 4.10) and the littoral drift in the surf zone will consequently be reduced.

6.3.4 Special Problems of a Groyned Foreshore

There is often a relatively thin layer of mobile beach material on a groyned foreshore; in particular shingle may be underlain either by a solid formation or by a dense relatively impermeable, sand–shingle mixture. A thin shingle tends to be an unstable shingle since, as described in section 6.1.3, drift at such points will be increased, leading to a further thinning. It is frequently noticeable that, for a similar reason, where there are steps in the alignment of a seawall, great difficulty may be found in retaining an adequate beach where the seawall is most exposed to the sea.

Another particular difficulty arises at a change in direction of the coastline where a promontory is formed. Here it may be necessary to provide a more substantial groyne to counter the combination of accentuated wave attack with a sudden change in the rate of drift, as illustrated in figure 6.6. The promontory may be associated with a geological feature causing offshore shoaling and the

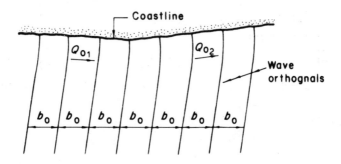

Figure 6.6 *Effect of promontory on longshore drift*

effect of such a complication should not be overlooked in designing the scheme.

The most intractable difficulty is the development of scour, downdrift from the terminal groyne, popularly known as 'the terminal groyne problem'. Russell and Stewart [12] describe a model experiment which confirmed that the volumetric scour, Q_s, developed downdrift of the terminal groynes, resulting from groyning the model foreshore, was equivalent to the reduction in littoral drift caused by the groynes, that is (see section 6.3.1)

$$Q_s = Q_0 - Q_g \qquad (6.3)$$

The shape and extent of the scour hole in plan may be roughly estimated by making the following assumptions, whose validity may be affected by factors of beach alignment, beach material and variation in exposure.

(1) Downdrift of the terminal groyne and clear of the shelter in the immediate lee of this, the angle of the foreshore to the prevailing wave crest line may be derived by application of equation 6.1 (and see section 4.8).

(2) The shape in plan of the scour hole remains constant (see figure 6.7) with the ratios of corresponding dimensions remaining unchanged.

(3) Downdrift of the scour hole, the foreshore line will be unaffected by the groyne system.

Application of these assumptions, with attention to the prevailing trend of the foreshore without the groyne system, will allow the scour to be predicted after a given period of operation of the groyne system.* It is then necessary to consider whether additional remedial works are necessary to counter this effect.

6.3.5 Seawalls and Parallel Revetments

Questions of wave forces on a seawall and overtopping are considered in chapter

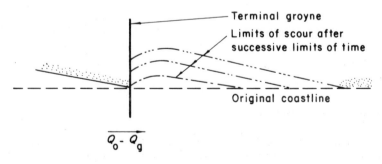

Figure 6.7 *Scour downdrift of terminal groyne*

---

*This approach is only valid if the original coast downdrift follows approximately the same alignment as the groyned length.

7. Here the hydrodynamic criteria to be used in the design and layout of a seawall or revetment are briefly discussed. The principal points are as follows.

(1) Any barrier will reflect a certain amount of wave energy and, on a mobile beach, this will cause modification to the beach profile. However, an irregular permeable revetment will be less destructive to that profile than a seawall.

(2) The higher the level of the beach fronting the barrier, relative to sea level, the less the effect on the beach profile will be.

(3) In the layout of a seawall, particular attention should be given to wave reflection and the possibility of a Mach stem (see section 7.2.2) developing, due to the high angle of obliquity of the oncoming waves.

Section 7.2.3 discusses questions related to the profile of the seawall. The hydrodynamic advantages of providing a stepped profile to a seawall are largely illusory so far as absorption of an appreciable fraction of the energy of storm waves is concerned, since the steps are usually too small by comparison with the wave height. A curved profile will help to avoid a violent reflection and a bull-nosed coping at the top of the wall will tend to deflect the plume from a breaking wave towards the sea — this effect is considerably reduced just when it would be most desirable, during periods of strong onshore winds. Consideration should be given to the several factors related to wall profile, apron, armouring (if any) and variation of beach levels which may determine the depth of scour, at the toe of a wall for the maximum waves to which it could be exposed, and how this may be controlled. On a sand beach, for example, where the wave may break against the vertical face of a wall at high water, the depth of scour may be of the same order as the wave height.

A permeable revetment may be built of some form of timber stockade, a rock bund or a mound of shaped units (see figure 6.8) similar to breakwater armouring units described in section 7.3. On grounds of efficiency, a permeable revetment is usually superior to a solid seawall, but it may be ruled out by considerations of space and amenity. A revetment will not normally lead to accretion of an already adequate natural foreshore, but it may be designed to destroy sufficient wave energy to achieve a dramatic improvement of a low foreshore or a thin beach.

6.3.6 Intermediate Barriers

The introduction of a revetment parallel to the shoreline at an intermediate position between high and low water is frequently advocated and occasionally constructed. Due to the principles, described in chapter 5, which control the beach gradient, the result is to cause a step at the revetment, to reduce the beach slope to shoreward and, more noticeably, to seaward of the revetment due to local wave reflection. Such a barrier has very limited application; whether or not any improvement will be caused to the beach will depend on the condition of the

Figure 6.8 *Revetment in Tripod Units, Seaford (A.H. Toms)*

shore and the fraction of the energy of the breaking wave absorbed by the revetment.

6.4 The Principles of Bays and Artificial Headlands

The principal features of natural bays are discussed in section 5.4.5. Here we are concerned with coast protection by the formation of artificial bays between bastions or the deepening (in plan) of natural bays by the reinforcement or extension of headlands.

Silvester [13] suggests a relationship between the distance between the headlands, depth of bay, and the angle between predominant waves and a line joining the headlands as shown in figure 6.9.

The erosion that occurs downdrift of a terminal groyne, illustrated in figure 6.7, is indicative of the shape of the updrift end of a bay. This can be seen in figure 6.10 — an aerial photograph which shows the way the sand cliffs are receding beyond a terminal groyne.

When a bay is in equilibrium with the predominant waves, including the most severe storm waves, the vector of wave momentum is normal to the shoreline at all points. However, littoral drift occurs in response to waves from other directions and may recur with lesser waves from the storm direction due to

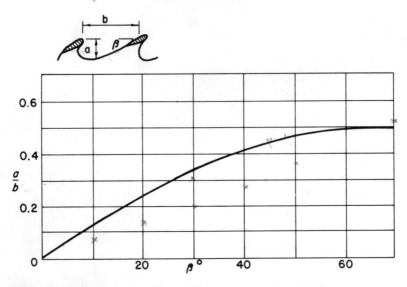

Figure 6.9 *Indentation ratio a/b against wave approach angle β*

Figure 6.10 *Erosion downdrift of a terminal groyne*

different effects of refraction, etc., but since wind and wave directions have a generally seasonal pattern over a period of about a year, the cumulative drift in an equilibrium bay tends to be zero.

In a non-stable bay the straight length of beach attached to the downdrift headland becomes stable long before the curved section adjacent to the updrift headland or 'strong point'. An artificial headland constructed at Barton-on-Sea achieved this stable beach within 3 years of construction (see figure 6.11). Meanwhile very active erosion continued downdrift of a concrete outfall structure, which as a result of frequent maintenance behaved as a complementary updrift headland. The updrift beach, shown in figure 6.12, has not yet reached equilibrium, and the predicted form is shown as a broken line. While this shape is being formed, the coarser material eroded from the shoreline feeds and extends the length of stable beach while finer material tends to be dragged off the beach and deposited as a bar at the low-water level.

Figure 6.11 *Artificial headland at Barton-on-Sea*

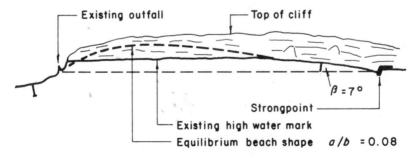

Figure 6.12 *Plan of evolution of bay between strong points, Barton-on-Sea*

Intense erosion may be expected of a shore of mobile material immediately downdrift of an artificial strong point or bastion. The feature may be so designed as to provide local shelter to the lee side and thus avoid the alternative of periodical strengthening of the root as the shoreline recedes.

When designing a scheme of coast protection using a bay formed between two artificial headlands, a logarithmic spiral may be used to predict the approximate stable shape of the bay. However, there is no physical justification for this and intelligent use of any particular part of the curve gives only a qualitative result. A fairly accurate solution to the bay formation may be obtained by solving the simultaneous equations for the rate of drift and for coastal change, using finite difference approximations (see section 4.8), with appropriate fixed time intervals and elements of coastline. An approach on these lines is described by Walton. [14]

A different type of bay is formed when the sea breaks through a stable, durable coastline over a sill or breaches a parallel revetment. Lulworth Cove, Dorset, is an example of such a bay. They tend to be symmetrical (geological factors permitting), have a depth to length ratio much greater than the type of bay described above and the formation is virtually independent of the direction of wave approach. [15]

6.5 Offshore Breakwaters

The commonest form of offshore breakwater is a rock mound constructed approximately parallel to the shoreline. The presence of an offshore barrier causes partial sheltering in its 'shadow' combined with diffraction of the waves at each end. On a sandy shore this tends to form tombolos.

Figure 7.7 indicates the approximate height of the reflected wave, H_R, and the transmitted wave, H_T, for an incident wave of height H_I and length L, encountering a plate extending from above sea level to a depth D, in a depth of water h. If the mound of height $(h - D)$ be considered as providing protection equivalent to a plate extending from the sea bed to a depth D, then the wave energy passing such a plate may be considered as equivalent to that reflected from the complementary plate extending from above sea level to depth D. Thus, if H'_T be the height of the wave transmitted past the mound, $H'_T = H_R$, where H_R may be read off figure 7.7 for representative values of h/L. A mound will cause less reflection than a plate of equivalent height but it will also destroy a fraction of the energy of the incident wave.

Caution should be exercised in using an approximation of this nature as $D \rightarrow 0$ since, on the one hand, an appreciable fraction of wave energy will be transmitted above mean sea level; on the other hand, a high enough wave will break above the mound. Each case will need to be considered individually, taking account of the ratio H_I/D.

In addition, a barrier with finite width will tend to cause a differential fraction of transmission and reflection of wave energy when the width of the mound bears a simple ratio to the wave length, in depth D. It must also be appreciated that this very simplified theory assumes no energy losses at the barrier.

From considerations of continuity, Lamb [16] established the heights of the transmitted and reflected waves at a sudden change in section of a canal. If we apply the same reasoning to the motion at the front and rear faces of a wide flat-topped mound with steep faces, we find that

$$\frac{H'_T}{H_I} = \frac{4C_1 C_2}{(C_1 + C_2)^2} \tag{6.4}$$

where C_1 and C_2 represent wave celerity in depths h and D respectively. Substituting for C_1 and C_2 in equation 6.4 from equation 3.11

$$\frac{H'_T}{H_I} = \frac{4 \tanh 2\pi h/L_1 \tanh 2\pi D/L_2}{(\tanh 2\pi h/L_1 + \tanh 2\pi D/L_2)^2} \tag{6.5}$$

where L_1 and L_2 relate to depths h and D respectively. The function 6.5 may be evaluated by using figure 3.2 to find $\tanh 2\pi h/L$ in terms of h/L_0 where the wave period, T, is known, and hence L_0 (equation 3.13).

In shallow water ($h/L \leqslant 0.04$), from equation 6.5

$$\frac{H'_T}{H_I} = \frac{4(hD)^{1/2}}{(h^{1/2} + D^{1/2})^2} \tag{6.6}$$

making use of equation 3.14.

In each of the above cases, no loss of energy is assumed to occur at the barrier and hence $H_R'^2 = H_I'^2 - H_T'^2$.

Since, for a constant period, the energy of a wave $\propto H^2$, end diffraction will be set up by the 'difference wave' of height $(H_I^2 - H_T^2)^{1/2}$ and the resulting composite wave may be obtained by superimposing the end diffraction pattern, given by figure 3.27, on the height of the transmitted wave obtained from figure 7.7. The result may vary considerably with the state of the tide where the range is high, since D/h will vary correspondingly. Breakwaters of this type have usually been constructed to cause interruption to littoral drift, often immediately updrift of a harbour threatened with excessive siltation.

The effectiveness of an offshore breakwater as a barrier to longshore drift on a straight foreshore will depend on [17]

(1) the length of the breakwater relative to the wave length of incident waves, L
(2) the length of the breakwater relative to its distance offshore.

The performance of existing offshore breakwaters [18,19] illustrates the desirable conditions of offshore bed gradients and low tidal variation. Short barriers may be considered to emphasise promontories (section 6.4). Barriers built (a) near the shoreline of a steep beach should be $2L$ to $3L$ long with a gap width of L, (b) in water depths of 1 m on a gentle beach, $3L$ to $5L$ long with a gap of L, (c) in water depth 2 m to 4 m, the length may be $2L$ to $6L$ with a gap of L; the distance offshore should be 0.3 to 1 times the breakwater length. [20]

Flexible offshore barriers have also been proposed from time to time (see section 7.3.4) and 'artificial seaweed', arranged in forests of plastic thongs attached to the sea bed, can modify bed currents leading to slight wave damping and local accretion of sand. [21,22] However, there are practical problems when artificial seaweed is used near areas of diving, of inshore shipping or pleasure boat routes where propellers may pick up the 'weed'.

6.6 Beach Replenishment

Chapter 4 describes methods of predicting quantitative and grading requirements of material for beach replenishment. A scheme for beach replenishment by importing sand or shingle must pay attention to two basic factors on which the success of the scheme will depend

(1) the material to be used should be suitable not only in quantity but in quality and grading

(2) the rate of replenishment along a frontage should be designed so as to repair the deficiencies in natural transport by littoral drift.

Point (1) will not arise in feeding schemes using coarse material from the foreshore; even from such a source, however, it is necessary to consider the possibility that, due to differential exposure of orientation, there may be some noticeable variation in particle size between the borrow pit and the frontage to be protected. It is also possible for the grain size characteristics of a borrow material to change during handling, particularly if the fill is moved with a dredger or transported hydraulically. [23] For sand replenishment the use of a material with a coarser grading than the naturally occurring sand will steepen the beach profile, thus moving the head of the beach seawards. A finer material will be taken to the foot of the beach or into deeper water.

Point (2) presents a more complex series of problems and there are the following possible situations to consider. First, the beach may be restored simply by feeding entirely at the updrift end and this is usually the case when beach feeding is combined with groynes, provided that erosion downdrift of the terminal groyne is otherwise controlled. Second, the foreshore may indicate that natural drift increases in the downdrift direction and thus that feeding is required at intermediate points to make good such a deficiency. Third, for a groyned foreshore, while it may be adequate to ensure that groyne compartments remain well filled by feeding from the updrift end, special attention should be given to areas of difficulties of the type described in section 6.3.4, such as those related to change in direction of coastline. These various cases are illustrated in figure 6.13.

When replenishing a sheltered beach entirely with sand, large quantities are required which, for economy, must be deposited fairly uniformly along the length of foreshore.

Where the beach feeding is carried out intermittently at selected points, at a rate in excess of the natural drift, a promontory will develop seawards. This will have the effect of acting as a temporary barrier to the natural drift and temporary protection will result in updrift of the tipping or discharge point. Downdrift,

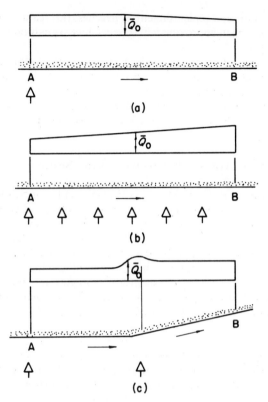

Figure 6.13 *Injection points for beach recharge*

beyond the immediate influence of such a promontory, there can be no
decrease in the rate of transport, and short-term erosion may occur in consequence. It is an inevitable and somewhat paradoxical conclusion, therefore, that
for a beach corresponding to the type illustrated by figure 6.13(b), the immediate
advantage from beach feeding is experienced updrift rather than downdrift of
the point of injection. In practice, this conclusion is confirmed and may result
in the required rate of recharge being less than that calculated to make good
deficiencies in natural drift.

Material at the feeding points must not be deposited in depths of water
beyond the limit of littoral drift; this criterion will be more critical for
shingle than for sand, for the reasons outlined in chapter 4. Where the material
is won from borrow pits on the foreshore, intended to be naturally replenished
by littoral drift, it is necessary to study the conditions of the sea and the form of
the borrow pit to preclude the possibility of a bar forming across its seaward
face which could convert it into a lagoon, which might be bypassed subsequently
by the littoral drift.

A beach in the process of adjusting its profile is more susceptible to longshore drift and this gives rise to difficulties especially when using a simple
equation for longshore movement (section 4.8) on a coast subject to an appreci-

able tidal range. For sand replenishment of beaches, this feature favours the restoration of the beach approximately to reproduce its natural (concave upwards) profile. [24]

A particular form of beach feeding is by the use of the 'refraction groyne' for the purpose, whereby recharge is concentrated at a point, the sand groyne retards longshore drift and offshore losses are reduced; by careful positioning and geometry, lee erosion may be avoided. Such a method is described by Führböter [25] and Dette [26] for the Island of Sylt in the North Sea.

6.7 Directions of Approach of Waves to the Shore

Section 6.1.2 assumes that information is available on the angle of incidence of waves to the coast, for the prevailing, or dominant, waves and also for the extreme storm waves. This is frequently the most difficult estimate to make in planning coast protection; judgement and experience may well compensate for some of the complexities of a rigorous analytical approach. Ideally, and essentially for an exposed coastline where long swell develops from storms far to sea, wave records are needed to establish the design wave climate. Otherwise the first necessity in studying the prevailing waves is for a wind rose, applicable to the area in which waves are generated, to be presented in some such form as that shown in figure 6.14. The wind rose must differentiate between periods of light and strong winds. It is the distribution with direction of the latter that concerns the coastal engineer. Some engineers construct a vector diagram from the wind rose to determine directly the approximate direction of the prevailing wave but this appears to be unsound for two reasons

(1) it takes no account of refraction of the deep water wave
(2) it disregards variations in fetch and shelter for the different points of the compass.

The use of an array of wave recorders such as wave-rider buoys may provide direct information on wave heights, periods and directions. [27] Alternatively, the approximate directions of swell on an exposed coastline may be derived indirectly from records of data from a single recorder in deep water, which are plotted daily or at more frequent intervals in the form of spectral density curves as described in section 3.3.6. These curves may then serve to construct contours of wave power on a plot of frequency against time. The area contained within a contour is then a direct measure of wave energy. Figure 6.15 shows how a 'storm' line may be constructed at an angle ϕ to the time base along the 'ridge' of a developing storm. Since wave velocity in deep water

$$C_0 = \frac{g}{2\pi f}$$

the distance travelled by a wave in time t s is

$$\frac{g^t}{2\pi f} = \frac{g}{2\pi} k \tan \phi$$

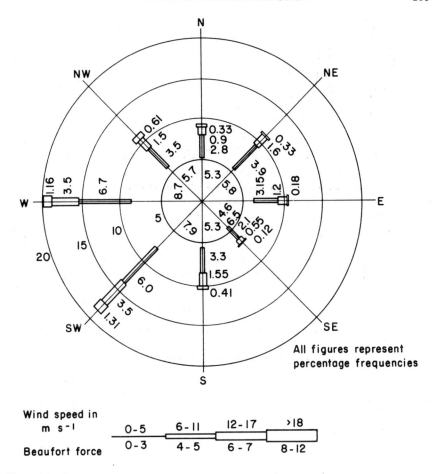

Figure 6.14 *Wind rose*

(where ϕ is measured from a plot similar to figure 6.5 adjusted by k for scales and units) and this will yield the approximate distance offshore of the storm centre. The use of a synoptic barometric chart for the day on which the 'storm line' intersects the time base will then reveal the position of the storm centre and the approximate origin of the swell waves.

Often it will be found adequate to determine, by observation, the approximate period of the dominant waves mainly responsible for littoral drift and to arrive at the deep water direction from the wind vector, ignoring winds from directions from which the coast is sheltered, and making allowance for a degree of wave refraction. A refraction study will then indicate the approximate angle of incidence of the prevailing breaking wave.

The longer the wave, the more nearly parallel to the coast will its crest be refracted. The most oblique wave to take into account in designing a groyne system (section 6.3.3) is therefore the steep short wave caused by strong winds

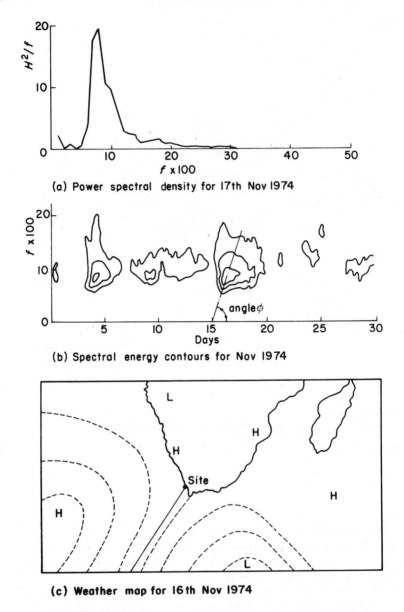

(a) Power spectral density for 17th Nov 1974

(b) Spectral energy contours for Nov 1974

(c) Weather map for 16th Nov 1974

Figure 6.15 *Example of wave direction analysis using wave spectra and weather maps*

of limited duration. For an exposed coast, a wave period of about 4 s may be taken (relating to a 20 m/s wind blowing for an hour—see figure 3.14) and a rudimentary refraction study will indicate the highest angle of incidence for a minimum predetermined significant breaking wave height (section 3.33 and 3.4).

Example 6.1

Prevailing waves strike a straight beach at an angle of 10°. It is required to prevent further erosion along a length of 2 km, currently occurring at an annual rate of 10 m³/m, by a system of groynes. At present, littoral drift at the updrift end of the beach is estimated at 50 000 m³/year. What must the groyne system achieve in maintaining a new orientation of beachline between groynes?

If it is assumed that 50 000 m³/year of beach material continue to enter the groyned beach at the updrift end, then at any intermediate point X m downdrift from here, the rate of littoral drift for the groyned beach must be reduced in the ratio

$$\frac{50\,000}{50\,000 + 10X}$$

Littoral drift is assumed proportional to sin 2α where α is the angle of incidence and since sin 20° ~ 20° (expressed in radians) the change of angle of the beachline at any point along this frontage is given by

$$10°(50\,000 + 10X - 50\,000)/(50\,000 + 10X) = 10°\,[X/(5000 + X)]$$
$$= 0° \text{ at an updrift end}$$

1°40′ where	$X = 1000$ m
and 2°50′ where	$X = 2000$ m

It should be noted that protection of the beach will tend to reduce erosion updrift of the protected length. Pelnard- Considère [28] indicates how, in the course of time, this effect on natural littoral drift may be calculated.

Example 6.2

It is required to reduce the offshore equivalent height of swell waves striking a beach from a maximum of 2 m to 1.6 m by means of a parallel offshore barrier in a depth of water of 8 m. What is the approximate level of the top of the barrier below the surface of the sea?

Since we are concerned with swell waves, we may assume that equation 6.6 is applicable for an approximate solution; that is

$$4/5 = 4 \times (8D)^{1/2}/(8^{1/2} + D^{1/2})^2$$
$$8 + 4(2D)^{1/2} + D = 10(2D)^{1/2}$$
$$D^{1/2} = 1.1 \text{ or } D = 1.2 \text{ m}$$

Example 6.3

Given a native beach material with grain size characteristics

$$nD_{84} = 0.15 \text{ mm}$$
$$nD_{16} = 0.28 \text{ mm}$$

and the characteristics of several potential borrow areas as follows

(A) $bD_{84} = 0.11$ mm, $bD_{16} = 0.18$ mm

(B) $bD_{84} = 0.18$ mm, $bD_{16} = 0.25$ mm

(C) $bD_{84} = 0.12$ mm, $bD_{16} = 0.35$ mm

which borrow material would result in the least long term losses when used for renourishment?

Referring to section 4.11

	Native	A	B	C
ϕ_{84}	2.74	3.18	2.47	3.06
ϕ_{16}	1.84	2.47	2.00	1.50
μ	2.29	2.82	2.23	2.28
σ	0.45	0.35	0.23	0.78
δ		1.18	-0.13	-0.02
σ_r		0.77	0.51	1.73
Overfill ratio		>10	2.00	1.25

Quite clearly material A would be unstable and material C would be the better of B and C.

References

1. A.M. Muir Wood, Characteristics of shingle beaches: the solution to some practical problems, *Proceedings of the 12th Coastal Engineering Conference, Washington, 1970*, pp. 1059-76
2. J.M. Armstrong, Low cost shore protection on the Great Lakes: a demonstration research programme, *Proceedings of the 15th Coastal Engineering Conference, Hawaii, 1976*, vol. III, pp. 2858-87
3. B.L. Edge, J.G. Housley and G.M. Watts, Low-cost shore protection, *Proceedings of the 15th Coastal Engineering Conference, Hawaii, 1976*, vol. III, pp. 2888-904
4. M. Porraz, J.A. Maza and M.L. Munoz, Low cost structures using operational design systems, *Proceedings of ASCE Specialty Conference 'Sediments 77', Charleston, 1977*, pp. 672-85
5. T.W. Richardson, Systems for bypassing at coastal inlets, *Proceedings of ASCE Specialty Conference 'Sediments 77', Charleston, 1977*, pp. 67-84
6. C.P. Jones and A.J. Mehta, A comparative review of sand transfer systems at Florida's tidal entrances, *Proceedings of ASCE Specialty Conference 'Sediments 77', Charleston, 1977*, pp. 48-66
7. E.C. McNair, A sand bypassing system using a jet pump, *Proceedings of the 15th Coastal Engineering Conference, Hawaii, 1976*, vol. III, pp. 1342-60

8. J. Duvivier, The Selsey Coast protection scheme, *Proc. Instn civ. Engrs.*, **20** (1961) 481-506

9. Hydraulics Research Station, Seaford Sea Wall — protection by artificial fill, Report No. EX 209 (1963)

10. *Shore Protection Manual* (U.S. Army C.E.R.C., 1975)

11. M.K. Gaughan and P.D. Komar, Groin length and generation of edge waves, *Proceedings of the 15th Coastal Engineering Conference, Hawaii, 1976*, vol. II, pp. 1459-76

12. R.C.H. Russell and C.F. Stewart, An investigation of a model shingle beach: the terminal groyne problem, Internal Hydraulics Research Station Report; see also *Hydraulics Research* (1960) D.S.I.R. pp. 65-7

13. R. Silvester, Headland defense of coasts, *Proceedings of the 15th Coastal Engineering Conference, Hawaii, 1976*, vol. II, pp. 1394-406

14. T.L. Walton, Equilibrium shores and coastal design, *Proceedings of ASCE Specialty Conference 'Sediments 77', Charleston, 1977*, pp. 1-16

15. R.G. Dean, Diffraction calculations of shoreline planforms, *Proceedings of the 16th Coastal Engineering Conference, Hamburg, 1978*, vol. II, pp. 1903-17

16. H. Lamb, *Hydrodynamics*, 6th edn. (Cambridge University Press 1945)

17. R.M. Noble, Coastal structures' effects on shorelines, *Proceedings of the 16th Coastal Engineering Conference, Hamburg, 1978*, vol. III, pp. 2069-85

18. I. Fried, Protection by means of offshore breakwaters, *Proceedings of the 15th Coastal Engineering Conference, Hawaii, 1976*, vol. II, pp. 1407-24

19. O. Toyoshima, Changes in sea bed due to detached breakwaters, *Proceedings of the 15th Coastal Engineering Conference, Hawaii, 1976*, vol. II, pp. 1572-89

20. O. Toyoshima, Design of a detached breakwater system, *Proceedings of the 14th Coastal Engineering Conference, Copenhagen, 1974*

21. W.A. Price, and K.W. Tomlinson, The effect of artifical seaweed in promoting the build-up of beaches, *Proceedings of the 11th Coastal Engineering Conference, London, 1968*, paper 135

22. H.G.H. Ten Hoopen, Recent applications of artificial seaweed in the Netherlands, *Proceedings of the 15th Coastal Engineering Conference, Hawaii, 1976*, vol. III, pp. 2905-15

23. R.D. Hobson, Sediment handling and beach fill design, *Proceedings of ASCE Specialty Conference 'Sediments 77', Charleston, 1977*, pp. 167-80

24. H. Christiansen, Economic profiling of beach fills, *Proceedings of ASCE Specialty Conference, 'Sediments 77', Charleston, 1977*, pp. 1042-8

25. A. Führböter, A refraction groyne built by sand, *Proceedings of the 14th Coastal Engineering Conference, Copenhagen, 1974*

26. H.H. Dette, Effectiveness of beach deposit nourishment, *Proceedings of ASCE Specialty Conference 'Sediments 77' Charleston, 1977*, pp. 211-27

27. D. Esteva, Wave direction Computations with three gauge arrays, *Proceedings of the 15th Coastal Engineering Conference, Hawaii, 1976*, vol. I, pp. 349-67

28. R. Pelmard-Considère, Essaie de théorie de l'evolution des formes de rivages en plages de sables et de galets, *IVième journées de l'Hydraulique*, Question III (1956)

7

Waves and Structures

7.1 Selection of Wave Characteristics

In selecting the characteristics of the design wave, different types of structure require different starting points.

(1) If the total loss of a structure is unacceptable, it must be designed for the maximum wave foreseen during the required life of the structure.

(2) The serviceability of a structure such as a breakwater or revetment may establish the acceptable limit of damage for a wave height to be expected to be exceeded on only a few occasions in the life of the structure. The choice of design wave will then be established mainly on the grounds of economics taking account of capital and maintenance costs during the life of the structure, including any consequential costs of damage and availability of materials.

In comparing alternative designs, the economies of each may be based upon these factors taking account of the possibility that, on account of (a), (b), (c) below, different design wave heights (and other characteristics) may be appropriate to different designs of structure.

(3) Where fatigue or progressive failure may be a concern, as for offshore structures, a unidirectional spectral wave analysis will be required (on the lines described in section 7.7); in certain instances, a multi-directional spectral analysis will be appropriate.

The height, H, of the design wave to the nature of the structure may be related [1] as follows

(a) for a rigid structure (for example, a concrete seawall) subject to sudden failure: $H_{1/100}$

(b) for a semi-rigid structure (for example, cantilevered steel sheet piling): $H_{1/100} - H_{10}$.

(c) for a flexible structure (for example, rubble mound breakwater): H_s.

Definitions of $H_s, H_{1/100}$ and $H_{1/10}$ are contained in section 3.3.5. The design wave period will often be T_z (section 3.3.5) but the use of T_p (peak energy) should, where known, be preferred.

The design wave parameters may be selected by the following procedure.

(1) Select design wave H_{des} ($H_{1/100}, H_{1/10}, H_s, \ldots$).

(2) Calculate maximum breaker height for H_{des}.
(3) If $H_{des} < H_{b\,max}$ use H_{des} for calculating stability.
(4) If $H_{des} > H_{b\,max}$ use $H_{b\,max}$ for calculating stability.
(5) Calculate H_{max} from data or assumed spectrum.
(6) If $H_{b\,max} < H_{max}$ use $H_{b\,max}$ for run-up and overtopping.
(7) If $H_{b\,max} > H_{max}$ use H_{max} for run-up and overtopping.

The design wave must be associated with appropriate conditions of tide, set-up and surge, recognising that the two latter factors, having a meteorological cause, may be related to the wave climate. Chapter 3 has discussed shallow water and the characteristics of the breaking waves. The choice of design wave will be related to the extent and reliability of wave data.

Design for a particular event of sea level, wave length and wave height assumes a regular train of waves. Model experiments frequently show, for revetments for example, that irregular waves may be more damaging than regular wave trains. Model tests simulating random seas or intermixing of two or more wave trains may be necessary to establish such questions.

Wave grouping may lead to occasional waves of extreme height in excess of those associated with waves of equal individual height dispersed throughout a wave train.[2] This further implies that laboratory experiments based on random waves may provide less severe exposure than in the real situation in which the order of succession of waves of different height and length may be an important contributory factor to local resonance and local extreme damage.[3]

The geometry of the sea bed in the vicinity of the structure may determine the maximum possible wave and it is not safe to assume that the maximum height of the incipiently breaking wave is limited to $0.78h$ (section 3.2.4); in adverse circumstances H may be as much as 1.4 since the changes leading to forming a breaker may extend over a distance of half the (shallow water) wave length. The orbital motions of the breaking wave remain to some extent unknown and can only be fully determined by a full instrumentation of a structure subjected to such a wave. Differential scale effects prevent a reduced size model from providing full information about the breaking wave.

7.2   Forces on Continuous Structures

7.2.1   The Continuous Vertical Wall in Deep Water

The classical analysis of the pressure distribution caused by a totally reflected wave against the vertical face of a wall founded in deep water is due to Sainflou.[4] The theory is based on the formation of a standing wave or clapotis at the face of the wall (see section 3.6). For a wave approaching the line of the wall transversely, the pressure diagram (to be superimposed on the hydrostatic pressure against the wall) requires the definition of three points to determine the pressure distribution on the vertical section (see figure 7.1).

(1) A represents the crest of the clapotis at which pressure is zero.
(2) B represents the still water surface level.
(3) C represents sea bed level, distance h below B.

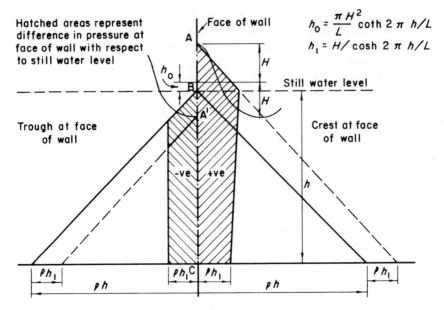

Figure 7.1 *Wave pressures against face of vertical wall*

The height of the clapotis, for an incident wave of height H, is $2H$. However, the mean wave level against the wall (the level of the orbital centre of the wave surface) is at a height h_0 above still water level where

$$h_0 = \frac{\pi H^2}{L} \coth \frac{2\pi h}{L} \tag{7.1}$$

Hence A is at a height $H + h_0$ above B, as defined above, the pressure at B being hydrostatic, that is

$$p_B = \rho (H + h_0) \tag{7.2}$$

with h_0 obtained from equation 7.1.

From equation 3.2, for an Airy wave the pressure at any point is given (in engineering units) by

$$\frac{p}{\rho} = \frac{1}{g} \frac{\partial \phi}{\partial t} - z \tag{7.3}$$

But, for a standing wave of height $2H$, from equation 3.33

$$\frac{\partial \phi}{\partial t} = gH \frac{\cosh 2\pi(z + h)/L}{\cosh 2\pi h/L} \sin \frac{2\pi x}{L} \sin \frac{2\pi t}{T} \tag{7.4}$$

and the surface level at any point is given by

$$\eta = H \sin \frac{2\pi x}{L} \sin \frac{2\pi t}{T} \tag{7.5}$$

Hence, from equations 7.3, 7.4 and 7.5

$$p = \rho \left[\eta \, \frac{\cosh 2\pi(z+h)/L}{\cosh 2\pi h/L} \right] - \rho z \tag{7.6}$$

where the factor

$$\frac{\cosh 2\pi(z+h)/L}{\cosh 2\pi h/L}$$

is known as the pressure response factor. At the bed $z = -h$ and the pressure at C

$$p_C = \rho \left(h \pm \frac{H}{\cosh 2\pi h/L} \right) \tag{7.7}$$

the higher value relating to the pressure beneath the crest (right side of figure 7.1) and the lower value to the pressure beneath the trough (left side of figure 7.1).

The simplified pressure diagram is as shown on figure 7.1, the pressures varying approximately linearly between A and B and, also, between B and C. For the minimum pressures when the wave trough is against the wall, A' is displaced to $H - h_0$ below B, and the pressure diagram varies linearly from B to A', then to the lower value of p_C (equation 7.4).

For a wall that would be overtopped by the wave, the part of the pressure diagram above the crest of the wall is lopped off and the remainder is assumed to be unchanged.

Sainflou's analysis, which leads to the derivation of equation 7.1, assumes a standing elliptical trochoidal wave, a shallow water variant of a Gerstner wave, where the particle orbits are represented as

$$x = x_0 + 2r \sin \frac{2\pi t}{T} \cos \frac{2\pi x_0}{L} \tag{7.8}$$

and

$$z = z_0 + 4 \frac{\pi r r'}{L} \sin^2 \frac{2\pi t}{T} + 2r' \sin \frac{2\pi t}{T} \sin \frac{2\pi x_0}{L} \tag{7.9}$$

where, at the free surface, $z_0 = 0$, $r = (H/2) \coth 2\pi h/L$ and $r' = H/2$.

A number of alternative theories for the pressure of a reflected wave at the vertical face of a wall have been derived, based on more complex initial assumptions for the wave form. Sainflou's analysis appears to be somewhat conservative but survives because of its relative simplicity, having regard to the margins of error essentially attached to the estimate of the characteristics of the design wave.

The procedure becomes more complex when it is required to calculate pressures against a vertical wall founded on a rubble mound or on a steeply shelving sea bed. Provided the water depth at the wall face remains deep enough to ensure clapotis without the wave breaking, a reasonable approximation may be obtained by basing the calculation on the depth of water at the face of the wall. The results of model tests are necessary for a more accurate assessment of wave forces in such a situation.

A true standing wave with nodal points midway between the antinodes only occurs in deep water. Generally, subsidiary incident and reflected wave crests may be observed travelling over the surface. Ultimately, when the ratio of H/L is such that the wave assumes the form of a solitary wave, the motion is entirely that of interpenetration of opposing systems of incident and reflected wave crests.

7.2.2 Reflection of the Solitary Wave

Where a vertical wall is fronted by a sloping sea bed, the depth of water at the nearest point of apparent clapotis $(L/2)$ of a solitary wave of length L will be greater than that at the wall. Partial breaking of the waves may occur at the position of this clapotis. Laboratory experiments by Danel reported by Wiegel [5] on the limiting heights of progressive and standing waves over a considerable range of H/L and h/L ratios, indicate that standing solitary waves may develop to a height of about $1.2h$, provided the distance between crests is appreciably greater than L_{sol} (see equation 3.58). Where the spacing between crests approaches L_{sol} the standing waves will partially break. This will limit the height of the reformed wave against the wall face.

Section 3.2.4 indicates the limitations on height of the solitary wave in relation to the depth of water. Up to the transitional point, from consideration of the wave as a periodical wave to a solitary wave, equation 3.81 may be used to determine the wave height. Thereafter, subsequent characteristics of the wave may be derived from equation 3.60.

If we accept the simpler form of the solitary wave (equation 3.48) total reflection of a train of solitary waves will create a system of apparent standing waves as a result of the encounter of a series of equal waves travelling in opposite directions. If $C = [g(h + H)]^{1/2}$ (equation 3.50) the result will be a 'standing wave' of peak crest height $2H$ and with zero particle velocity, on a vertical section at the maximum crest height, by considerations of conservation of energy. Between positions of clapotis, the crest height will fall to the height H above surface level.

Assuming no loss of energy of the solitary wave entering deep water, equation 3.60 implies that wave height is related to water depth at points 1 and 2 by the relationships

$$\frac{8}{3}\,\rho g h_1^2 H_1 \left(\frac{H_1}{3h_1}\right)^{1/2} = \frac{8}{3}\,\rho\,g h_2^2 H_2 \left(\frac{H_2}{3h_2}\right)^{1/2} \tag{7.10}$$

that is

$$\frac{H_1}{H_2} = \frac{h_2}{h_1} \tag{7.11}$$

and the height is inversely proportional to the still depth of water. For a regular train of waves, the nearest 'standing wave' to the wall face will be at a distance S where

$$S = \frac{CT}{2} \text{ or } \frac{1}{2}\int C\,dT \tag{7.12}$$

where T is the wave period and the integral may be solved by a knowledge of the relationship between depth of water and distance from the wall. It will then be possible to establish whether or not partial breaking will occur at this point.

Wiegel [5] states that a solitary wave is reflected symmetrically from a vertical wall provided its crest line makes an angle, α, to the wall, less than $45°$. For a greater angle of incidence, say $45° < \alpha < 70°$, close to the wall, each crest alters its alignment to create a wave travelling along the face of the wall with increased crest height, known as a Mach stem. The height of crest gives rise to a velocity u equivalent to the component of the incident wave's celerity in this direction, that is $u = C \csc \alpha$. Since the waves do not strike the face of the wall, no reflection occurs. The variations in the effect have been studied for walls with inclined faces.

7.2.3 Impact of the Breaking Wave

Where a wave breaks on a sloping beach, assumed here to be smooth and impermeable, it is possible by means of a simplified treatment (but see also section 7.3.1) to derive expressions for the height of run-up and the forces applied to the face of a seawall in the swash zone.

(1) At the instant of breaking, 75 per cent of the height, H_b, of the crest of the breaker is assumed (on the basis of model tests) to be above still water level, which corresponds to a depth of water h_b.[6]

(2) The forward motion of water particles in the crest is assumed to be

$$u_b = C_b = (gh_b)^{1/2} \tag{7.13}$$

and confined to that part of the crest above still water level.

(3) Equating pressures on the face of a wall seaward of the shoreline (see figure 7.2) to the rate of destruction of momentum of the advancing wave crest, the dynamic component of pressure expressed as head of water

$$P_v = \rho\,\frac{u_b^2}{g} = \rho h_b \tag{7.14}$$

and the total pressure diagram on the face of a vertical wall is as illustrated in figure 7.2.

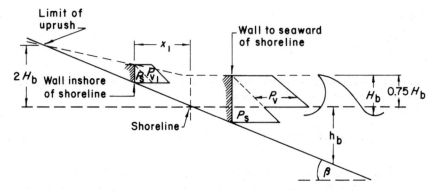

Figure 7.2 *Forces and run-up inshore of the breaker zone*

(4) Inshore of the shoreline, the uprush or swash is assumed to decrease linearly in quantity and in velocity, to the point of maximum uprush situated at a height of $2H_b$ above still water level (or a value provided by equation 7.26). Thus, for the vertical wall illustrated in figure 7.2 static pressure increases linearly from zero at the swash surface to

$$P_s = 0.75 \, \rho H_b \left(1 - \frac{X_1 \tan \beta}{2H_b} \right) \tag{7.15}$$

at beach level while the dynamic pressure

$$P_{v1} = P_v \left(1 - \frac{X_1^2 \tan^2 \beta}{4H_b^2} \right) \tag{7.16}$$

where P_v is derived from equation 7.14.

For a wall (or for part of the profile of a wall) with a face inclined to the horizontal at an angle θ ($\theta > 90°$, that is, the face does not oversail), the dynamic component of the wave force may be considered as applied transverse to the wall face, and the dynamic pressure

$$P_{v, \, \theta} = P_v \sin^2 \theta \text{ or } P_{v1, \, \theta} = P_{v1} \sin^2 \theta \tag{7.17}$$

with P_v or P_{v1} evaluated from equations 7.14 and 7.16 respectively. For a wall of fairly flat slope, the maximum wave pressure will not occur at all levels simultaneously; for such a wall it is in any event improbable that problems of over-all stability, requiring the application of equation 7.17, will arise. Section 3.4.4 indicates how H_b may be derived from the characteristics of the deep water wave and the refraction coefficient.

The degree of asymmetry of a wave after passing through shoaling water (see section 3.4) will affect its breaking characteristics.[7]

7.2.4 Impulsive Forces on Seawalls

Seawalls have frequently been damaged in such a way as must have required forces considerably greater than those explained by a purely hydrodynamic analysis. Bagnold [8] studied a number of such instances and measured maximum forces caused by waves striking model walls. He concluded that the mechanism involved the compression of a cushion of air between the wave front and the wall.

Where a large cushion of air is involved, pressure on the wall face will not be greatly increased and the bubble will 'explode' to cause a plume of water to rise against the face of the wall. Where, however, the air is confined in extent over the area of the face of the wall, as may occur close to the breaking point when the wave front is approximately parallel to the face of the wall, Bagnold suggested the model illustrated in figure 7.3. Assume that a 'piston' of water of length K compresses a unit area of a cushion of air in a confined horizontal space of length l and of constant cross-sectional area. Assume the 'piston' arrives with initial horizontal velocity u_0, with the contained air at pressure p_0. Then, for adiabatic compression, when the length of pocket has been reduced to a length x

$$p = p_0 \left(\frac{l}{x}\right)^\gamma \tag{7.18}$$

[where γ (= 1.4 for air) is the ratio of specific heat of a gas for constant pressure to that for constant volume]. The velocity u of the piston is given by

$$p = \frac{\rho K}{g} \frac{u\, du}{dx} + p_0 \tag{7.19}$$

or, from equation 7.18

$$\frac{\rho K}{g} u \frac{du}{dx} = p_0 \left[\left(\frac{l}{x}\right)^\gamma - 1\right] \tag{7.20}$$

whence, by integration and substitution for $u = u_0$ when $x = l$

$$u^2 = u_0^2 - \frac{2 p_0}{\rho k} \left\{ \frac{l}{\gamma - 1} \left[\left(\frac{l}{x}\right)^{\gamma-1} - 1\right] - (l - x) \right\} \tag{7.21}$$

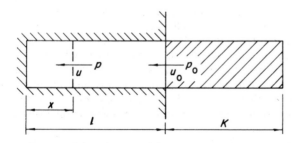

Figure 7.3 *Reference diagram for Bagnold's piston model*

and p attains its maximum value when $u = 0$. By graphical integration Bagnold
obtained an approximate value of

$$p_{max} \approx p_0 + 2.7 \frac{\rho u_0^2 K}{gl} \tag{7.22}$$

From results of his own laboratory experiments and from full-scale measurements made at Dieppe, Bagnold concluded that maximum shock pressures could
occur when the vertical height of the air cushion was about $0.4 H_b$ (where H_b is
the crest height of the breaking wave at the face of the wall) and with a value of
K of about $0.2 H_b$. Thus, from equation 7.22

$$p_{max} \approx p_0 + \frac{0.54 \, \rho u_0^2 H_b}{gl} \tag{7.23}$$

but such extreme values are only likely to occur against a near-vertical smooth-
faced wall.

Denny [9] subsequently extended model research on wave pressures against
a vertical wall. In the laboratory, he measured a maximum pressure, for about
1500 waves, equivalent to a head of $110 H_b$ (mode $42 H_b$),* but found that with
only minor irregularities in the wave form the maximum shock pressure for more
than 400 waves amounted to less than $80 H_b$ (mode $25 H_b$),* with these pressures
confined to the upper 60 per cent of the wave height from trough to crest. In
practice, it is apparent that there are many factors, including the dynamic response of the wall, and the geometry of the face [10] to modify such laboratory
results. It appears, nevertheless, that the maximum impulse, (that is, the time
integral of the shock force) may be represented universally as approximately
$\frac{1}{2}\rho \, g^{1/2} H_b^{5/2}$ per unit length of wave crest, for the most adverse circumstances.

One practical indication of shock forces against concrete seawalls is the
manner in which ill-designed or badly constructed lift joints become rapidly ex-
ploited by the sea.

7.3   Dissipation of Wave Energy

A wave breaking against a vertical wall may have undesirable consequences, related to the magnitude of the forces against the seawall: the plumes of water in
times of storm, or the damage caused by the high water particle velocities which
accompany clapotis. The principles governing the protection which may be provided by different types of wave barrier are here discussed briefly.

The economic form and profile of a wall are closely related to the materials
and method of construction. The scope of this book precludes discussion of the
many factors, other than the hydrodynamic aspects considered in this chapter,
which contribute to the optimum design. These factors principally concern the

*Mode: the peak value for a single-peaked frequency diagram, that is, here the
most probable value of shock pressure.

local geology, the tidal range and the position of the wall in relation to high and low water, limitations on access and availability of structural components including natural durable rock. The versatility of concrete for marine work is well known but the capabilities of bitumen as a carpet or a grouting medium for rock fill are less familiar.[11] The durability of different materials is an important consideration; apart from corrosion, erosion of a marine structure caused by the abrasion and impact of mobile beach material may be the most significant factor determining the life of the structure.

For breakwaters and other barriers founded in deep water in exposed situations, the economic solution is to be found in a permeable structure designed to dissipate wave energy harmlessly. As indicated in section 6.2, the same principle has applications in the design of coast protection works.

7.3.1 Effect of the Profile of the Wall

An important object in the design of a seawall on a soft or erodible bottom is to minimise wave reflection. Accepting, for the present, an impermeable type of wall, the aim must be to destroy—or, more correctly, to transform into heat— as much of the wave energy as possible, by causing the wave to break at the wall and, by a suitable selection of wall profile and degree of surface roughness, to promote maximum turbulence of the swash over the surface of the wall. Where the wall is providing protection against flooding by the sea, it is also important to ensure that, in the worst combination of circumstances, the run-up of breaking waves does not cause unacceptable overtopping. Hunt [12] summarises useful analytical and experimental data concerning these factors in relation to walls with inclined seaward faces of simple or composite form, with and without berms, encountered by unbroken waves. The most important conclusions are as follows.

(1) The slope of the face of a seawall to the horizontal to ensure breaking of the wave is given by

$$\tan \alpha \approx \frac{8}{T} \left(\frac{H_I}{2g}\right)^{1/2} \tag{7.24}$$

Such a slope will cause $H_R/H_I \approx 0.5$. Where no great variation in wave height occurs between deep water, H_0, and the oncoming wave at the wall, H_I, then $H_I \approx H_0$ and $L_0 = gT^2/2\pi$ (from equation 3.13). Equation 7.24 then gives

$$\frac{H_0}{L_0} \approx \frac{\tan^2 \alpha}{5.1} \tag{7.25}$$

Hence the minimum slope of the face of the wall—or at least the apron up to the point of breaking—may be determined in relation to the longest wave of critical height. The above criterion for $\tan \alpha$ determined analytically by Iribarren and Nogales, is supported by model tests on regular wave trains.

(2) The run-up, R, of a breaking wave, measured vertically above mean surface level of the sea at the time, may be related to H_I by consideration of a number of factors set out by Hunt in non-dimensional form. Model tests suggest that

$$\frac{R}{H_I} = \frac{K \tan \alpha}{\frac{8}{T} \left(\frac{H_I}{2g}\right)^{1/2}} \tag{7.26}$$

where K is a constant for a smooth plane surface with a value of about 2.3. For a surging wave $R/H_I \not> 3$ and Miche has shown that theoretically in the absence of friction

$$\frac{R}{H_I} = \left(\frac{\pi}{2\alpha}\right)^{1/2} \text{ for } \frac{\pi}{4} < \alpha \leqslant \frac{\pi}{2} \tag{7.27}$$

The *Shore Protection Manual* [1] provides a series of design curves for run-up for different breakwater sections based on model test results by Savage. Droyosz-Wawrzyniak [13] provides factors of coefficient of roughness r, defined as ratio of rough to smooth run-up as follows

concrete slabs $r = 0.9$
stone sets $r = 0.75$ to 0.80
rounded stones $r = 0.6$ to 0.68
rubble (2 layer) $r = 0.5$ to 0.55

Other results suggest $r = 0.8$ for a single layer of rubble and $r = 0.5$ for tetrapods. It is clear that r is affected by permeability of the face as well as its roughness.

(3) For composite slopes equation 7.26 may be used for breaking waves with a value of α intermediate between the lower and upper wall slopes, α_1 and α_2. Where α_1 or α_2 predominates, by consideration of the point of breaking of the wave, then equation 7.26 may be used with the appropriate value of α_1 or α_2 substituted for α. Equation 7.26 requires in addition the introduction of a factor S ($S < 1$) to account for turbulence losses at the change in slope. Model tests indicate that, where the change in slope occurs approximately at sea level

$$S \sim 0.9 \text{ where } \alpha_1 \text{ (or } \alpha_2) = \tan^{-1} \frac{1}{3} \text{ and } \alpha_2 \text{ (or } \alpha_1) = \tan^{-1} \frac{1}{6}$$

and

$$S \sim 0.8 \text{ where } \alpha_1 \text{ (or } \alpha_2) = \tan^{-1} \frac{1}{3} \text{ and } \alpha_2 \text{ (or } \alpha_1) = \tan^{-1} \frac{1}{10}$$

with S independent of whether the slopes are 'synclinal' or 'anticlinal'. For anticlinal (that is, convex upwards) slopes, Saville [14] indicates that a reasonable estimate of run-up may be related to an equivalent plane slope which intersects the actual slope at the position of breaker point and at the extreme of run-up.

An iterative procedure is needed to determine such a plane; this method under-estimates run-up for concave slopes, the common profile for natural beaches.

(4) An inclined berm in a seawall provides an effective means of reducing run-up. Provided the width of berm represents a significant part, say 20 per cent, of the wave length, then the effect of the berm is approximately the same as if its slope were continued to the crest of the wall, but there is an evident economy in construction.

(5) Wall roughness may considerably reduce run-up but the factor is too complex to express quantitatively except in relation to special cases. The effect of roughness will be greater on a gentle slope, where velocities are greater and the total distance travelled by the swash is also greater.

A suitably curved wall profile will cause less marked reflection of the non-breaking wave than a vertical wall. A stepped or irregular wall profile below the level of the sea surface will have little effect on the breaking characteristics of the wave unless the steps are constructed to a scale representing an appreciable fraction of the height of the wave. Economic design for a large-scale project is usually based on model tests and results are available on a number of typical wall profiles.[15]

Weggel [16] provides a basis for design curves for estimating overtopping, Q, based on a knowledge of the height of run-up, R, above still water level (for structure extended to control overtopping), H_0, equivalent deep water wave height, h_s, water depth at toe of structure, h height of crest of structure above sea bed (at foot). An empirical coefficient is defined as $K = 0.06 - 0.0143 \, ln$ (sin α) where α is angle to horizontal of the (smooth-faced) structure

$$Q = (gQ_0*H_0'^3)^{1/2} \exp \left[\frac{-0.217}{R} \tanh^{-1} \left(\frac{h - h_s}{R} \right) \right] \qquad (7.28)$$

and

$$Q_0* = \left(\frac{\epsilon}{2K} \right)^2 \frac{(gTH)^2}{H_0'^3} \tanh^2 \left(\frac{2\pi h_s}{L} \right) \qquad (7.29)$$

L being deep water wave length, H breaking wave height and ϵ a dimensionless 'block factor' depending on wave profile, $\frac{1}{2}\pi$ for sinusoidal waves. The 'equivalent' deep water wave takes no account of dissipation of wave energy between deep water and shore (section 3.4.1).

7.3.2 Rubble Mound Breakwaters

Traditionally, rubble mound breakwaters were constructed in rockfill, with stone, natural or cleaved, used as a protective capping. A study of the perform-ance of rubble breakwaters provided the basis for Iribarren's formula, for a wave breaking on a breakwater, which relates the weight of stone, W, wave height H, densities of rock and water, ρ_r and ρ and the stable angle of the exposed face of the mound α thus

$$W = \frac{K\rho_r H^3}{(\rho_r - \rho)^3 (\cos \alpha - \sin \alpha)^3} \tag{7.30}$$

where K is a dimensional factor.

Hudson [17] subsequently presented the formula in a more general form to take account of the coefficient of friction μ between the capping and the core

$$W = \frac{K'\rho_r\rho^2 \, \mu^3 H^3}{(\rho_r - \rho)^3 (\mu \cos \alpha - \sin \alpha)^3} \tag{7.31}$$

Such a formula assumes that the hydrodynamic uplift F (see figure 7.4) on each portion of capping stone is caused by jets acting over the projected area of the stone and transverse to the face of the mound. The force, F, is further assumed to be proportional to the wave height, H.

As a result of subsequent laboratory studies, Hudson [18] reanalysed the problem and stated the relationship as

$$\frac{\rho_r^{1/3} H}{[(\rho_r/\rho) - 1] \, W^{1/3}} = f\left(\alpha, \frac{h}{L}, \frac{H}{L}, \Delta\right) = N_s \tag{7.32}$$

where Δ represents a damage parameter (that is, the proportion of displaced or unstable armouring units) and N_s is defined as the stability number. Hudson found that, for constant values of h/L and H/L, equation 7.32 could best be expressed as

$$W = \frac{\rho_r H^3}{K_D \, [(\rho_r/\rho) - 1]^3 \, \cot \alpha} \tag{7.33}$$

where K_D represents a non-dimensional factor. By comparing equations 7.32 and 7.33 it is apparent that $N_s = (K_D \cot \alpha)^{1/3}$ and that hence, by finding the best fit

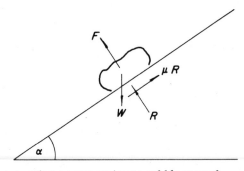

Figure 7.4 *Forces acting on armouring to rubble-mound*

for a straight-line relationship between N_s and cot α plotted to a log–log scale, K_D may be estimated.

Equations 7.32 and 7.33 have the merit over equations 7.30 and 7.31 that they contain no term relating to a coefficient of friction which, for armour units interlocked to a rock core, is difficult to evaluate.

Values of K_D have been obtained from model tests for a number of different types of capping stone and specially designed armouring units. While the values obtained for any particular form of armouring vary to a certain degree, depending on the wave steepness and breaking characteristics, the weight of a special concrete unit may be a relatively small fraction of that of natural stone needed to withstand comparable conditions. For example, where a stone capping in a double layer may have a value of K_D of 1 to 3 (depending on its angularity and density), values for special concrete units would usually be 10 or more. The most effective units possess a high degree of interlock, a high voids ratio, and tend to 'heal' where any local wave damage may occur; furthermore, proclivity to damage should not increase too suddenly with increasing wave height.[19]

For breakwaters, where each unit may weigh 20 000 kg or more in exposed situations, there is an obvious economy in choosing the most efficient, and hence the lightest, unit to be handled, provided its shape is not so complex as to create particular difficulties in casting. Equation 7.33 is normally held to apply between the top of the breakwater and a level of $-H$ below still water, where H is wave height. For the remainder of the face, lighter units may be used. There are, in addition, certain conditions to observe to ensure that the rock core is not disturbed beneath the armouring.

For an initial stage of design, values of K_D and N_s may be used from the published results of model tests, for economic comparison between types of unit. A model should then be made to reproduce the specific design, with attention paid to these particular aspects.

(1) Is h at the toe of the breakwater always beyond the breaker limit? If not, the maximum wave will break and will be more destructive to the armouring than the non-breaking wave.

(2) Do the published results relate to a mound made entirely of armouring units or to a mound with a rock core?

(3) Will the wave attack be accentuated locally along the length of the breakwater? This could occur, particularly at an exposed end and at points of change of direction.

A word of caution is, however, necessary in relation to the degree of damage acceptable to each type of unit and to the ease of local repair, particularly for units that need to be assembled to a specified pattern. A further word of caution is necessary in relation to units which have, in the course of development, changed their relative dimensions which may affect the effective void ratio. Whereas in general a high void ratio (up to a critical limit) will lead to high hydrodynamic efficiency, the void ratio may need to be reduced to obtain a sufficiently robust unit.

The Hudson formula equation 7.33 makes no provision for wave length. From section 7.3.1 for a given face slope α, longer waves will tend to surge up the face; this surge may cause high velocities under the surface layer of armour, an appar-

ent consideration for the Dolos unit [19] *inter alia*. For a similar reason, the
critical wave for Dolos units has been found in laboratory tests to approach at
about 60° to the normal. The acceptable damage depends considerably on the
type of unit. A higher degree of damage is acceptable for quarry stone than for
Dolos units, with most other units intermediate between the two.[19]

Hudson's formula implies that the flatter the slope the lower the required
weight of unit. Experiments with Dolos [20] indicate that their stability depends
on interlock and the stability coefficient decreases with increasing slope. Price
[21] describes simple laboratory experiments from which he concludes a critical
difference in behaviour depending on whether or not the armour is at a critical
slope such that one unit bears upon another.

Brown [22] concludes that many factors of geometry and packing affect the
value of K_D. In the case of Tribars, for example, this may result in a unit weight
variation by a factor of 4, material usage by 37 per cent and damage rate by a
factor of 10.

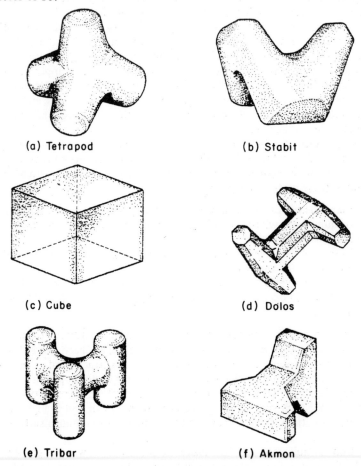

(a) Tetrapod   (b) Stabit

(c) Cube   (d) Dolos

(e) Tribar   (f) Akmon

Figure 7.5 *Geometry of various armour units*

TABLE 7.1 *Armour unit design parameters (Note: Values show in this table represent first approximations which require confirmation for each specific application)*

Armour Unit	Stability Coefficient K_D		Porosity $P(\%)$	Layer Coefficient C	Run-up R/H	Steepest Slope $\cot \alpha$
	0% damage	up to 5% damage				
Akmon	11	29	60	0.9	0.95	1.5
Cube	6	13	47	1.1	1.0	1.5
Dolos	15	23	63	1.0	0.83	1.5
Stabit	10	19	55	0.9	1.0	1.33
Tetrapod	8	18	50	1.04	1.0	1.5
Tribar	7	22	54	1.02	1.0	1.5
Quarrystone	2.5	9	37–45	1.15	1.1	1.5

Note: The number of armour units per unit area and the thickness of the armouring layer can be calculated from the following

$$N_r = AnC(1 - P/100)(\rho_r/W)^{2/3} \qquad r = nC(W/\rho_r)^{1/3}$$

where N_r is the number of individual units covering an area A, n is the number of layers and r is the total thickness of the armouring.

Thus, the value of K_D (see table 7.1) has to be chosen in relation to many factors, which may include size of unit, slope of breakwater, method of placing (hence density and porosity) and degree of acceptable damage. Figure 7.5 shows the general geometry of the armour units listed and the approximate limits of damage may be broadly classified as

0%   Nil
0 to 2%   Units rocking (movement less than length of unit)
2 to 4%   Few units displaced but armour layer otherwise stable
4% upwards   Increased displacement of units with time
14%   Incipient total failure

In addition roundheads of breakwaters need special attention, because of wave concentration, the reduced lateral protection of units and the angle of wave attack, including around the lee face.

It will be noted from equation 7.33 that other factors remaining constant the weight of unit

$$W \propto \rho_r/(\rho_r - 1)^3$$

if ρ is assumed to be unity and ρ_r expressed in tonnes/m^3. Thus the increase in density from 2.4 to 2.6 tonnes/m^3 leads to a reduced weight of unit in the ratio 6.35/8.75, that is, a ratio 1 : 1.37. Many factors are involved in the selection of the economic density of unit; this example simply indicates the need to take account of this possible modification by the inclusion of heavier aggregates or a dense concrete mix.

Similar design procedures may be used for coastal revetments but, where these are situated in shallow water, the maximum waves are limited and the minimum weight of unit, being proportional to H^3, may be appropriately reduced. In these circumstances, a geometrically simple shape of unit will deserve consideration to minimise casting costs. If such a revetment is subjected to breaking waves, particular caution has to be taken in stabilising the toe, either by the introduction here of more massive units or of a positive anchorage. In addition, special consideration should be given to the design of riprap slope protection as a result of recent research involving model tests [54] and full scale field trials.[55]

Caldwell [23] describes the results of a number of model tests carried out to measure the proportion of wave energy of solitary waves reflected from a wall with a permeable face, set at angles between about 5° and 90° to the horizontal, backed either by an impermeable core or by open water. He found that, provided the permeable face was formed of units of a certain size arranged with constant voids ratio, the proportion of reflected wave energy was unaffected by the presence of an impermeable core.

7.3.3 Pervious Vertical Breakwaters

Experiments by Wiegel [5] show that, when a wave train encounters a line of piles, the transmitted wave energy, due to local diffraction around the piles, results in wave heights about 25 per cent greater than those predicted by a simple formula

$$\frac{H_T}{H_I} = \left(\frac{E_T}{E_I}\right)^{1/2} = \left[\frac{b}{d+b}\right]^{1/2} \tag{7.34}$$

which assumes that transmitted energy is proportional to the 'gap ratio'. Here, d represents pile diameter, and $d + b$ the pitch between pile centres.

Hayashi *et al.* [24] describe a model study of long low waves encountering a screen of circular piles in shallow water and an accompanying analysis carried out in the following steps.

(1) The horizontal velocity at a vertical section is assumed to be constant with depth.

(2) By Bernoulli, the horizontal velocity between piles at any instant is given by

$$V = \frac{C_V \left[2g(\eta_I + \eta_R - \eta_T)\right]^{1/2}}{\left[1 - \left(\frac{b}{d+b}\right)^2\right]^{1/2}} \tag{7.35}$$

where C_V is a velocity coefficient and η represents height above still water level (see figure 7.6).

(3) By the principle of continuity of flow

$$VC_c bh = V_T(d + b)h \tag{7.36}$$

where C_c is a contraction coefficient, and hence from equations 7.35 and 7.36

$$V_T = C_c C_V \frac{b}{d+b} \left[\frac{2g(\eta_I + \eta_R - \eta_T)}{1 - \left(\frac{b}{d+b}\right)^2}\right]^{1/2} \tag{7.37}$$

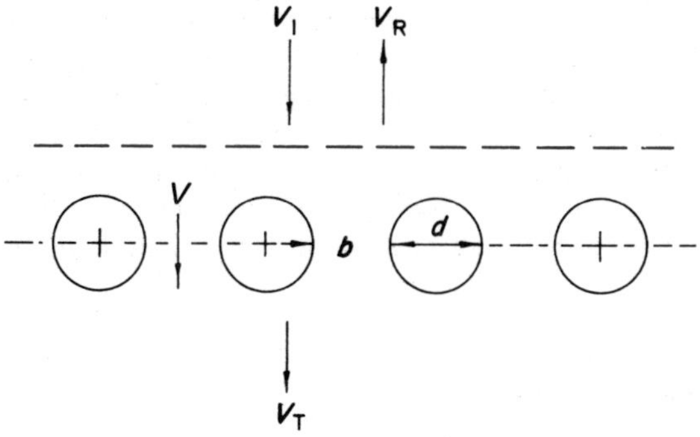

Figure 7.6 *Line of vertical piles*

but η_I, η_R and η_T are proportional to wave heights H_I, H_R and H_T and $V_I = (g/h)^{1/2} \eta_I$, etc., and $V_I h + V_R h = V_T h$. Hence $H_R = H_I - H_T$ and

$$H_T = 4h\Sigma \left[-\Sigma + \left(\Sigma^2 + \frac{H_1}{2h} \right)^{1/2} \right] \qquad (7.38)$$

where

$$\Sigma = C_c C_v \frac{b/(d+b)}{\left[1 - \left(\dfrac{b}{d+b} \right)^2 \right]^{1/2}} \qquad (7.39)$$

Energy loss is thus given by

$$\frac{E_{loss}}{E_I} = 1 - \left(\frac{H_T}{H_I} \right)^2 - \left(\frac{H_R}{H_I} \right)^2 = 2 \frac{H_T}{H_I} \left(1 - \frac{H_T}{H_I} \right) \qquad (7.40)$$

It is then possible to derive the forces on the piles by consideration of the momentum loss of the wave motion approaching the piles. Model tests indicated a good agreement with theory provided $C_c C_v = 1$. Thus, for $b/d = 0.5$, $H_T/H_I = 0.8$, and for $b/d = 1$, $H_T/H_I = 0.9$. In fact, the coefficients C_c and C_v are each less than unity, but this appears to be compensated for by the fact that the analysis assumes full loss of velocity head represented by $(V^2 - V_T^2)/2g$.

From time to time proposals are advanced for a perforated vertical breakwater. A particularly interesting type of such a breakwater was constructed at Baie Comeau, on the St. Lawrence River, in 1962; the concept of the breakwater and model tests to prove its efficiency are described by Jarlan [25] and Marks.[26] Essentially, the breakwater comprises a series of cellular compartments with perforated front wall and continuous rear wall. The basis of the design relies on the destruction of wave energy by the creation of high jet velocities through the perforations of the front wall. To be fully effective it is essential that oscillations of water level within the cells should be out of phase with the contact face of the wall and Jarlan established that this condition would obtain for the range of design waves. The greater the wave steepness, the greater the phase shift, the relationship evidently depending on the spacing and size of the holes in the front wall and the distance between front and rear walls. The cross-walls prevent any considerable longitudinal movement of water within the cells which could other-wise impair the function of the breakwater when subjected to oblique waves. More elaborate types of permeable breakwater have recently been described.[27, 28]

7.3.4 Floating Breakwaters

The kinetic energy of a prism of water dx dz of unit width parallel to the crest of an Airy wave (x horizontal and z vertical, positive upwards from still water level) is

$$Ek(z) = \rho \, \frac{u^2 + w^2}{2} \, dx \, dz \qquad (7.41)$$

where u and w are respectively horizontal and vertical velocities. From equation 3.17 the ratio of the kinetic energy at depth z to that at the surface, $Ek(0)$, is

$$\frac{Ek(z)}{Ek(0)} = \frac{\cosh 4\pi(h + z)/L}{\cosh 4\pi h/L} \qquad (7.42)$$

Hence, as a first approximation, the ratio of energy, E_R, reflected from a plate extending from above the water surface to a depth D to that of the incident wave E_I is

$$\frac{E_R}{E_I} = \frac{\int_{-D}^{0} \cosh \left[4\pi(h + z)/L \right] dz}{\int_{-h}^{0} \cosh \left[4\pi(h + z)/L \right] dz} = \frac{\sinh 4\pi h/L - \sinh \left[4\pi(h - D)/L \right]}{\sinh 4\pi h/L} \qquad (7.43)$$

But the kinetic energy of a wave is $\propto (H)^2$ and hence, if we assume no loss of energy, the ratio of the reflected wave height, H_R, to the incident wave height, H_I is

$$\frac{H_R}{H_I} = \left[\frac{E_R}{E_I} \right]^{1/2} = \left[1 - \frac{\sinh \left[4\pi(h - D)/L \right]}{\sinh 4\pi h/L} \right]^{1/2} \qquad (7.44)$$

The height of the transmitted wave

$$H_T = [H_I^2 - H_R^2]^{1/2} = \left[\frac{\sinh \left[4\pi(h - D)/L \right]}{\sinh 4\pi h/L} \right]^{1/2} H_I \qquad (7.45)$$

In deep water, where $h/L \gg 0.5$, $\sinh 4\pi h/L \approx \cosh 4\pi h/L \approx e^{4\pi h/L}$ so, from equation 7.45

$$H_T/H_I = e^{-2\pi D/L} \text{ and } H_R/H_I = (1 - e^{-4\pi D/L})^{1/2} \qquad (7.46)$$

H_T/H_I and H_R/H_I are plotted in figure 7.7 for $h/L = 0.05$ and 0.5. Over a complete wave period there will be no residual horizontal force on the plate.

Lochner et al. [29] demonstrate that the motion of a floating vertical breakwater extending to a depth D, subjected to low waves in deep water, may be re-

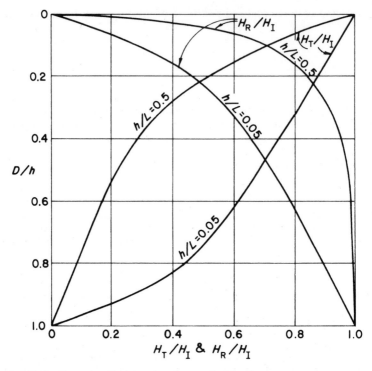

Figure 7.7 *Reflected and transmitted wave height for waves*

presented approximately as an oscillation of period T about a point at depth γ below mean surface level (see figure 7.8) where

$$\gamma \approx \frac{L}{2\pi} \ e^{-2\pi D/L} \tag{7.47}$$

If the resultant wave pressure on the breakwater is represented by a force $P \sin 2\pi t/T$ acting at a height n above the centre of mass of the structure, itself at a depth below mean surface level of $\gamma - l_G$, then, considering accelerations of the structure of the effective mass M

$$P = \frac{2\pi^2}{T^2} \ H_T l_G M \tag{7.48}$$

and

$$Pn = \frac{2\pi^2}{T^2} \ H_T M R_G{}^2 \tag{7.49}$$

where R_G represents the radius of gyration of the structure. From equations 7.48 and 7.49, n is seen to be equal to $R_G{}^2/l_G$.

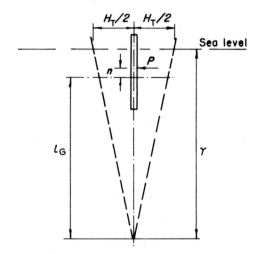

Figure 7.8 *Motion of floating breakwater*

For maximum efficiency the breakwater must have a high effective mass (representing the sum of the mass of the structure and that of the body of the water that moves with it), high damping characteristics, and possess natural frequencies of vertical and angular oscillation appreciably lower than those of the longest design wave. Lochner *et al.* [29] explain how the above reasoning led to the design of Bombardon. This was a structure of cruciform cross-section 7.6 m x 7.6 m with a buoyancy tank in the upper arm which penetrated the water surface and had a beam of only 1.5 m. Units 61 m long were moored 15 m apart; with two such parallel lines of units separated by 244 m, with staggered centres, H_T/H_I was found to be approximately 0.3 for waves of 46 m length and 3 m height.

Floating breakwaters used off the coast of Japan to protect fish-farming have been provided with U-shaped anti-rolling tanks to achieve the same object of low frequency and high damping.

A number of alternative laminar types of floating breakwater have formed the subject of experiments in the laboratory or at sea. These may be subdivided into semi-rigid and flexible types. The latter include floating plastics rafts containing compartments filled, or partially filled, with water or other liquids. The movement of the contained fluid provides a certain degree of damping, but these flexible breakwaters present considerable mooring problems. Appreciable protection is provided by such a mattress extending about half a wave length.

If relatively rigid sheets are floated on the water surface, model experiments indicate that, if the width in the direction of wave transmission is about $5L$, where L is the wave length, $H_T/H_I = 0.5$, but the effect depends on the dynamic characteristics of the raft.[5] It seems improbable that an economic breakwater could be developed along such lines. Stoker [30] treats problems of floating plates and beams in considerable mathematical detail.

Off the coast of Guyana considerable protection is provided by mud in suspension, in sufficient concentration locally as 'sling mud' to develop thixotropy. Other informal methods of protection have been proposed, such as floating mats of tyres, [31] usually effective for short waves $(T \not> 4$ s) only.

A considerable literature has developed on the abstraction of energy from waves; floating devices for this purpose have much in common with floating breakwaters.[32, 33]

Submerged devices resting on the sea bed such that locally the depth of water is suddenly and appreciably decreased may be developed to abstract a reasonable fraction of wave energy with practical benefits concerning the economics of mooring and of power transmission.

7.3.5   Pneumatic Breakwaters

The Brasher pneumatic breakwater, used first in 1915 off the coast of California, provided protection against relatively short waves by bubbles from a compressed-air pipe laid along the sea bed. Subsequent uses of the same principle include the temporary protection of the Dover train-ferry dock during a repair of the lock gate. Evans [34] describes model experiments to establish the mechanism of operation of the pneumatic breakwater. As had been suggested previously, the reduction of wave height was shown to be caused by horizontal water currents at the surface, set up by the rising curtain of bubbles. Evans showed that water jets along the surface could produce similar results.

For a thick layer of opposing surface current, the steepness of a deep water wave is increased and, if it is close to limiting steepness, the wave will break and energy will thereby be dissipated. From section 3.4.3 it may be shown that, on the assumption that $C = (gL/2\pi)^{1/2}$ remains valid, no deep water wave will penetrate a current exceeding a quarter of the celerity of the incident wave. Where the surface current is confined to a thin layer, the mechanism is somewhat different, energy being partially destroyed in turbulence at the interface.

The analysis of the effects of a uniform surface current and a surface current decreasing uniformly with depth of the layer, by Taylor [35] provides the relationship between the depth and the velocity of the surface layer needed to form a barrier to a deep water wave of given properties. The current is further related by Taylor to the rate of discharge of air bubbles by consideration of the angle of diffusion of the rising bubble curtain.

The pneumatic breakwater is found to be inefficient for protection against long waves. It is of interest to note that the same principle has, however, been successfully used to provide cushioning against the shock of underwater blasting, as a stirring mechanism to prevent ice forming across a navigation channel in a lake and, also, to confine floating oil slicks.

7.3.6   Resonator Basins

Protection against waves of length L travelling along a channel, relatively narrow with respect to L, may be provided by means of resonator basins, let into the side walls, each $L/4$ in length and with a fully reflecting end wall; these operate

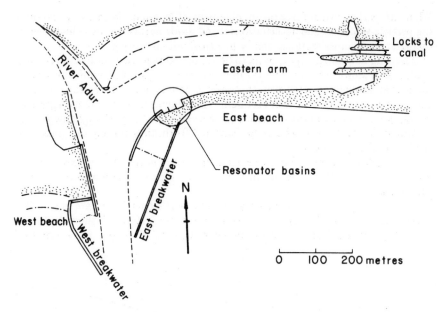

Figure 7.9 *Resonator basins at Shoreham*

on the same principle as acoustic cavity resonators. The width of the basin should not exceed about $L/4$ and, since the basin will only be effective against waves whose length approximates to L, a wide range of periods will require more than one size of resonator.

Figure 7.9 indicates a series of three resonator basins constructed in 1966 to reduce wave action, within Shoreham Harbour, Sussex, which was affecting lock gates at the east end of the harbour. Model tests indicated that a series of three resonator basins proportioned to 6, 7 and 8 s waves would be effective over the range of wave periods of 5 to 9 s. For a straight channel, $0.8L$ wide, sets of three resonator basins on each side reduced waves to about 40 per cent of their original height. At Shoreham, the curve of the harbour was found to affect the areas sheltered by the resonator chambers which are provided on one side only of the channel.

7.4 Wave Forces on Cylinders

7.4.1 Long Slender Cylinders

The wave forces on a fully submerged cylinder may be derived from the wave particle velocities and accelerations using the 'Morison equation'

$$\frac{\mathrm{d}F}{\mathrm{d}z} = \frac{1}{2}\,C_{\mathrm{D}}\rho du\,|u| + C_{\mathrm{M}}\rho A\,\frac{\mathrm{d}u}{\mathrm{d}t} \tag{7.50}$$

Where dF is the normal force on an increment of length dz from a wave producing particle velocities and accelerations u and du/dt normal to the cylinder with
diameter d and cross-sectional area A in a fluid with density ρ.

The drag coefficient C_D appears to be similar to that used for hydrodynamic
loading in a uniform flow where it can be expressed as a function of Reynolds
number and roughness. However, this analogy should not be taken too far because the mechanism of vortex production is influenced by the oscillatory nature
of the flow. In uniform flow, vortices are generated and swept away downstream; in waves, they may be swept back and forth, thus altering the pressure
field around the cylinder.

For an ideal, inviscid fluid accelerating uniformly normal to the axis of a
long cylinder the inertia coefficient C_M has been shown by Lamb [36] to have a
theoretical value of 2.

In oscillatory flow the drag coefficient and inertia coefficients are physically
dependent on each other as may be seen from figure 7.10 which shows both
plotted against Keulegan-Carpenter number, $N_K = \hat{u} \, T/d$ where $\hat{u}$ is the amplitude

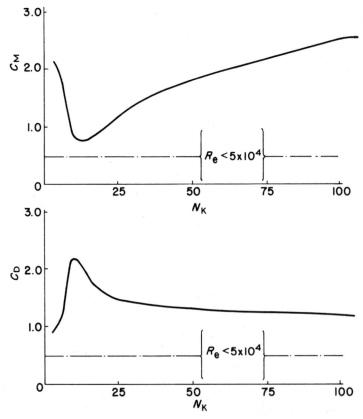

Figure 7.10 *Suggested values of C_M and C_D at subcritical Re for wave force
normal to axis of smooth cylinder; after Keulegan and Carpenter
[37]*

of the horizontal oscillatory velocity.[37] For linear wave theory N_K is related to the maximum drag, F_D and inertia, F_M forces as follows

$$\frac{F_{D\,max}}{F_{M\,max}} = \frac{C_D\, N_K}{C_M\, \pi^2}$$

For linear (Airy) waves, Morison's equation may be written

$$\frac{dF}{dz} = \frac{1}{2} C_D \rho d\, K_z^2 \left| \sin \frac{2\pi t}{T} \right| \sin \frac{2\pi t}{T} + C_M \rho\, \frac{d^2}{4}\, \frac{2\pi^2 K_z}{T} \cos \frac{2\pi t}{T} \quad (7.51)$$

where

$$K_z = \frac{\pi H}{T}\, \frac{\cosh 2\pi(z + h)/L}{\sinh 2\pi h/L}$$

Thus, the maximum loadings at depth z will occur for values of t given by

$$\frac{2K_z T}{\pi^2 d} \left| \sin \frac{2\pi t}{T} \right| \frac{\cos 2\pi t/T}{\sin 2\pi t/T} = \frac{C_M}{C_D} \quad (7.52)$$

that is, for $0 \leqslant t/T \leqslant 0.5$

$$\frac{2K_z T}{\pi^2 d} \cos \frac{2\pi t}{T} = \frac{C_M}{C_D}$$

and, due to symmetry, points of numerical maxima will be separated by half a wave period.

In practice the determination of drag and inertia coefficients for design is based on empirical data derived from laboratory and full-scale experiments. A comprehensive survey of the available data has been published by Hogben et al. [38] The results for vertical smooth cylinders are summarised in figure 7.11.

Lighthill [39] has indicated that the direct application of Morison's equations for linear wave motion involves an oversight, which may lead to serious error in calculating C_M and C_D from experimental data, expressed as interaction between variable velocity and variable extension (for example, variation in horizontal spacing between two small closely spaced floats) of the wave. This has the effect of adding to equation 7.51 an additional second-order term

$$\frac{dF_S}{dz} = 2.5\, \rho\, \frac{d^2}{L} \sin \frac{2\pi t}{T} \cos \frac{2\pi t}{T} \quad (7.53)$$

For $C_M = 2$ and $C_D = 1.5$, figure 7.12 indicates the effect of introducing the term of equation 7.53 into equation 7.51 for a deep water wave height of $3.2d$ and wave length $33.5d$.

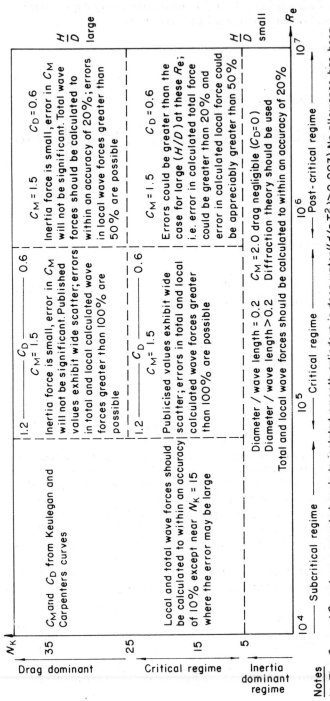

Notes

1. The C_M and C_D values suggested apply to isolated smooth cylinders in deep water ($(d/g T^2) > 0.003$) No allowance has been made for roughness, orientation, slamming, interaction with other members and other effects

2. No allowance has been made for the interactive effects of the currents and waves

3. The C_M and C_D values suggested and their reliability estimates are subjective

4. The values of R_e and N_K specifying the boxes are not well defined experimentally

5. The C_M and C_D values suggested should be used with a wave theory appropriate to the enviromental conditions considered. The chosen wave theory should be used to evaluate R_e and N_K but approx. values are adequate when using this figure.

Figure 7.11 *Summary of suggested values of C_M and C_D as functions of R_e and N_K; after Hogben et. al. [38]*

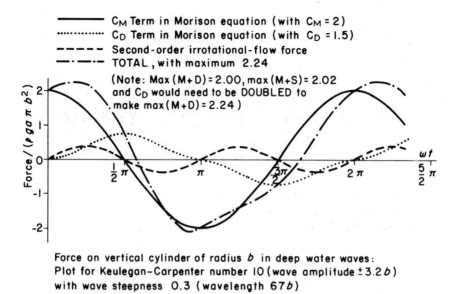

——— C_M Term in Morison equation (with $C_M = 2$)
············· C_D Term in Morison equation (with $C_D = 1.5$)
– – – – Second-order irrotational-flow force
—·—·— TOTAL, with maximum 2.24
(Note: Max $(M+D) = 2.00$, max $(M+S) = 2.02$
and C_D would need to be DOUBLED to
make max $(M+D) = 2.24$)

Force on vertical cylinder of radius b in deep water waves:
Plot for Keulegan–Carpenter number 10 (wave amplitude $\pm 3.2\,b$)
with wave steepness 0.3 (wavelength $67\,b$)

Figure 7.12 *Second-order effect on Morison's equation*

At laboratory scale surface roughness will affect the drag coefficient. Consequently it may be expected that in a marine environment the growth of barnacles, mussels, seaweed and other organisms will influence both the coefficient and the effective diameter of the member, which may in some parts of the structure and areas of the world be increased by as much as 300 mm.

There is at present no experimental data available directly relating to the loading on inclined members. Usually the force normal to the member is assumed to be independent of the tangential force and is calculated from the normal component of velocity and acceleration using the Morison equation. The tangential component of loading is generally regarded as insignificant.

The presence of a current or tidal stream may alter the load coefficients. Where the current and waves are from approximately the same direction it is usual vectorially to sum the velocities before calculating Reynolds numbers and forces.

There is recent evidence to show that waves can produce significant transverse 'lift' loadings on rigid vertical members which can be larger than the 'in line' loading (see figure 7.13). These loads appear to arise from the mechanism of vortex formation around the cylinder which is as yet not fully understood.[40] Locally the transverse loads may be significant. However, the time history appears not to be correlated to the time history of wave particle motions and it is probable that the vector sum of these loads tends to zero in a structure with large numbers of members. Offshore and laboratory experiments are at present being undertaken to investigate transverse wave-induced loading.

Horizontal or near horizontal structural members that enter the water during the passage of a wave can be subject to impulsive forces known as 'wave slam'

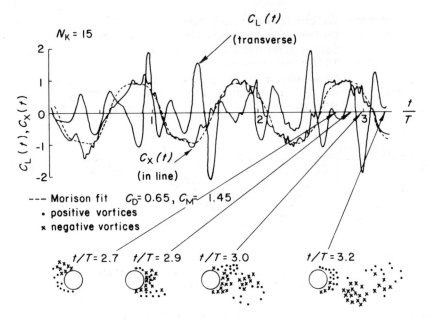

Figure 7.13 *Variation of non-dimensional transverse and in-line forces with time for $N_K = 15$; after Stansby [40]*

in addition to the change in hydrostatic loading. Theoretical and experimental investigations have been reported by Miller [41] and Sarpkaya.[42] The loading arises from the impact of the water surface on the cylinder and may be calculated from the velocity of the water surface normal to the plane of the surface and the dynamic characteristics of the cylinder. For effectively rigid cylinders

$$\left(\frac{dF}{dS}\right)_{slam} = \frac{1}{2} C_{slam}\, \rho d V |V| \qquad (7.54)$$

where $(dF/dS)_{slam}$ is the load per unit length, and V the normal velocity of the water.

The slamming coefficient is generally taken as 3.5, although theoretically for an infinitely rigid cylinder with small immersed area and added mass it can be shown to be equal to 4.

7.4.2 Large Cylinders

It is implicit in the use of the Morison equation that the dimensions of the cylinder are small enough in relation to the wave length for it to be assumed that the wave is unaffected by the existence of the obstruction and that the acceleration is instantaneously uniform in the vicinity of the cylinder.

For large cylinders, where these assumptions are not valid (generally cylinders with a diameter greater than 20 per cent of the wave length), a diffraction analysis may be used to calculate the pressure distribution and forces on the cylinder. In practice the mathematical functions used in a diffraction analysis satisfy only a linearised water surface boundary condition. For vertical cylinders of uniform diameter d between the sea bed and the water surface, MacCamy and Fuchs [43] have provided a closed-form analytical solution for the total horizontal force on the cylinder at depth z below the surface

$$F(z) = \frac{\rho g H L}{\pi} \frac{\cosh 2\pi(z + h)/L}{\cosh 2\pi h/L} f_A \cos\left(\frac{2\pi t}{T} - \alpha\right) \tag{7.55}$$

where

$$\tan \alpha = \frac{J_1'(\pi d/L)}{Y_1'(\pi d/L)} \tag{7.56}$$

and

$$f_A = \frac{1}{\{[J_1'(\pi d/L)]^2 + [Y_1'(\pi d/L)]^2\}^{1/2}} \tag{7.57}$$

J_1' and Y_1' are differentiated Bessel functions of the first and second kind, α is the phase lag angle and the coordinates are shown on figure 7.14. f_A and $\tan \alpha$ have been presented graphically by Wiegel [5] as shown in figure 7.15. It will be noted that the force equation reduces to the inertia term of the Morison equation with $C_M = 2$ when d/L approaches zero.

Other analytical solutions for axisymetric structures are listed by Hogben *et al.*[38]

Where no appropriate analytical solution is available it is necessary to use a numerical technique. For finite element analysis, the external surface of the structure is defined in terms of elements of area which are sometimes referred to as facets. At the centre of each facet is a node at which the pressure disturbance caused by the wave is computed in terms of its amplitude and phase lag. The variations in pressure have the same period as the wave, assumed to be linear.

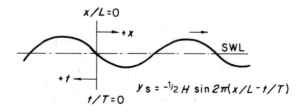

Figure 7.14 *Coordinate system, MacCamy–Fuchs large caisson, theory*

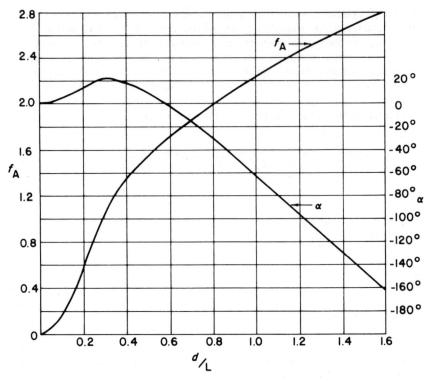

Figure 7.15 *Function for MacCamy–Fuchs large cylinder equation*

The force is found by integrating the pressure over the surface area taking account of the phase angles.

Hogben *et al.* provide a list of some of the published finite element modelling programs available for diffraction analysis.[38]

Where a non-linear wave profile is required for the analysis of a structure large enough to justify the use of a diffraction analysis, it is generally prudent to increase the loads in the ratio of the non-linear wave particle acceleration to the linear wave particle acceleration.

7.4.3 Forces on Pipelines

A special case involving wave forces on cylinders is that of a pipeline on the sea bed. Here, due to vorticity induced around the top of the pipe, horizontal wave orbital velocities and currents will provoke vertical lift forces. Experiments by the Hydraulics Research Station, Wallingford, indicate a value for the lift coefficient, C_L, of about 0.5, that is, maximum uplift forces in dynamic units $F_L = 0.5\, \rho v^2 d/2$ per unit length for the maximum water velocity vector, v, transverse to the line of the pipe, that is $F_L \approx 2.5$ kN/m for a current of 1 m/s and a pipe diameter of 1 m.

7.4.4 Flutter

'Flutter' is the name given to oscillation of a body caused by eddies which are formed alternately to each side of the wake, known as vortex streets. The oscillations are transverse to the direction of flow as illustrated diagrammatically in figure 7.16 and, for steady flow (see for example Scruton and Flint [44]) the Strouhal number, for a long cylinder, is defined as $S = d/T_e v$ where d is cylinder diameter, T_e the interval between the shedding of adjacent eddies in the same side of the wake, and v the current velocity. For values of Reynolds number, Re, between about 10^3 and 2×10^5, S is found to be about 0.2. In the sea, flexible cylinders oscillate in a strong current and consideration should be given to the possibility of the natural period of lateral oscillation approximating to T_e, or of in-line oscillations approximating to $T_e/2$.[45] While a considerable amount of study has been made of the alternating lift coefficient, C_L, for different amplitudes of oscillation up to an upper limit $\sim d$, in a steady current, [46, 47] there is inadequate information on the corresponding effects of wave motion. Certain structures have been noted to oscillate transversely in waves with frequencies of an order to be accounted for by 'flutter' and it is known, from experiment, that where this occurs, a considerable increase in the drag coefficient may be caused. Mass and drag coefficients in waves need to be related to a fully consistent theory for the more complex problem of flutter of structures in waves to become better understood (see section 7.4.1). Even less information is available on structural members of other than circular form.

7.4.5 Forces on Cables and Flexible Moorings

A special class of problem is presented by the study of the effect of sea currents on the locus of, and resulting stress in, mooring cables in deep water. Wilson [48] treats the problem for the case of uniform current, taking account of the longitudinal and normal components of drag. Wilson [49] develops the theory somewhat further by a numerical approach to the case of variation of current velocity with depth. Bracannot [50] provides graphical solutions for the simpler case of uniform current, neglecting the longitudinal drag. Zajac [51] treats the comparable problems encountered in the laying and recovery of submarine cables.

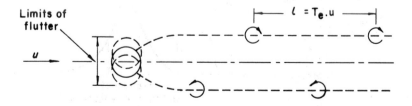

Figure 7.16 *Vortex sheet downstream of cylinder*

7.5   Spectral Analysis of Wave Loadings

Since the loads in a structure subject to wave action are constantly varying, it is useful to extend the spectral analysis methods described in chapter 3 to produce load or stress spectra which may be used to predict extreme values or as the basis for a fatigue analysis.[52]

The crucial step in the application of spectral methods is the transfer from a sea state input spectrum of sea surface elevation to a response spectrum. The function which specifies this relationship over the frequency range is called a transfer function. For a linear system it can be shown that this function is unique and is obtained by applying a unit amplitude at appropriate frequencies and measuring or calculating the corresponding responses. The transfer function ordinate at each frequency considered is the response amplitude squared. The ordinates of the response spectrum are obtained by multiplying the ordinates of the input spectrum by the ordinates of the transfer function.

The variance of the response is defined by the area under the response spectrum. If the response is assumed to have a probability distribution which is fully defined by its variance (for example, Gaussian or Rayleigh), then the probability of various response levels being exceeded may be calculated.

To illustrate the procedure described above, consider the steps involved in determining the spectrum of mud line moment for a cylindrical free-standing cantilever with a uniform diameter in depth of water h, as shown in figure 7.17. The sea state is represented by the spectral density function $S^{\eta\eta}(f)$ where f is the frequency (see section 3.3.6).

The Morison equation, which defines the force per unit length on the cantilever (see section 7.4) is used to form the transfer functions. It will be noted, however, that the drag term is non-linear, being a function of velocity squared. The Morison equation must therefore be linearised for use in this type of analysis. Borgman [53] has provided a method which minimises the errors involved

$$\frac{\mathrm{d}F}{\mathrm{d}S}\,(z',t) = C_\mathrm{M}\rho\,A\,\frac{\mathrm{d}v}{\mathrm{d}t}\,(z',t) + C_\mathrm{D}\rho\,\frac{d}{2}\left(\frac{8}{\pi}\right)^{1/2}\,\sigma_v\,(z')\,v\,(z',t) \qquad (7.58)$$

where $\sigma_v\,(z')$ is the standard deviation of the velocity in the sea state at distance

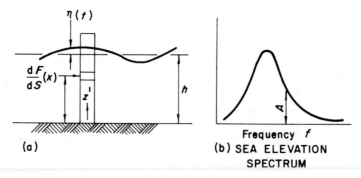

Figure 7.17 *Reference diagram for spectral analysis*

z' from the sea bed. (Note that in all other sections of this book except chapter 1 z is measured upwards from the sea surface, that is, $z' = z + h$.)

Since the mud line moment is the force per unit length multiplied by its lever arm, the spectral density function of bending moment can be written as

$$S^{mm}(f) = \frac{C_M^2 \rho^2 A^2 \omega^4}{\sinh^2 2\pi h/L} \left[\int_0^h z' \cosh 2\pi z'/L \, dz' \right]^2 S^{\eta\eta}(f)$$

$$+ \frac{8 C_D^2 \rho^2 (d/2)^2 \omega^2}{\pi \sinh^2 2\pi h/L} \left[\int_0^h z' \sigma_v^2(z') \cosh 2\pi z'/L \, dz' \right]^2 S^{\eta\eta}(f) \quad (7.59)$$

where

$$\sigma_v^2(z') = \int_0^\infty \left(\omega \, \frac{\cosh 2\pi z'/L}{\sinh 2\pi h/L} \right)^2 S^{\eta\eta}(f) \, df \quad (7.60)$$

These spectra can then be integrated to define the variance of the bending moment, from which a maximum value of known probability can be calculated. The procedure involved is illustrated in figure 7.18 where the drag and inertia terms are shown on separate diagrams.

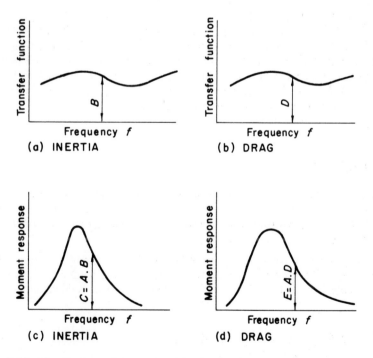

Figure 7.18 *Distribution of drag and inertia terms*

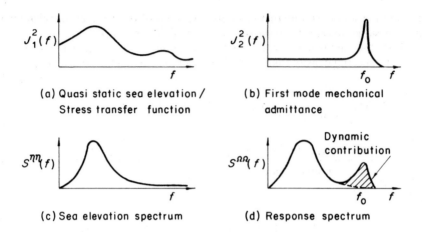

Figure 7.19 *Loading spectral analysis*

The spectral analysis method is particularly useful for the analysis of structures with significant dynamic response to waves. Through inclusion of the mechanical admittance of the structure in the transfer functions, the variance obtained from the area of the response curve will include the dynamic contribution as shown in figure 7.19(d).

Since linearity is essential to the method, linear wave theory must be used. For any wave with finite amplitude, the loading changes non-linearly as the surface elevation passes the structure. It is therefore also necessary to adopt a suitable equivalent loading function, which is assumed to act at still water level. In consequence the method is not reliable for analysis of parts of the structure in the splash zone. In practice, the method is more appropriate to large structures in deep water, where wave heights are small in relation to depth and where the structure is likely to be more flexible.

Example 7.1

What will be the net maximum load against a vertical wall exerted by a 4 m high wave with 10 s period in 8 m depth of water? What will be the bending moment about the base of the wall, assuming still water at the sheltered side of the wall? (Density of seawater = 1020 kg/m³.)

The length of wave in deep water = $1.56 \times 10^2 = 156$ m by equation 3.13, that is, $h/L_0 = 5.1 \times 10^{-2}$ whence, from figure 2.2, $h/L = 9.2 \times 10^{-2}$, so $L = 87$ m. From equation 7.1, the orbital centre of the wave surface is raised above sea level by

$$(\pi H^2/L) \coth 2\pi h/L = \pi 16/87 \coth 2\pi \times 8/87$$

$$= 0{\cdot}58 \times 1{\cdot}9 = 1{\cdot}1 \text{ m}$$

The pressure response factor at the sea bed by equation 7.7 = $1/\cosh 2\pi h/L$ = 0.85. Whence when the crest is against the wall from A to B (see figure 7.1), the net pressure against the wall increases from zero to $(4 + 1.1)$ 1020 kg/m^2 where A is 5.1 m above B. From B to C the net pressure against the wall will decrease linearly from 5.1 x 1020 to 4 x 0.85 kg/m^2. Thus

$$\text{total net load} = \tfrac{1}{2}\, 5 \cdot 1^2 \times 1020 + \tfrac{1}{2}\, 8(5 \cdot 1 + 3 \cdot 4)1020$$

$$= 13\,200 + 34\,800 = 48\,000 \text{ kg/m}^2$$

moment about the base

$$= 13\,200\,(8 + \tfrac{1}{3} \times 5 \cdot 1) + 20\,900 \times \tfrac{2}{3} \times 8 + 13\,900 \times \tfrac{1}{3} \times 8$$

$$= 276\,000 \text{ kg m/m}$$

Example 7.2

A train of waves of crest height 1 m, in 4 m of water and 16 s period, is totally reflected by a vertical wall standing in 2.5 m of water. The wave crests are parallel to the line of the wall and the bed shoals towards the wall at a slope of 1:40. What will be the crest height of the nearest clapotis to the wall?

It is first necessary to establish the type of wave to be considered. In a depth of water of 4 m equation 3.58 indicates

$$L_{sol} \approx T_{sol}(gh)^{1/2} \approx 100 \text{ m for } T_{sol} = 16 \text{ s}$$

But table 3.2 indicates a lower limit of L_{sol} of

$$2\pi/M \text{ where } M \approx (3H/h)^{1/2} = 0 \cdot 865 \text{ for } H/h = \tfrac{1}{4}$$

Thus the limiting value of $L_{sol} \approx 30$ m so that the wave in question may be treated as a solitary wave from a point some distance offshore from the 4 m depth of water.

From section 7.2.2 the distance S from the wall to the nearest clapotis is given by

$$S = \tfrac{1}{2}\!\int\! C\, \mathrm{d}T \text{ or } T_{sol/2} = \Sigma \Delta S/C$$

in finite difference form where

$$C = [g(h + H)]^{1/2} \text{ and } ah = 4 \text{ m}^2$$

(from section 7.2.2). ΔT for successive increments of ΔS may then be calculated with values of C centred for each length of ΔS, taken as 10 m.

S (m)	0	5	10	15	20	25	30	35	40	45	50	55	60
h (m)	(2.5)	2.63		2.88		3.13		3.38		3.63		3.88	
H (m)		1.52		1.39		1.28		1.19		1.10		1.03	
C (m/s)		6.4		6.5		6.6		6.7		6.8		6.9	
ΔT			1.6		1.5		1.5		1.5		1.5		1.4
$\Sigma\Delta T$			1.6		3.1		4.6		6.1		7.6		9.0

By linear interpolation, $T_{sol/2}$ of 8 s corresponds to $S \approx 53$ m. The height of the standing wave formed here will be about $2H$ for the appropriate value of h, that is, crest height $= 2 \times 4/(2.5 + 53/40) = 1.8$ m.

Example 7.3

The conditions of example 7.2 remain unchanged apart from the tide falling by 1.5 m. What will be the maximum force applied to the wall by the wave?

If the solitary wave be assumed to break in a depth of water given by $H_b/h_b = 0.78$, then, since by section 7.2.2

$$H_b \times h_b = a \times h = 4\,\text{m}^2$$

$$h_b = (4/0.78)^{1/2} = 2.26\,\text{m and } H_b = 1.77\,\text{m}$$

From section 7.2.3, since the wall is now inshore of the breaking point but seawards of the shoreline, the pressures against the wall comprise two components. P_s increases linearly with depth from zero at the level of the wave crest to ρh_w at the foot of the wall where $h_w = (0.75\,H_b + 1)$ m from figure 7.2 the foot of the wall being 1 m below still water level. $0.75 H_b$ may be approximately equated to H_b, that is

$$\text{total static load} = \tfrac{1}{2}(1.77 + 1)^2 \times 1020$$

$$= 3900\,\text{kg/m}$$

On the same basis, the dynamic load of the breaking wave may, by equation 7.14 be computed as

$$P_v = 1020 h_b H_b = 1020 \times 4 = 4100\,\text{kg/m}$$

that is, total horizontal load on wall caused by breaking wave $= 3900 + 4100 = 8000$ kg per linear metre.

Example 7.4

The face of a seawall slopes at 1:3 to 3 m below extreme high water and then at such a slope to ensure breaking of the maximum waves. What will be the approximate height of run-up of a wave 4 m high and 15 s period? What will be the run-up for a similar height of wave of 8 s period?

From equation 7.24, in order to ensure breaking

$$\tan \alpha < \frac{8}{T} \left(\frac{H_I}{2g} \right)^{1/2} = \frac{8}{15} \left(\frac{4}{2 \times 9 \cdot 81} \right)^{1/2} = \frac{1}{4.15}$$

If we assume a lower slope of the wall of 1:5, then, by equation 7.26 run-up for $T = 15$ s

$$R = H_I SK \frac{\tan \alpha}{\dfrac{8}{T} \left(\dfrac{H_I}{2g} \right)^{1/2}}$$

where $K \approx 2.3$ and S, from section 7.3.1, will be about 0.9. Hence

$$R = 4 \times 2 \cdot 3 \times 0 \cdot 9 \times \tfrac{1}{4} \times 4 \cdot 15$$

$$= 8 \cdot 5 \text{ m (using a mean value of 1:4 for the wall slope)}$$

For $T = 8$ s, by substituting in the equation above for T

$$R = 8/15 \times 8 \cdot 5 = 4 \cdot 5 \text{ m}$$

Example 7.5

Model tests indicate a stability number N_s of 2.5 for a certain type of concrete armour unit for a slope of breakwater face of 1:3. What will be the weight of unit to withstand 5 m waves?

From equation 7.33 *et seq.*, we have

$$K_D \cot \alpha = N_s^3$$

that is

$$K_D \cot \alpha = 15 \cdot 6$$

substituting in equation 7.33

$$W = \frac{\rho_r H^3}{K_D \left(\frac{\rho_r}{\rho} - 1\right)^3 \cot \alpha}$$

where $\rho_r = $ (say) 2.3 tonnes/m^3

$$\frac{\rho_r}{\rho} = 2.3$$

Hence

$$W = \frac{2 \cdot 3 \times 5^3}{15 \cdot 6 \times (1 \cdot 3)^3} = 8.4 \text{ tonnes}$$

Example 7.6

A train of waves of height 4 m and period 12 s strikes a cylindrical pile of 0.5 m diameter standing in a depth of 8 m of water. What will be the maximum force on the pile at 4 m below still water level?

From section 7.4 we shall assume values of C_D and C_M of 1.5 and 2.5 respectively. At $T = 0$ and $T = 6$ s, that is, when the surface level at the pile corresponds to still water, we have, from equation 7.51, the force

$$F = \pm \frac{C_M}{g} \rho \frac{2\pi^2}{T} \frac{d^2}{4} K_z$$

(the + sign relating to $T = 0$ and the − sign to $T = 6$ s). When $T = 3$ and 9 s we have, from equation 7.51, the force

$$F = \pm \frac{\frac{1}{2}C_D}{g} \rho d K_z^2$$

(The + sign relating to $T = 3$ and the − sign to $T = 9$ s), where

$$K_z = \frac{\pi H}{T} \frac{\cosh 2\pi(z + h)/L}{\sinh 2\pi h/L}$$

and $H = 4$ m, $T = 12$ s. $h = 8$ m and $z = -4$ m. $L_0 = 1.56 \times T^2 = 224$ m and $h/L = 0.078$ from figure 3.2. Hence

$$K_z = \frac{\pi \times 4}{12} \frac{\cosh 2\pi \times 0 \cdot 039}{\sinh 2\pi \times 0 \cdot 078}$$

$$= \frac{\pi}{3} \frac{1 \cdot 03}{0 \cdot 51} \text{ (from figure 3.2 or from tables)}$$

$$= 2 \cdot 1$$

Hence, where $T = 0$ and 6 s

$$F = \pm \frac{2 \cdot 5}{9 \cdot 81} \ 1020 \ \frac{2\pi^2}{12} \ \times \ \frac{0 \cdot 5^2}{4} \ 2 \cdot 1 = \pm 56 \text{ kg/m}$$

When $T = 3$ and 9 s

$$F = \pm \frac{1}{2} \frac{1 \cdot 5}{9 \cdot 81} \ 1020 \times 0 \cdot 5 \times (2 \cdot 1)^2 = \pm 172 \text{ kg/m}$$

From equation 7.52, the maximum wave force will occur for $0 \leqslant t \leqslant 6$ s when

$$\cos \frac{2\pi t}{T} = \frac{C_M}{C_D} \times \frac{\pi^2}{2K_z T}$$

$$= \frac{2 \cdot 5 \times \pi^2 \times 0 \cdot 5}{2 \times 2 \cdot 1 \times 12} = 0 \cdot 246$$

that is

$$2\pi t / T = 1 \cdot 32 \text{ rad}$$

and

$$t = 12 \times 1 \cdot 32 / 2\pi = 2 \cdot 5 \text{ s}$$

A maximum force in the opposite direction will occur half a wave period later, that is, when $t = 2.5 + 6 = 8.5$ s.

The maximum value of the wave force, obtained by equation 7.51 is

$$F = 172 \sin^2 (1 \cdot 32 \text{ rad}) + 56 \cos(1 \cdot 32 \text{ rad})$$

$$= 172 \times 0 \cdot 93 + 56 \times 0 \cdot 246$$

$$= 160 + 14 = 174 \text{ kg/m}$$

Example 7.7

A rubble mound breakwater is to be constructed on a beach slope 1:100 and to withstand a significant wave height of 4 m, period 7 s. The depth of water ranges between 4 m and 6 m. The stability coefficient may be taken as 3.5 for unbroken waves and 3.0 for breaking waves. If the nominal armour size is

*4 tonnes and has density 2.6 tonnes/m³, what must be the slope of the break-
water face and the crest level if there is to be no overtopping? Assume the
density of seawater to be 1.03 tonnes/m³.*

Using equation 3.102

$$a = 4.46 \times 9.81 \times (1 - e^{-19/100}) = 7.57$$

$$b = \frac{1.56}{(1 + e^{-19.5/100})} = 0.86$$

$$\frac{H_b}{h_b} = 0.86 - 7.57 \times \frac{4}{9.81 \times 7^2} = 0.8$$

$$h_b = 5 \, m$$

Consequently at 4 m depth the wave height will be limited by breaking to 0.8 x 4
= 3.2 m.

For $h = 6$ m the wave is unbroken so that using equation 7.33

$$\cot \alpha = \frac{2.6 \times 4^3}{4 \times 3.5 \times \left(\frac{2.6}{1.03} - 1\right)^3} = 3.36$$

For $h = 5$ m the wave is breaking so that

$$\cot \alpha = \frac{2.6 \times 4^3}{4 \times 3.0 \left(\frac{2.6}{1.03} - 1\right)^3} = 3.9$$

and for $h = 4$ m

$$\cot \alpha = \frac{2.6 \times 3.2^3}{4 \times 3.0 \left(\frac{2.6}{1.03} - 1\right)^3} = 2$$

so that the breakwater slopes for 4 m, 5 m and 6 m water depth should be
$1:3\frac{1}{2}$, 1:4 and 1:2 respectively.

For the 6 m depths using equation 7.26 with $K \approx 2.3$

$$R = \frac{2.3 \times 1/3.5}{\frac{8}{7} \left(\frac{4}{2 \times 9.81}\right)^{1/2}} \times 4 = 5.1 \, m$$

for a smooth slope. Using the appropriate coefficient in section 7.3.1 (that is, 0.55) the run-up on a rough slope would be approximately 0.55 x 5.1 = 2.8 m so that the crest elevation must be 2.8 m above high water.

For the 5 m depth

$$R = \frac{2.3 \times 1/4}{\frac{8}{7}\left(\frac{4}{2 \times 9.81}\right)^{1/2}} \times 4 = 4.46 \, \text{m}$$

for a smooth slope and 4.46 x 0.55 = 2.45 m for a rough slope.

For the 4 m depth

$$R = \frac{2.3 \times 1/2}{\frac{8}{7}\left(\frac{3.2}{2 \times 9.81}\right)^{1/2}} \times 3.2 = 8.0 \, \text{m}$$

for a smooth slope and 8.0 x 0.55 = 4.4 m for a rough slope.

This shows that whereas steeper slopes require less volume to construct, run-up heights are greater.

References

1. *Shore Protection Manual* (U.S. Army C.E.R.C., 1975)
2. R.R. Johnson, E.P.D. Mansard and J. Ploeg, Effects of wave grouping on breakwater stability, *Proceedings of the 16th Coastal Engineering Conference, Hamburg, 1978*, vol. III, pp. 2228-43.
3. P. Bruun and A.R. Gunbak, New design principles for rubble mound structures, *Proceedings of the 15th Coastal Engineering Conference, Hawaii, 1976*, vol. III, pp. 2429-73
4. M. Sainflou, Essai sur les digues maritimes verticales, *Ann. Ponts Chauss.*, **4** (1928) 5-48
5. R.L. Wiegel, *Oceanographical Engineering* (Prentice-Hall, Englewood Cliffs, N.J., 1964)
6. R.L. Wiegel and K.E. Beebe, The design wave in shallow water, *J. Waterways Div. Am. Soc. civ. Engrs.*, **82**, WW1 (1956)
7. P.H. Kemp and M.D. Adeyemo, Effect of backwash on wave asymmetry close to breakers, *Proceedings of the 11th Coastal Engineering Conference, London, 1968*, paper 118
8. R.A. Bagnold, Interim report on wave-pressure research, *J. Instn civ. Engrs,* **12** (1939) 202-26
9. D.F. Denny, Further experiments on wave pressures, *J. Instn civ. Engrs.*, **35** (1951) 330-45
10. N.L. Ackermaun, Impact pressures produced by breaking waves, *Proceedings of the 14th Coastal Engineering Conference, Copenhagen, 1974*
11. Baron W.F. Van Asbeck, *Bitumen in Hydraulic Engineering* (Elsevier, Amsterdam, 1961)

12. I.J. Hunt, Design of seawalls and breakwaters, *Proc. Am. Soc. civ. Engrs.*, **85**, WW3 (1959) 123-52

13. L. Droyosz-Wawrzyniak, Calculation of height of wave rushing up the slopes and the range of slope revetments, *Arch. Hydrotech.*, **4** (1965) 323-36

14. T. Saville, Wave run-up on composite slopes, *Proceedings of the 6th Coastal Engineering Conference, Gainsville, 1958*, pp. 691-700

15. T. Saville, Laboratory data on wave run-up and overtopping on shore structures (U.S. Army Corps of Engineers, Beach Erosion Board) Tech. Memo No. 64 (1955)

16. J.R. Weggel, Wave overtopping equation, *Proceedings of the 15th Coastal Engineering Conference, Hawaii, 1976*, vol. III, pp. 2737-55

17. R.Y. Hudson, Wave forces on breakwaters. Engineering aspects of water waves: a symposium, *Trans. Am. Soc. civ. Engrs.*, **118** (1953) 653-74

18. R.Y. Hudson, Laboratory investigations of rubble-mound breakwaters, *J. Am. Soc. civ. Engrs.*, **85**, WW3 (1959) 93-121

19. A.F. Whillock and W.A. Price, Armour blocks as slope protection, *Proceedings of the 15th Coastal Engineering Conference, Hawaii, 1976*, vol. III, pp. 2564-71

20. M. Brorsen, H.F. Burcharth and T. Larsen, Stability of Dolos slopes, *Proceedings of the 14th Coastal Engineering Conference, Copenhagen, 1974*

21. W.A. Price, Static stability of rubble mound breakwaters, *Dock Harb. Auth.*, (1979) 2-7

22. C.T. Brown, Blanket theory and low cost revetments, *Proceedings of the 16th Coastal Engineering Conference, Hamburg, 1978*, vol. III, pp. 2510-27

23. J.M. Caldwell, Reflection of solitary waves (U.S. Army Corps of Engineers) Tech. Memo No. 11 (1949)

24. T. Hayashi, T. Kano, M. Shirai and M. Hattori, Hydraulics research on the closely spaced pile breakwater, *Proceedings of the 10th Coastal Engineering Conference, Tokyo, 1966*, paper 2.6

25. G.E. Jarlan, A perforated vertical wall breakwater, *Dock Harb. Auth.*, **XLI** (1961)

26. W. Marks, A perforated mobile breakwater for fixed and floating application, *Proceedings of the 10th Coastal Engineering Conference, Tokyo, 1966*, paper 66

27. T. Ijima, E. Tanaka and H. Okuzono, Permeable sea wall with reservoir and the use of WAROCK, *Proceedings of the 15th Coastal Engineering Conference, Hawaii, 1976*, vol. III, pp. 2623-42

28. N. Shiraishi, R.Q. Palmer and H. Okamoto, Quay wall with wave absorber IGLOO, *Proceedings of the 15th Coastal Engineering Conference, Hawaii, 1976*, vol. III, pp. 2677-96

29. R. Lochner, O. Faber and W.G. Penney, The 'Bombardon' floating breakwater, The civil engineer in war, 2, docks and harbours (Institute of Civil Engineers, 1948) pp. 256-90

30. J.J. Stoker, *Water Waves* (Interscience, New York, 1957)

31. R.C. McGregor and N.S. Miller, Scrap tyre breakwaters in coastal engineering, *Proceedings of the 16th Coastal Engineering Conference, Hamburg, 1978*, vol. III, pp. 2191-208

32. B.M. Count, On the dynamics of wave power devices, *Proc. R. Soc. A*, **363** (1978) 559-79

33. J.K. Dawson, *Wave Energy*, Dept. of Energy Paper No. 42 (HMSO, 1979)

34. J.T. Evans, Pneumatic and similar breakwaters, *Proc. R. Soc. A*, **231** (1955) 457-66

35. G.I. Taylor, The action of a surface current used as a breakwater, *Proc. R. Soc. A*, **231** (1955) 466–78
36. H. Lamb, *Hydrodynamics*, 6th ed. (Cambridge University Press, 1945)
37. G.H. Keulegan and L.H. Carpenter, Forces on cylinders and plates in an oscillating fluid, *J. Res. natn. Bur. Stand.*, **60** (1958) 423–40
38. L. Hogben, B.L. Miller, J.W. Searle and S. Ward, Estimation of fluid loading on offshore structures, *Proc. Instn civ. Engrs.*, **63** (1977) 515–62
39. J. Lighthill, Waves and hydrodynamic loading, BOSS 79 Opening Address (London, 1979)
40. P.K. Stansby, Fluid loading and the discrete vortex method, *J. Soc. underwat. Technol.*, (1978)
41. B.L. Miller, Wave slamming loads on horizontal circular elements of offshore structures, Royal Institution of Naval Architects Spring Meeting, 1977, paper 5
42. T. Sarpkaya, Wave impact loads on cylinders, *Proceedings of the 10th Offshore Technology Conference, Houston, 1978*, paper 3065
43. R.C. MacCamy and R.A. Fuchs, Wave forces on piles: a diffraction theory U.S. Army Corps of Engineers, Beach Erosion Board, Technical Memo No. 69 (1954)
44. C. Scruton and A.R. Flint, Wind-excited oscillations of structures, *Proc. Instn civ. Engrs.*, **27** (1964) 673–702
45. R.N. Sainsbury and D. King, The flow-induced oscillations of marine structures, *Proc. Instn civ. Engrs.*, **49** (1971) 269–302
46. A.D.K. Laird, Water forces on flexible oscillating cylinders, *J. Waterways Div. Am. Soc. civ. Engrs.*, **88** (1962) 125–37
47. R.E.D. Bishop and A.Y. Hassan, The lift and drag forces on a circular cylinder oscillating in a flowing fluid, *Proc. R. Soc. A*, **277** (1964) 51–75
48. B.W. Wilson, Characteristics of anchor cables in uniform ocean currents, *P.I.A.N.C. Bull.*, **I** (1964) 21–53; **II** (1964) 81–115
49. B.W. Wilson, Characteristics of deep sea anchor cables in strong ocean currents, *Proc. Instn civ. Engrs.*, **32** (1965) 598–99 (synopsis only)
50. M. Bracannot, Abaques donnant la figure d'equilibre et les tensions dans un cable soumis à un courant permanent uniforme, *Houille Blanche*, **8** (1965) 771–80
51. E.E. Zajac, Dynamics and kinematics of the laying and recovery of submarine cables, *Bell Syst. Tech. J.*, **36** (1957) 1129–207
52. D.J. Cronin, P.S. Godfrey, P.M. Hook and T.A. Wyatt, Spectral fatigue analysis for off shore structures, in *Numerical Methods in Offshore Engineering*, ed. (Wiley, New York, 1978) chapter 9
53. L.E. Borgman, The spectral density for ocean wave forces, University of California, Berkeley, Hydraulic Engineering Laboratory, Wave Research Projects, HEL-9-8 (1965)
54. D.M. Thompson and R.M. Shuttler, Design of riprap slope protection against wind waves, CIRIA Report No. 61 (1976)
55. R.M. Young, P. Ackers and D.M. Thompson, Riprap design for wind-wave attack: prototype tests on the offshore bank of the Wash, CIRIA Technical Note No. 84 (1977)

8

The Acquisition of Data

This final chapter presents a brief account of the instruments and techniques available to the coastal engineer for acquiring and recording pertinent data about currents, waves, water depths, sediment transport and littoral drift. Instruments in these fields continue to develop rapidly and it is intended, primarily, to provide an introduction to the principles and the available choice of techniques rather than to attempt a detailed descriptive account of particular instruments, which would rapidly become obsolete.

8.1 Current Measurements

In selecting instruments for current measurement a distinction needs to be made between those instruments which continuously measure velocities in two (or even three, see section 8.1.3) directions and thus integrate effective transport at a point, and the direct-reading instrument which tunes into the current and integrates in effect the total movement at a point. The latter types of instrument, described in sections 8.1.1 and 8.1.2, record revolutions of a propeller by means of a reed switch which, moreover, measures revolutions in either direction, so short-term turbulence or orbital velocities caused by waves may give rise to overestimating average current velocities and affect the indication of direction of the resultant.

8.1.1 Direct-reading Current Meter

The most widely used instrument for measuring currents at sea is the direct-reading current meter (DRCM) which is lowered over the side of a moored vessel by means of a cable with multicore conductors for electrical circuits between the current meter and the recording head. The depth of the instrument is usually recorded automatically by means of a pneumatic depth gauge, alternatively visual observations are made of a marked cable. Current velocity measurements are obtained by measuring the speed of rotation of a propeller. The instrument is sensitive to velocities of 0.05 m/s (0.1 knots). Current direction is measured by orientation of the vane in relation to the magnetic meridian.

Current profiles are obtained by raising and lowering the instrument in stages and taking readings at predetermined levels. For subsequent plotting of results it is normally most satisfactory to obtain readings at the lower levels at approximately the same heights above sea bed throughout the tidal cycle.

In a strong current it is necessary to ensure that the instrument is controlled in position in plan, either by the use of a sinker or by confining the DRCM and its supporting cable, at intervals, to travel down a heavily weighted line. Unless the vessel from which readings are to be taken is moored fore and aft, movement of the vessel may affect current readings. Swinging of the ship at slack water will not only cause some variation in the position at which the readings are taken but, and this may be more serious, the currents measured near slack water will also be subject to error unless allowances are made for such movement.

8.1.2 Recording Current Meters

Self-recording current meters (SRCM) similar to that shown in figure 8.1 measure the speed and direction of currents by the use of the same principle as the DRCM described above. The information is, however, recorded within the immersed body of the instrument, in binary coded form, on film or on magnetic tape, for subsequent processing and decoding. An additional refinement of such instruments is a timing switch, which may be pre-set to obtain readings over short periods at predetermined intervals: this capability may be important to increase the period of life of the unattended recorder. With more complex types of recording meter, the information on current

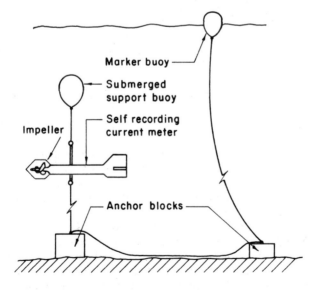

Figure 8.1 *Self recording current meter*

speed and direction may be obtained by telemetry—by acoustic pulse through
the water—on demand from an interrogatory signal from within a range of about
500 m. The latter capability permits a periodic check on the satisfactory operation of the instrument, which is highly desirable. Such instruments are usually
used in groups to record currents simultaneously at different situations or levels
and the lack of results at one point cannot be subsequently restored by taking
further readings.

8.1.3 Current Meters without Moving Parts

In certain situations, particularly following foul weather and close inshore,
propeller-type current meters are liable to become entangled in seaweed or
fouled by marine growth (in clear warm waters within a week). Furthermore,
these are fairly delicate instruments and there is therefore an incentive to use
alternative types of current recorders. Perhaps the simplest of all current
recorders is the National Institute of Oceanography jelly bottle described by
Carruthers.[1] Instruments of greater complexity but similar type have been
used, based on measurements of the inclination of a cable attaching a submerged buoy to a sinker. Ortolan [31] for instance, describes such an instrument for measuring bottom currents, making use of a photographic self-
recording clinometer.

Lowe et al. [2] describe the use of a rigid air-filled filament-wound pipe
spar supported on the sea bed and projecting above the sea surface. Accelero-
meters in orthogonal directions in the upper part of the spar measure the
components of tilt, and hence transport rate (that is, velocity integrated over
the depth). A fast Fourier transform analysis filters out the effects of short-
period waves. The device may also be used to detect direction of sea swell and
temporal characteristics of edge waves.

Instruments are available for the laboratory, and may be expected to be
developed for use at sea, which measure water velocity in three mutually
perpendicular directions by exploiting the Doppler effect on the frequency of
transmission of ultrasonic signals between transducer heads. Lasers are also
used, in comparable laboratory methods, for measurement of velocities at a
point.

Where over-all transport measurements are required in a relatively narrow
channel, consideration may be given to the exploitation of the electromagnetic effect of the motion of the sea setting up a potential difference across
the channel, measured by an insulated cable on its bed, as described in section
2.5. Interpretation of the results would be difficult in an estuary, or elsewhere
where appreciable variation in the salinity, and hence the conductivity, of the
water is to be expected.

Several electromagnetic current meters are now available which operate on
the same principle, setting up a local magnetic field and determining water
current vectors by measuring e.m.f in two (or three) perpendicular directions.
A spherical instrument is used for measuring the three components of velocity,
and an oblate sphere circular in plan for measuring horizontal velocities only.
Such instruments will record velocities down to 0.01 m/s and provide either

instantaneous velocities, say, for a period of 0.2 s, or mean velocities over a longer, say 20 s period. For purposes of calibration it is also necessary to determine conductivity, periodically for the open sea or continuously in or near a river estuary or where any appreciable variation may be expected.[3, 4]

8.1.4 Floats and Drift Recorders

It is frequently necessary, for an engineering project, to obtain information on the pattern of tidal streams over an appreciable area. The usual manner of obtaining this information is by the use of surface floats, such as that illustrated in figure 8.2. The float is designed to present minimum wind resistance and to represent water movement at a selected shallow depth below the surface, thereby minimising the effect of local wind-drift. Although compensation for wind effects may be made, the area of the drogue must be large in relation to the area of pennant and other projection above water surface. Several floats are placed in the sea in the area under observation and their movement followed, preferably over a tidal cycle for a representative spring and neap tide. Each float carries an identifying pennant and the positions are recorded by means of one or more launches using appropriate position-fixing equipment or, for a minor operation, a sextant. Alternatively shore or sea-based radar may be used to follow the floats or, in the absence of such a facility, synchronised fixes by three land-based theodolites. Stereoscopic photography may also be used. The movements of floats may be recorded by pairs of air photographs separated by

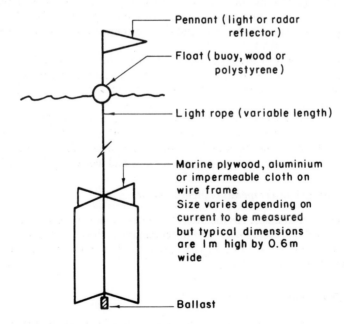

Figure 8.2 *Surface float*

a short interval, which permit the movement of each float during the interval to be estimated; this method is only economical where a large number of floats are involved.

Sasaki *et al.* [5, 6] have used a system 'Stereo-bacs' whereby floats released in the surf zone are photographed at regular intervals by remotely controlled cameras suspended by balloons. The resulting film provides immediate information of circulation, drift and rip currents, and provide data for systematic analysis.

A point frequently overlooked in designing float tests is that a reliable interpretation requires the tidal stream at any particular locality to be estimated throughout the tidal cycle; a series of float courses diverging from the centre of interest will provide information difficult to interpret. (In fact it will relate to Lagrangian rather than Eulerian equations of motion − see section 1.1.) It may therefore be necessary to determine the general set of tidal streams by a preliminary series of tests, followed by a full-scale series in which each float is introduced at a predetermined time and place to travel through the area of primary interest. Velocity profiles by current meter will usually be required to translate the results of float tests into overall transport. This relationship may be complex where salinity currents occur, as in estuaries, or where tests are carried out close inshore. Here the floats may be combined with a drogue—operating as a storm anchor—suspended at a desired level below the float.

Alternatively, for coastal waters subject to continuous wave action and where the main water movements are wind driven, currents can be established using a system of fixed buoys or drogues. The first drogue is fixed to the sea bed, the second attached to it by rope and the third attached to the second by a weighted rope or chain. The current velocity and direction can be approximately established by measuring the angle and distance between the drogues using land-based survey equipment.

Where wind drift of the surface layer of the sea forms a part of the study, drift cards may be used; these consist of reply-paid cards in plastics envelopes, designed to float flat or on end, requesting the finder to record the time and place of recovery. Plastics drift indicators, with slight negative buoyancy, have been used where the circulation of bottom currents represents the subject for study; interpretation of results of bottom drift tests is open to considerable doubt in relation to movement of bed load which, essentially, requires a certain minimum threshold value of shear stress and hence of velocity.[8, 9]

8.1.5 Salinity and Temperature Measurement

Instruments are available for the direct or recorded measurement of sea salinity, based on conductivity, and of temperature, the latter being necessary for the interpretation of conductivity as salinity. For recording instruments, the compensation is automatic.

8.1.6 Tidal Gauges

A tide gauge should preferably be sited in a sheltered area and be fitted with a chamber to damp out short period waves.

Tidal readings taken in the open sea may be subject to error due to the variation of mean sea level that accompanies steep waves in shoaling water particularly near a lee shore (see section 3.7.1).

The simplest type of recording tide gauge for sheltered areas is also, at present, the most satisfactory. A heavy float rises and falls with the tide within a well and the movement is transmitted by a vertical wire tensioned around a spindle. The well is situated in deep water in an area subject only to surface waves. Thus, by confining connection with the sea to holes near the foot of the well, whose total area is a fraction of the surface area of the well, adequate damping of wind waves is assured.

Where it is necessary to record tidal movements in the open sea, some form of pressure capsule is normally used for the purpose, fitted with a porous or electronic filter to minimise short-period fluctuation created by waves.

Tide gauges based on the measurement of electrical properties of a circuit including immersed electrodes, have been developed for use in fresh or saline water. The gauge can measure both short-period changes, that is, waves, or the mean water level, that is, tides.

Transmitting tide gauges, usually based on mechanical movement of floats, emit the information periodically or on demand by radio frequency transmitter. The recorder may therefore be housed remotely in an office. A special use of such a wave gauge is in controlling dredgers and survey vessels; for certain of these, soundings are thus automatically adjusted in relation to datum.

Section 2.5 describes the correction factors that have to be applied to separate direct tidal movement from variation in sea level caused by wind and weather.

8.2 Wave Measurements

8.2.1 Direct Observation of Waves

Until the introduction of wave measuring instruments in the last thirty years, records of wave characteristics at sea were based for the greater part on visual estimates by mariners, supplemented to a smaller degree by observations against graduated staffs attached to the piles of exposed piers.

Hogben and Lumb [10] provide over 3000 tables of statistics based on nearly two million sets of visual observations of heights, periods and directions of waves reported under a scheme organised by the World Meteorological Organisation from ships in service on the major shipping routes of the world over the 8 year period from 1953 to 1961. First published in 1967, this source has been used extensively and is expected to be up-dated from time to time. The world is divided up into 8 areas, the data from each area being the responsibility of one country. Each area is then subdivided into Marsden squares (10° squares) each square having a code. The data on wave height and period are presented in tabular form for (1) all seasons for all directions, all seasons with direction in 20° arcs and (2) as for (1) but using 2-monthly intervals. The engineer can obtain *all* data (up to the present) for any sea area that he wishes to examine by specifying the sea area to the country indicated as responsible for data collection.

Aerial photography may be used to study refraction patterns of long swell. In the Second World War such photographs were used to allow the offshore topography to be deduced from the refraction pattern of waves of known deep water characteristics.

A U.S. satellite SEASAT, launched in 1978, is designed to provide all-weather global monitoring of sea surface temperature, significant wave height and the speed and direction of surface wind.[11]

8.2.2   Use of Instruments on the Sea Bed

A number of the early spectral analyses of waves were based on records obtained by means of pressure gauges (collapsible air-bags or transducer heads) or inverted echo sounders resting on the sea bed (see, for instance, ref. 12). The former type of instrument may only be used in shallow water, the depth being related to the minimum length of wave to be recorded where the pressure response factor (see section 7.2.1) is adequate. The recorded pressure may also be modified by the effect of the presence of the instrument on orbital velocities in the vicinity. The latter type records the length of path of a pulse of sound reflected from the water surface and will only provide a reliable record where the depth of water above the transmitter/receiver head represents a fairly small fraction of the wave length, the acceptable ratio depending on the degree of focusing of the signal. Where foam is present in storm waves, the echo from the surface is obscured.

8.2.3   Use of Recorders at or above Sea Surface

Vertical gauges, recording wave heights by electrical resistance (see section 8.1.6), pressure reading or similar direct method, require some means of support without presenting an obstruction sufficient to modify the wave characteristics. Such gauges are therefore normally attached to open-framed structures such as drilling platforms or marine oil rigs. They may also be used close inshore and, in particular, for recording waves within harbours; here, it is necessary to ensure that the type of gauge is immune from fouling by flotsam or oil. For this reason, a gauge that may be set above the sea surface is frequently selected, emitting a sonic or radar pulse and measuring the period between transmission and reception of the reflected signal.

8.2.4   Recorders for Long Waves

A particular problem is presented by the recording of long waves or seiches which may have an amplitude of only a few centimetres, combined with a long period of from, say, 20 s to several minutes. A sensitive gauge is required, which may be damped to exclude short-period waves. The simplest means for detecting the existence of seiches is to examine the record of a tide gauge near high and low water, when long-period fluctuations in level may be distinguished from the tidal movement. Tide gauges may be used for the recording of seiches, adopting

an appropriate method for compensating the record for tidal effects so that the
seiche appears throughout the tidal cycle as a periodic departure from an
approximately horizontal line, possibly combined with an increase of drum
speed. One such method makes use of two float-type tide gauges, with one
operating as a normal tide gauge; the chamber of the second is connected to the
first by a pipe with restricted bore.[13] One float will rise and fall with the tide
and with superimposed seiche movements, the other will respond to tidal movements only. The recorder is so arranged as to indicate the difference between the
vertical height of the two floats and thus records seiches only. A method of
spectral analysis will be required to identify the predominant periods of seiches.

8.2.5 Wave Recorders

There are a number of types of wave-recording buoy, including the wave-rider
buoy [14] which is shown in figure 8.3. This instrument incorporates an
accelerometer and transmits data by radio over a distance of about 20 km.
Information obtained by a fixed pattern of such buoys, for example, the clover-
leaf buoy of the National Institute of Oceanography [15] may be processed

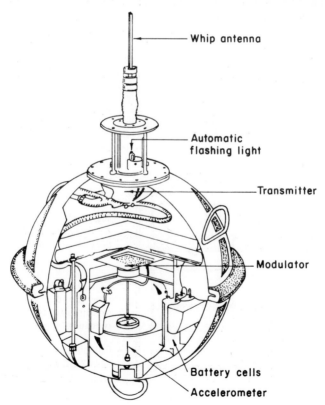

Whip antenna

Automatic
flashing light

Transmitter

Modulator

Battery cells

Accelerometer

Figure 8.3 *The waverider buoy*

to provide information on wave direction, but Esteva [16] discusses the limitations of such arrays in that (1) the lower limit of analysable wave period depends on layout and water depth (2) there is a dependence on orientation of the array for short period waves (3) accuracy depends on the nature of the wave field, that is, a wide or narrow spectrum. The method is not now generally recommended and entails a great amount of analysis.

There remains a need for a simple type of instrument to indicate the direction of approach of waves. The coastal engineer usually needs to obtain records over an extended period in, probably, a remote situation and is reluctant to invest in costly equipment to operate unattended and vulnerable to damage or depredation. Readily assimilable records are also required.

The DOSO [17] meter records directly the direction but not amplitude of the horizontal component of orbital wave motion by means of a brush-type sensor mounted on the head of the instrument drum, see figure 8.4. The forward and return motion of each passing wave causes the brush to tilt a freely mounted pendulum which contacts an annular coil, such that resistance is directly proportional to angle measured clockwise from zero, so that a measured potential directly records wave direction. A practical problem lies in differentiating between waves and superimposed background currents so the instrument should be used in combination with a SRCM (section 8.1.2).

Two land-based methods, each yielding a reasonable indication of wave direction, which can then be back tracked into deep water, are (1) by using a clinometer (a simple instrument visually aligned with the wave crest) from a high vantage point on the coast, close to deep water, and (2) by using radar [18] whereby direction can be established for the whole zone up to 2 km from the

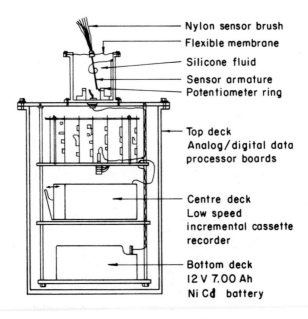

Figure 8.4 *The DOSO meter*

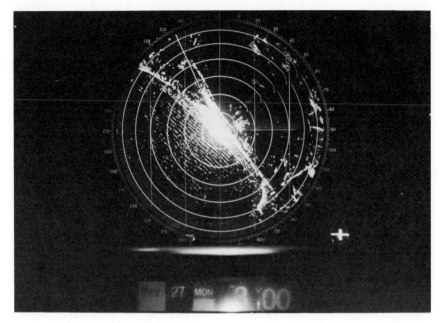

Figure 8.5 *Time lapse radar recording of wave direction*

coast but, since this method is dependent on reflections from normally large steep waves, it is only possible to record, say, 30 to 40 per cent of the waves annually. The radar records of wave direction can be taken photographically with the exposure time equal to the complete sweep time of the radar scanner as shown in figure 8.5. In addition by recording wave direction on successive cinefilm frames a two-dimensional picture of the wave fronts can be established as they diffract.

Finally, there is the ship-borne wave recorder, exemplified by the NIO instrument [19] which combines the record from an accelerometer with pressure transmitted from sensors attached to the hull and open to the sea. Lightships provide particularly appropriate vessels for obtaining such records, the instrument being arranged to record automatically for a few minutes in each hour over an extended period.

Section 3.3.5 describes the analysis of wave records, a process carried out by hand or by computer.

8.3 Hydrographic Surveys

8.3.1 Depth Recording

While a survey-type of echo-sounder may have an error, in favourable conditions of a firm bottom and a calm sea, of less than 100 mm, the over-all accuracy of a marine survey may be more dependent on a satisfactory establishment of the level of the sea surface (see section 2.5) and the precise positioning of the survey vessel (by Decca Hi-fix or comparable system, generally to within 2 to 10 metres, depending on the geometry of the land-based stations or by one of the more precise systems developed for the offshore oil industry), augmented as required by visual, radio-wave or laser instrument sights. For surveys close inshore, confidence may be increased where tidal range permits overlap between hydrographic survey at high water and beach survey at low water.

The echo-sounder requires calibration at the beginning and end of every period of survey (the bar check), by means of a metal bar slung beneath the vessel at predetermined levels. Other practical precautions are needed to ensure uniform speed of rotation of the recorder and synchronisation with time of emission of the sound pulse. The most accurate interpretation requires precise knowledge of the speed of sound through the water, dependent on salinity and temperature. The emitted beam is fairly narrow but will be reflected by the high points on a rugged bottom where distance between peaks and valleys is small in relation to the depth of water. Systems of binary digital recording may be used for depth and position records to allow immediate processing of the record without recourse to the visual trace on the recorder—special circuits have been devised to ensure continuity of record from the bed without interference with other echoes (from fish or other cause of false reading).

For a muddy bottom, often encountered in estuaries and occasionally in the open sea, the gain may be altered or a dual system used, a pulse of, say 210 kHz identifying the surface of the mud and a 30 kHz pulse the surface of the consolidated layers beneath, but there remain problems in calibration.

The problem of measuring sea bed profiles in the surf zone has prompted the Scripps Institute to develop a tracked vehicle capable of travelling 450 m offshore and into a depth of water of 10 m. Horizontal position and vertical profiles are obtained by gyroscopes, fluxgate compass and by odometers on each tread.[20]

8.3.2   Other Survey Techniques

A number of geophysical profiling systems may be used at sea. A survey vessel traverses the area under study with an underwater source and receiver of energy pulses. The depth of penetration to which reflecting surfaces below sea bed may be detected depends on the energy and frequency of the pulse, the nature of the ground, the sensitivity of the receiver and the electronic gain of the amplifier. Certain profiling systems may be used to indicate the depth and type of sediment overlying the solid bottom and, as such, provide a valuable survey tool for the coastal engineer.

Another geophysical technique concerns the use of transit sonar (also called 'oblique asdic' and 'echo ranging'). A narrow transverse beam of sound energy pulses is transmitted to one or both sides of a vessel following a steady course. Echoes are recorded as darker marks on a continuous record, the shade representing the strength of the return signal, and the surface topography within 500 m or more of the vessel's course may in consequence be, to a certain extent, deduced in the interpretation of the record. The strength of the return signal is related to the angle of the bed (thus parallel sand waves will appear as alternate dark and light bands). Interpretation requires an approximate knowledge of the topography of the sea bed so the technique is usually combined with a depth record and, where interpretation of geological relief is required, with a geo-physical reflection survey. This is also an excellent technique for locating pipe-lines, wrecks and other sea bed obstructions.

There are a number of techniques for obtaining samples from the sea bed but each is appropriate to a fairly narrow range of materials. The sampler may be allowed to fall freely (the drop-sampler) or it may be forced into the seabed (the piston-sampler or explosive-sampler). The in situ density of sediments, and the variation with depth, may be established by the use of a nuclear probe. For a particular material, calibration may be made against reconstituted samples of the same material.

8.4 Measurement of Sediment Movement

8.4.1 Material in Suspension

Several types of sampler collect suspended sediment in a container by settlement from natural flow entering an orifice and flowing at reduced velocity through the container. Generally, the results will be of qualitative value only of the rate of sediment transport.

The most effective method entails the pumping of samples and the filtering out of sediment. Interpretation as a rate of transport requires the simultaneous recording of current velocity. These requirements are achieved, for example, by the HRS Flux Meter.[21] Another method for measuring suspended load at some distance away from the bed is to use oceanographers' sampling bottles, suspended at intervals on a wire, with top and bottom lids simultaneously closed by messenger. Sampling of the sediment may subsequently be achieved by means of the Coulter counter, which automatically counts particles in a capillary, traversing the field of view of a microscope. Variations of the same technique have been developed for use in rough and breaking seas.[22, 23, 24]

8.4.2 Bed Transport

There is no satisfactory method of direct measurement of bed transport at sea, although it is possible to obtain some information, where there is a firm bottom, by means of a trap such as the BTMA (bottom transport meter, Arnhem) which has a rectangular orifice and perforated container mounted on a sledge frame; material down to about $300\,\mu$m is retained. Interest in measuring bed transport usually relates to areas where there is a soft bottom, unsuitable in consequence for such an instrument because of local disturbance, uncertainty in the relative level of orifice and bed, and the likelihood of 'dredging' during the course of recovery.

Where there are sand waves or dunes it might be supposed that the rate of transport could be gauged by periodic surveys along the line of advance of the waves. At sea, such a survey requires a high precision in position fixing and sufficiently detailed mapping to reveal a consistent trend, taking account of effects of weather and of periodic variations; it is not known that any attempt of quantitative analysis of this nature has proved successful. In the laboratory, the movement of sand waves has been studied in unidirectional flow by means of a pair of downward facing echo-sounders and at sea such an approach might well provide qualitative information on the changes of sand wave forms with tide and weather.

At present, apart from over-all determination of siltation and scour, by computing volumetric differences between periodic marine surveys, the greatest amount of information is obtainable by means of tracers.

Clays, silts, sands and larger particles may be labelled by attachment (by adsorption or mechanically for larger particles) of certain radioactive tracers. An alternative technique is based on irradiation of an artificial material, of similar particle size and density as the natural sediment; for this a chemically treated ground glass is suitable.[25, 26] The movement and distribution of the tracer are subsequently surveyed at intervals by means of a Geiger counter or scintillation counter lowered by cable to the sea bed. Generally, the results of such a survey may only be interpreted qualitatively, but in certain circumstances it is possible to examine distribution of the tracer with respect to depth and hence to make a quantitative interpretation, at least over limited areas. The Atomic Energy Research Establishment, Harwell, has engaged in a considerable amount of work in this field. The isotope used for a particular study has to satisfy requirements for high gamma ray activity, and a half-life to suit the period of the experiment, while satisfying considerations of health and safety in use. It is necessary to study the initial background radioactivity and it is the strength and variation of this background which determine the maximum area of distribution of the tracer, for the results to be interpretable. It is possible that new developments in technique will permit not only the strength but the energy level of radioactivity to be measured. This would permit the identification of two or more tracers used simultaneously. Thus differences in rates and direction of transport might be determined for different particle sizes initially deposited together. See also Heathershaw and Carr.[27]

There is at present no satisfactory technique for using radioactive tracers in the inshore zone. If all the bed movement were strictly parallel to the shore, core sampling combined with determination of radioactivity would permit a direct estimate of the transport rate. Changes in the bed profile, transverse to the shoreline, however, prevent reliance on such a method. If a regular rate of dosing with radioactive material were used, similar to the process described for fluorescent tracers in section 8.5.2, it should be possible to devise a technique of detection that could, in the long run, eliminate the errors due to bed profile changes. Because of the time dependence of the strength of radioactivity, it is here that the 'double-labelling' by two tracers would be essential to indicate the maximum amount of information about tracer movement. A further practical difficulty arises, however, due to the wide difference in the excursion (that is, the total range of movement), during a tidal or other cycle, between material transported in suspension and bed transport. In consequence, the former will tend to become widely dispersed while the latter remains relatively highly concentrated, with resulting difficulty in designing the scheme for detection.

It has been found possible in certain localities to use sources of rare minerals or natural radioactivity from areas of erosion, to trace prevailing direction but not the magnitude of bed or littoral movement.

8.5 Measurement of Littoral Drift

8.5.1 Direct Methods of Measurement

As discussed in chapter 5, it is locally possible to make direct measurement of littoral drift. Where physiographical or structural features provide a complete barrier, it is only necessary to measure the rate at which material is accumulating on the updrift side—or diminishing on the downdrift side. Where sand is involved, a survey, from which quantitative information may be derived, will have to extend to some distance offshore (and, if wind is involved, inshore as well). Shingle drift, on the other hand, is usually confined to the littoral band; the exceptions concern only those localities where there are rapid currents to take the shingle into deep water or where the shingle accretion extends into deep water (see figures 6.1 and 6.3).

Volumetric computation, based on orthodox topographical methods of surveying over a wide area, is a laborious process on a foreshore affected by tidal movement. If a storm occurs during the course of the survey, there may be sufficient movement of material between one part of the beach and another to invalidate the apparent results of the survey.

A satisfactory and economical method is to compute beach quantities at predetermined sections from periodic aerial surveys. Adequate ground controls are provided to permit levels to be derived from stereoscopic pairs of aerial photographs. If the levels are obtained at corresponding points for each survey, the results may be fed directly into a standard computer program with minimum revision of data. The aerial survey is carried out on a calm day near low water of spring tides to ensure maximum exposure of the foreshore; if necessary the beach slope may locally need to be extrapolated below sea level but, on a shingle beach, this will not normally introduce a significant error. On a sand shore the aerial survey will need, in any event, to be supplemented by an offshore survey and changes offshore will not normally be occurring with great rapidity.

On a groyned beach, errors will be introduced if beach levels are obtained too close to the groynes since local sheltering may cause these to be unrepresentative of beach levels within the groyne bay. A satisfactory rule is to determine levels on sections at quarter points along the length of the groyne bay.

On a steep beach, backed by a seawall or breastwork of known height, it is possible to carry out a beach survey directly by photography. A conspicuous rope or tape is laid down the beach on the section whose profile is to be determined and a photograph taken from an unvaried viewpoint. A simple grid laid

over the photograph, with the horizontal determined from the line of the sea
horizon and levels related to that of the seawall or breastwork at the line of the
section, then permits the profile to be established. Alternatively, a high viewpoint will allow photographs to be taken in calm weather at selected stages of
the tide and hence approximately to map foreshore contours.

Yet another method of determining a beach profile is by means of an inclino-
meter, supported by two or more wheels, which is pushed down the beach. The
instrument maintains a continuous record of inclination—and hence beach
gradient—and distance traversed. All levels may be attached to sea level at the
head of the beach.

8.5.2 Indirect Methods of Measurement

Indirect methods of measurement of littoral drift require the use of tracers.
While radioactive tracers have proved of the greatest value offshore (see section
8.4.2), fluorescent tracers have been most widely adopted for determination of
littoral drift, with particular success on shingle beaches. Earlier experiments
required the particles to be coated with the tracer dye, but more recent applications have used artificial beach material made from a crushed concrete containing a resin and the fluorescent dye. For a shingle beach, the pebble grading
and density are matched by the concrete, using where necessary a heavy
aggregate such as hornblende. The material is rounded by the sea and the
difference in shape has normally been found to be unimportant. A number of
different fluorescent dyes of distinctive colour may be used to allow two or
more tracers to be distinguished simultaneously. Aluminium pebbles with a
variety of shapes and the same density of the natural beach material, have been
used.[28] These pebbles are expensive and their recovery, using a metal detec-
tor above low water mark, is time-consuming and rarely more than 60 per cent.

The usual procedure is to deposit the tracer at a steady rate at predetermined
positions on the foreshore and to detect its presence, at regular intervals of time
and distance along the foreshore, by means of an ultraviolet lamp, used within a
square frame laid on the beach. Calculations of littoral drift are based on recording the count of visible particles and assuming uniform mixing of the tracer with
the natural beach.[29] A simple method of calculating littoral drift compares
the distribution pattern of tracer material detected on a foreshore with a model,
based on the assumption that the probability of any particle being transported
in one direction along the foreshore, during a given interval of time, maintains
a constant ratio to the probability of a similar movement in the opposite direction.
This is obviously a crude model and greater refinements in the technique involve
the introduction of a diffusion factor, to account for the scatter of the tracer
superimposed on the trend of littoral drift, and to abandon the notion of a
constant trend of littoral drift, which is a gross oversimplification.

Thus, for studying the movement of material offshore, with waves giving
rise to a mean drift current $\bar{U}$ (equation 3.40), the steady-state equation for
concentration c of a tracer placed at a steady rate q at a given point is

$$\frac{\partial c}{\partial t} + \bar{U} \frac{\partial c}{\partial x} = \frac{\partial}{\partial x} \left(\epsilon_x \frac{\partial c}{\partial x} \right) + \frac{\partial}{\partial y} \left(\epsilon_y \frac{\partial c}{\partial y} \right) \tag{8.1}$$

or where the diffusion constants $\epsilon_x = \epsilon_y = \epsilon$ and ϵ is contant, equation 8.1 reduces to

$$\frac{\partial c}{\partial t} + \bar{U}\frac{\partial c}{\partial x} = \epsilon\nabla^2 c \qquad (8.2)$$

An equation of similar, but simpler, form may readily be derived for the 'linear' case of littoral drift with tracers.[30]

Finally, a mention should be made of studies of the composition of beach material whereby the original source, or sources, may be determined by relation to rock type or mineral content. Variations of this nature along a beach or around a bay may provide information on the rates and directions of littoral drift and their historical significance (see also section 8.4.2).

References

1. J.N. Carruthers, *Fishing News*, No. 2362 (1958) 6-7
2. R.L. Lowe, D.L. Inman and C.D. Winant, Current measurements using a tilting spar, *Proceedings of the 14th Coastal Engineering Conference, Copenhagen, 1974*
3. C.R. King, The performance of an electromagnetic current meter in oscillating flow, Hydraulics Research Station INT-157 (1976)
4. D.A. Huntley and A.J. Bowen, Field measurements of nearshore velocities, *Proceedings of the 14th Coastal Engineering Conference, Copenhagen, 1974*
5. T.O. Sasaki, K. Horikawa and S. Hotta, Nearshore currents on a gently sloping beach, *Proceedings of the 15th Coastal Engineering Conference, Hawaii, 1976*, vol. I, pp. 626-44
6. T.O. Sasaki and K. Horikawa, Observations of nearshore currents and edge waves, *Proceedings of the 16th Coastal Engineering Conference, Hamburg, 1978*, vol. I. pp. 791-809
7. H.R. Oakley and E.A. Dyer, Investigations of sea outfalls for Tyneside sewage disposal, *Proc. Instn civ. Engrs.*, 33 (1966) 201-30
8. P.M.J. Woodhead and A.J. Lee, A new instrument for measuring residual currents near the sea-bed (International Commission for the Exploration of the Sea, 1960) Hydrography Committee Report No. 12
9. A.W. Phillips, A sea-bed drifter investigation in Morecambe Bay, *Dock Harb. Auth.*, **XLVI** (1968) 9-13
10. N. Hogben and F.E. Lumb, *Ocean Wave Statistics* (National Physical Laboratory, London, 1967)
11. C. Schneider, Visual surf observations/marineland experiment, *Proceedings of ASCE Specialty Conference 'Sediments 77', Charleston, 1977*, pp. 1086-100
12. N.F. Barber, Ocean waves and swell, *Maritime Waterways Div. Instn civ. Engrs.*, 7 February 1950
13. C.F. Stewart, Measurement of long-period waves and methods of analysis, *Proceedings of the 21st International Navigation Congress, Stockholm, 1965*, paper S II-1
14. L. Draper, Wave recording instruments for civil engineering use, *Proceedings of National Institute of Oceanography Conference on Wave Recording for Civil Engineers, 1961*, pp. 7-17

15. D.E. Cartwright and N.D. Smith, Buoy techniques for obtaining directional wave spectra, Buoy Technology, Washington Marine Technology Society, 1964, pp. 112–21

16. D. Esteva, Wave direction computations with three gauge arrays, *Proceedings of the 15th Coastal Engineering Conference, Hawaii, 1976*, vol. I. pp. 349–67

17. G. de F. Reteif and A.P.M. Vonk, A low cost inshore wave direction indicator, *Proceedings of the 14th Coastal Engineering Conference, Copenhagen, 1974*

18. E. Loewy, K.G. Witthaus, L. Summers and R.J. Maddrell, Data collection and analysis for coastal projects, *Proceedings of the 15th Coastal Engineering Conference, Hawaii, 1976*, vol. I, pp. 43–59

19. M.J. Tucker, A shipborne wave recorder, *Trans. Instn nav. Archit.*, **98** (1956) 236–50

20. R.J. Seymour, A.L. Higgins and D.P. Bothman, Tracked vehicle for continuous nearshore profiles, *Proceedings of the 16th Coastal Engineering Conference, Hamburg, 1978*, vol. II, pp. 1542–54

21. H. Crockmore and N. Akenhead, Pump samplers for measuring sand transport in tidal waters, *IERE Conference on Instrumentation in Oceanography, Bangor, 1975*

22. F.A. Kilner, Measurement of suspended sediment in the surf zone, *Proceedings of the 15th Coastal Engineering Conference, Hawaii, 1976*, vol. II, pp. 2045–59

23. E.G. Thornton and W.D. Morris, Suspended sediments measured within the surf zone, *Proceedings of ASCE Specialty Conference 'Sediments 77', Charleston, 1977*, pp. 655–68

24. J.P. Coakley, H.A. Saville, M. Pedrosa and M. Larocque, Sled system for profiling suspended littoral drift, *Proceedings of the 16th Coastal Engineering Conference, Hamburg, 1978*, vol. II, pp. 1764–75

25. D.B. Smith and T.V. Parsons, Silt movement investigation in the Oxcars spoil ground, Firth of Forth, using radioactive tracers, 1961 and 1964, AERE-R 4980 (HMSO, 1965)

26. D.B. Smith, T.V. Parsons and R.L. Cloet, An investigation using radioactive tracers into the silt movement in an ebb channel, Firth of Forth, 1956, AERE-R 5080 (HMSO, 1965)

27. A.D. Heathershaw and A.P. Carr, Measurement of sediment transport rates using radioactive tracers, *Proceedings of ASCE Specialty Conference 'Sediments 77', Charleston, 1977*, pp. 399–416

28. P. Wright, J.S. Cross and N.B. Webber, Shingle tracing by a new technique, *Proceedings of the 16th Coastal Engineering Conference, Hamburg, 1978*, vol. II, pp. 1705–14

29. W.J. Reid and H.D. Morgan, Modern techniques for determining sediment movement and their uses, P.I.A.N.C. 20th Congress, section II, subject 5 (1961)

30. G.T. Csanady, Turbulent diffusion in the environment, *Geophysics and Astrophysics Monographs*, vol. 3 (Driedel, Dordrecht, 1972)

31. G. Ortolan, *Int. Hydrogr. Rev.*, **43**, No. 2 (1966) 179–88

Index